THE TRUTH ABOUT THE WAR AND

no 19 bus

THE COMING GLOBAL ENERGY CRISIS

Stephen Hamilton-Bergin

Thanks to Maggie for clarifying chaos. Trudi for being a design genius. David for intellectual encouragement. Peter for developing my imagination. Christine for everything. The monks of Worth Abbey for their silent inspiration and hospitality. All my teachers past present and future.

First Published in the United Kingdom by
Literary Workshop Ltd.
Earthsure Foundation,
Grove House, Ditchling Common,
West Sussex RH 15 0 SJ
Tel 01444 47 11 22

www.**no19bus**.org.uk

First Edition Published by Literary Workshop Ltd
September 2003.

A catalogue record for this book
is available from the British Library

ISBN 0-9545318-1-7

Typeset by Pink Designs Ltd
Hove
www.pinkdesigns.co.uk

Printed and bound in Great Britain by
Wyndeham Heron
The Bentall Complex Colchester Rd
Heybridge Essex CM9 4 NW

Every attempt has been made to avoid offence.
Anyone who takes offence is welcome to contact the author
personally. There are no lawyers on call to interfere with the
process of respect, good manners and gentleness which I
believe should be at the heart of all human dialogue.
The human journey cannot be undertaken
alone.

For Rita

the website:
www.no19bus.org.uk

Contact number:
01444 47 11 22

CONTENTS

HAPPY 21st BIRTHDAY!

Birthday Greetings!

To everyone born on the 4th September 1982
you are twenty one today.
Congratulations!
You are now grown up and it is time to
think about a career. It is very
difficult to give specific advice. For the
next forty or so years you will be
dismantling an unbalanced and
dysfunctional Global trading
juggernaut and replacing it with an
ecologically sensitive trading system
based on your local community
needs. It is uncertain if you will
have time to follow a conventional
career. Don't worry! Everyone will be
in the same boat trying to paddle to
safety. As a member of the older
generation I must apologise for the
profligacy with which we gobbled up
the finite energy resources. I'm
certain you will do a much better job!
Hope you have a lovely day.
Have fun.

John x

Nicle

grannie
+
Marmar AMY

grandpa xx

Mum (Regimie
xxx

FOREWORD

By C. J. Campbell

This is an unusual book. Thoughts, facts, interpretations, ideas and insights follow one another in an enthusiastic avalanche. One wonders where it might be going but if you persevere the vision becomes clear.

It has a refreshing candour. One reads on to find that indeed it delivers a penetrating analysis not only of the facts but of what they mean for Mankind. We are spared having to read turgid science or probability theory, and we don't have to be bored by arcane and pedantic economic arguments. Above all, we are spared slick expressions and clever buzz words. Instead, we find a humanitarian and intuitive common sense in the best sense of that expression, having nothing common about it. It really does not matter if all the numbers and observations are exactly right: they are close enough to deliver a sound message.

In short, the author has correctly identified that the world supply of oil and gas is set to decline over the next few decades. He points out how the provision of these fossil fuels drove the prosperity of the past Century, before pausing to remind us that by describing them as fossil fuels we admit to depletion. Clearly, production has to start at zero following discovery and end at zero on exhaustion passing one or more peaks around the midpoint of depletion, when half the total has been consumed. It seems so very obvious, yet the notion of the decline of the premier energy supply on which the world runs is strangely counter intuitive. It is very hard to accept the consequences that must change the world beyond recognition, yet that is what Nature ordains.

The author's great strength is his humanistic view of Mankind in a spiritual sense. He pauses to wonder if we have really been so much happier crunching down the endless shopping malls than were our grandfathers with their pitch forks gathering the autumn harvest mid the hedgerows of rural England. He asks if the oil-based affluence has really led to a better life. In the developed world, divorce, crime, drunkenness and excess reach new heights, blasted hourly by television screen and loudspeaker. Profiteering was previously regarded as morally repugnant, and usury was a sin. Now they are central to a kleptocratic world, run by dictatorial power-elites, who have cloaked themselves in democratic imagery that fails to represent the true interests of the people at large. In the so-called Third World, exports yield incomes for the local elites, often to be used to buy land mines or helicopter gun-ships, divorcing the populace ever further from the sustainable roots of their existence. Resource wars have broken out as desperate consumers vie for access to dwindling supplies of oil, yet patriots in the desert fight on. Terror becomes universal with daily bombings in the capitals of the world. Permeating the entire edifice is the hidden role of finance whereby the United States for example has been able to import growing amounts of physical oil in exchange for an extension of domestic debt. The debt itself cannot be serviced without yet more debt, imposing an unfulfillable need for perpetual growth. Even god-fearing Norway has over-produced its oil to such an extent that it cannot begin to consume the proceeds, forcing it to invest in an Oil Fund, now with a notional value of 120 billion dollars, making it the biggest single investment in the World. Investment is probably not the right word as the markets will decline in parallel with the oil that drives industry and agriculture. It would have been better to have left the oil in the ground for the use of the later generations allowing the Norwegians to live the simpler and more rewarding lives they knew in the past. Britain for its part puffed away its windfall of oil and gas in two or three short decades, without a thought to the future when it will be crippled by the cost of imports. Weeds will grow on the presently choked motorways.

But the author rises above this hideous image of a world gone wrong to suggest that the decline of the instant wealth that we have extracted from the Earth's inheritance may be an enormous blessing in disguise. It may lead to the localisation of markets and the emergence of communities respecting themselves, each other and their environment.

It is entirely possible that Mankind will follow many other over-adapted species in the fossil record who died out when their environmental niche changed, but the author does not think so. He believes that if people and governments listen to his wake-up call they can react in time and in a sensible way to find a sustainable future.

In short, his book truly is essential reading.

C. J. Campbell
Former oil executive [FINA]
Founder of the Association for the Study of Peak Oil [ASPO]
County Cork
Ireland

August 2003.

no 19 bus

The no 19 bus comes in four parts

PART I

THE TRUTH ABOUT THE WAR & OIL
- The Coming Global Energy Crisis

A series of seven essays analysing the research, science and politics behind the major issues confronting humanity over the next 30 years.

PART II

no 19 bus
the novel

Ten volumes tracing the lives of forty people through 2007 - 2012 and then onto 2070.

Volume One published simultaneously with The Truth about the War & Oil

PART III

The Website
www.no19bus.org.uk

Interact with the ideas, stay in tune with the latest developments.

Connects to paralell websites worldwide.

PART IV

EARTHSURE FOUNDATION

To rehabilitate the Earth by letting us touch its soul.

Healing the Earth's broken ecosystems through a coming together of local community spirit and enterprise

Introduction

October 2nd, 2003

What you are about to read is going to impart some vital information which is being systematically ignored by mainstream media. The reasons for this are numerous but the principal reason is that the facts which are about to be presented to you are very unpalatable. One might go further and say that these facts are quite frightening. What you are about to read questions the very foundations on which our present democracy is based. Our political leaders are lying to us. This in itself is very frightening. There are many different ways of telling lies. One way is simply to avoid looking at the truth.

I would like to invite you to take a roller coaster ride with me. Follow a series of ideas down a slippery slope and then return to your own counsel.

What exactly is the government and the media hiding from us?

This can be answered very simply indeed. They are hiding from us the fact that the physical energy systems which keep the Western World economies rollicking along are at critical levels.

In the last few weeks, just as I am about to go to press, New York, London Denmark, Sweden and the whole of Italy have experienced major breakdowns of the national grid. These are just symptoms of an energy system on the verge of crisis.

Politicians and the Chief Executives of national power companies are telling us we shouldn't worry. It's just a glitch. A lack of investment in the infrastructure. More investment will therefore solve the problem. They are mistaken. It is not a **coincidence** that the largest failures of National Electrical grids in history occurred within a few weeks of one another. The explanations provided by the electricity companies and the governments are so spurious and pathetic they are simply laughable. In Italy, 58 million people apparently lost power because two trees fell down in Switzerland. Power systems across the Globe are at critical levels and working far beyond the capacity they were designed for.

The World is also experiencing the first real shortage of oil and gas. In America they are drilling every little gas well they can find to try and keep up with demand. They are failing to do so. National grids need power fed into them constantly. Any disruption to the fuel supply coming in means there will a disruption to the power going out. Everything is being run at its limits. When a system is run at its limits it breaks down at its weakest point. Of course every one can understand and forgive that a tree coming down on power lines may cause a temporary local power failure but when such events knock out an entire National Grid and the hydrocarbon fuel source is reaching demand limits it is obvious that systemic failure is just around the corner.

All the major Western powers are now beginning to squabble over the world's remaining oil and gas resources. They are shrinking. No one wants to face the political or economic realities of shrinking hydrocarbon supplies. War is a temporary brutal answer. Terrorism is the consequence. This problem will not go away through wishful thinking. Alternatives will not fill the demand gap. Prices will soon soar. Speculators are already active in the market.

As you read this book you will frequently come across the concern that the imminent depletion of our oil and gas resources is getting no real coverage in the Mainstream Media. On the day I am going to press however [October 2nd] an article finally arrives! The timing could not be more appropriate.

In an article in the Independent Newspaper October 2nd 2003 the headlines state.

"World Oil and gas supplies are heading for a production crunch sometime between 2010 and 2020 when they cannot meet supply because Global reserves are 80 per cent smaller than had been thought."

The squabble over our hydrocarbon resources has turned into war in Iraq. Pipelines are being blown up all round the world on a daily basis. The pot of politics is poisoned. Politicians are suggesting, or rather they are trying to pretend, that it is business as usual but the wheels are about to come off this particular fantasy.

The war in the Middle East is still raging. It appears there are many Iraqi's who don't welcome the liberating coalition armies. Most people in the West are confused about the reasons for the War. A large and growing minority are becoming aware that the main reason for the war was so America and Great Britain could establish military control over Iraqi oilfields. But why? What on earth has oil got to do with it? To most people oil is just black stuff from which we get our daily dose of petrol. In fact it is a great deal more than that. It is the very vital blood that is needed to pump energy constantly through the heart of Capitalism.

Mankind is about to go through the most momentous changes in the shortest space of time since the story of human evolution began.

What form will these changes take? This is the essence of the work which I am now about to present to you. This is an "invitation" to take a journey over the next thirty years of human history.

It is my conclusion that the Western psyche is collectively refusing to look at inevitable future realities head on.

One short word about the structure of this work. It is appearing in eleven volumes. The first volume is the book that you are presently reading. This book is called the 'The Truth About The War and Oil'. It is to be followed by ten volumes of a novel.

'no 19 bus - the novel'

The series of novels traces the lives of about forty to fifty people from 2003 through 2007 and onto 2012. The first volume of the novel is being simultaneously published with this book 'The Truth About The War and Oil' which is a series of seven essays.

These essays explore all the background research that I have done for the novel. The more I researched the more I discovered that humanity is on the threshold of an extraordinary discovery. Hydrocarbon energy, most specifically oil and gas, which has enabled our economic societies to flourish is shortly about to be slowly, but inexorably, withdrawn. In these essays I will present the academic science which verifies these conclusions.

Increasingly over the last few years the effect that mankind's industrial activities are having on the global environment has become a matter of serious importance. Indeed many people from many different spheres of life would agree that environmental issues are becoming critical. The heat waves that struck Europe and North America in the summer of 2003 were without precedence. Calculations are presently being made to determine how much additional carbon dioxide these forest fires released into the atmosphere. It will amount to many additional millions of tons. These events are beginning to demonstrate that the environmentalist's worst predictions are rapidly becoming reality. We are probably at the beginning of positive feedback loops. The hotter it gets the more we will burn and the more we burn the hotter it gets. The heat waves have caused a precipitous drop in the European Union's agricultural production. For the first three years of this century we are actually beginning to grow less food than we consume. The grain surpluses which have been artificially engineered by chemical agricultural practices are no longer able to compensate for the effects of a deteriorating eco system. It is also becoming clear that you cannot separate economic and environmental issues. The one causes the other. Many people are coming simultaneously to the conclusion that continued economic growth and development will not solve the environmental problems but will almost certainly only make them worse.

It is becoming clear that the system needs to unwind itself.

But how is this to be achieved?

Now that I have finished this series of books I am in the same position as any other author. It is necessary for me to present my work to the public. My least hope is that it will create some vigorous debate. My great hope is that we are on the threshold of a new illumination which will reconnect humanity to the finest and most noble principles of creation.

Over the next thirty years everyone upon the planet will become increasingly conscious of the fact that our hydrocarbon resources, specifically oil and gas, are depleting. For the last few hundred years we have become used to having more and more of them available for us to develop our economic systems. This is now about to change. Very shortly we will have less and less resources. We need these resources to increase if we are to maintain growth. We need to maintain growth in order to stop the world debt falling in on top of us. It is a problem of planetary proportions with no easy solution.

Hydrocarbons are fossil fuels like coal and oil and gas.

The rate of depletion of these fuels cannot be determined because the future is not yet known. The rate of depletion will depend simply on the degree to which we are determined to find as much of it as possible and burn it as soon as possible.

For very simple **physical** reasons oil is about to become a depleting resource.

This is the main background to the book.

The reason this is the main background is because it is the most significant and entirely predictable event that will take place over the next thirty years.

There is a solution. The natural intelligence within the Earth's eco systems simply rebalances. Unfortunately this rebalancing may lead to the extinction of the human species within the next few generations. The only possible course of action to ensure our survival is to change direction rapidly and learn how to live with nature as a friend rather than an enemy to be constantly conquered. Although this is the only possible course of action it is not being followed. In fact the human economic system is trying desperately to continue going in the opposite direction.

It is my hope that hidden away from mainstream conventional thinking is a growing number of people who are finally reaching breaking point. It is becoming clear that we need a total change of emphasis. Instead of charging continuously forward we need to stop and look back at the wake of environmental destruction we have left behind us. Nearly half the world's fisheries are on the point of complete collapse. The atmosphere spinning above every one of us in our "personal little environments" is thoroughly choked with industrial chemicals and effluents that we may not have made personally but we certainly use. Nearly every day we hear that we have more and more choice but in fact the opposite is true. We can only choose from what's on offer. The political powers in control do not offer us an alternative lifestyle. Our present political masters are spinning a web of lies but they spin so fast they are not conscious of their own deceptions. There is an alternative. It just so happens that this alternative contradicts conventional economic wisdom and it is therefore universally rejected. Help however is at hand. Nature is about to withdraw the benefit of more and more hydrocarbons. Once we start to get to grips with this idea we will be better placed to understand that an alternative lifestyle is about to be designed for us. Nature is withdrawing her bounty so she can conserve her overstretched resources. Nature is preparing to send humanity back to school where we will learn that the teacher was often right. We just forgot to listen because we had overfilled ourselves on our own ideas.

It is my considered conclusion that never before, in the history of evolving humanity, has the situation been on such a knife edge. I am aware that doom laden prophecies have proliferated since the beginning of time. There have been so may it is not surprising that we ignore them. All of them have been wrong. Why is it different this time? There is no short simple answer to that question. In fact it may well be that Doomsday prophecies have universally failed to become reality for the simple reason that these prophecies act as a warning. I hope to illustrate through the following essays the nature of the problem confronting us. I am not yet ready with all of the solutions. The reason it is more acutely critical this time is because the whole Global economic system is intimately related. You can't pull on one strand of nature without realising you are pulling on all the others. The Crisis we are going to have to face is of our own making. We may worry about an asteroid hitting the earth or think aliens are going to annihilate us. Unfortunately the real problem is somewhat more banal and ordinary. We are about to pay the price for populating the earth at breakneck speed and using up it's limited resources faster than they can be renewed. We can put off looking at this problem for a while but we can't put it off indefinitely. Something in the system is going to fundamentally break down before too long. The longer we put off the looking the worse the breakdown will be. This may be the moment when those of us who are concerned to preserve the human species beyond the next few generations begin to unite in a common cause.

What might that cause be?

I hope my book can throw a little light on the subject. Some of these essays are quite technical but please don't worry about understanding all the technical details. The essence of the message is the most important thing to take on board. The essence of the message is quite easy to describe. We are going to need to rapidly change our behaviour if we are to survive for more than a few more generations.

There is a web site for anyone who would like to follow through the themes in this book.

www.no19bus.org.uk

Stephen Hamilton-Bergin

West Sussex
October 2nd 2003

A SHORT SYNOPSIS OF THE NEXT 30 YEARS

- OVER THE NEXT 30 YEARS THE GLOBAL ECONOMY WILL BE HIT BY A SERIES OF OIL INDUCED SHOCK WAVES.

- AN OIL SHOCKWAVE PRECEDED ALL OF THE WORLD'S MAJOR RECESSIONS.

- THERE ARE TWO TYPES OF OIL SHOCKWAVE: THE FIRST IS CAUSED BY A DRAMATIC INCREASE IN THE OIL PRICE. THE SHOCK WAVES WE HAVE EXPERIENCED IN THE LAST 30 YEARS ARE OF THIS TYPE. THESE ARE BUT TREMORS BEFORE THE EARTHQUAKE.

- THE SECOND TYPE OF SHOCKWAVE WILL BE CAUSED BY ACTUAL PHYSICAL SHORTAGES.

- OIL IS A FINITE RESOURCE. ABOUT 90 PER CENT OF THE PLANET'S OIL HAS ALREADY BEEN FOUND.

- THE TOTAL AMOUNT OF CONVENTIONAL OIL REMAINING IN RESERVES IS ABOUT ONE TRILLION BARRELS [ONE THOUSAND BILLION BARRELS].

- WE ARE CURRENTLY [IN 2003] USING OIL AT THE RATE OF 26 BILLION BARRELS A YEAR OR 75 MILLION BARRELS A DAY. A BARREL IS EQUIVALENT TO 42 US GALLONS.

- WE ARE CURRENTLY ONLY FINDING ONE BARREL OF OIL FOR EVERY FIVE WE USE. THIS RATIO WILL REDUCE EVEN FURTHER OVER THE NEXT FEW YEARS.

- BETWEEN THE YEAR 2000 AND 2010 OIL WILL REACH A POINT OF PEAK PRODUCTION. AT THIS POINT THE AMOUNT OF OIL AVAILABLE FOR USE IN THE GLOBAL ECONOMY WILL BE REDUCED BY ABOUT THREE PER CENT PER YEAR.

- THE REASON WE CANNOT BE MORE SPECIFIC ABOUT THE DATE IS THAT THE ACTUAL EVENT OF OIL PEAK PRODUCTION WILL NOT BE KNOWN UNTIL SOME YEARS AFTER THE EVENT.

- ANTICIPATING AND PLANNING FOR THIS CRISIS WOULD SOFTEN ITS INEVITABLE, AWESOME, DESTRUCTIVE POWER.

- 95 PER CENT OF GLOBAL TRANSPORTATION SYSTEMS, SHIPS, PLANES, LORRIES, CARS AND TRAINS ARE FUELLED BY OIL IN THE FORM OF PETROL, DIESEL OR KEROSENE.

- THERE ARE NO READILY AVAILABLE ALTERNATIVES TO LIQUID COMBUSTIBLE OIL.

- HYDROGEN, OFTEN PROCLAIMED AS THE NEXT "GENERATION" ENERGY RESOURCE IS NOT READILY ACCESSIBLE. ALTHOUGH HYDROGEN IS ONE OF THE MOST COMMON ELEMENTS IN CREATION IT IS LOCKED UP IN WATER. TO RELEASE HYDROGEN FROM WATER AND LIQUIFY IT IS AN ENERGY INTENSIVE EQUATION.

- HYDROGEN FUELED VEHICLES, POWERED BY FUEL CELLS COULD, IF DEVELOPED QUICKLY ENOUGH, PROVIDE MANY OF OUR PUBLIC AND PRIVATE TRANSPORTATION NEEDS BUT IT WILL NOT SUPPLY THE ENERGY FOR GLOBAL FREIGHT TRANSPORTATION SYSTEMS AT AT ECONOMIC COST.

- THE ESTIMATED COST TO DEVELOP A HYDROGEN ENERGY SYSTEM FOR USE SIMPLY BY CARS AND BUSES IS PUT AT A TRILLION DOLLARS A YEAR.

- OIL SHOCK WAVES WILL INCREASE IN INTENSITY.

- OIL SHOCK WAVES WILL SLOWDOWN THE GLOBAL ECONOMIC SYSTEM.

- THE EFFECT ON THE CAPITALISTIC FINANCIAL STRUCTURE WILL BE INCREASINGLY SEVERE.

- THE WESTERN INDUSTRIAL GLOBAL ECONOMY IS BASED ON GROWTH AND GROWTH IS RELIANT ON INCREASING SUPPLIES OF OIL ENERGY.

- WHEN OIL SHOCKWAVES REVERBERATE THROUGH THE WORLD ECONOMY A RECESSION IS INDUCED.

- WHEN A RECESSION IS INDUCED THE AMOUNT OF OIL CONSUMED IS REDUCED. THIS HAS THE EFFECT OF REDUCING OIL PRICES WHICH IN TURN CAN RE -INTRODUCE GROWTH.

- VERY SOON THE OIL ENERGY AVAILABLE TO PROMOTE GROWTH WILL AUTOMATICALLY AND DRAMATICALLY START TO DECLINE. THE IMMINENT SHORTAGES OF OIL WILL HAPPEN FROM TWO DISTINCT BUT CLOSELY RELATED CAUSES. OIL AS A PHYSICAL RESOURCE IS BECOMING MORE AND MORE SCARCE AND OIL PIPELINES ARE BEING DESTROYED BY LOCAL GUERILLA MOVEMENTS.

- SIMULTANEOUS WITH A REDUCTION IN THE AMOUNT OF OIL AVAILABLE TO STIMULATE THE ECONOMY. WE PRESENTLY HAVE AN UNBALANCED WORLD FINANCIAL SYSTEM.

- DEBT LEVELS, BOTH PERSONAL, CORPORATE AND GOVERNMENT ARE AT HISTORICAL HIGHS. INTEREST RATES ARE AT HISTORICAL LOWS. WE WILL BE UNABLE TO PROMOTE GROWTH THROUGH CREATING MORE DEBT. THE DEBT MOUNTAIN CANNOT GROW ANY BIGGER.

- DEBT CREATION IS THE MOST IMPORTANT PRACTICAL FUNCTION OF THE GLOBAL ECONOMIC SYSTEM.

- THE SCENARIO AS DESCRIBED IN THE ABOVE IS NOT RECOGNISED PRESENTLY BY POLITICIANS OR BUSINESS.

- OIL SHOCK WAVES ARE ABSOLUTELY INEVITABLE HOWEVER. THEY WILL ARRIVE AS RELIABLY AS THE SUN ARRIVES EACH MORNING.

THE ONLY ISSUES ARE:

- WHEN WILL THE SHOCK WAVES ARRIVE?

- WHAT KIND OF ECONOMIC/FINANCIAL/SOCIAL/ POLITICAL EFFECTS WILL THEY PRODUCE?

- THE HUMAN RACE MIGHT HAVE BEEN ABLE TO AVOID THE SHOCKWAVES IF WE HAD BEEN LESS PROFLIGATE IN OUR USE OF OIL AND SIMULTANEOUSLY, WE HAD BEGUN TO DESIGN THE INFRASTRUCTURE FOR AN ALTERNATIVE ENERGY ECONOMY. IT IS NOW ALREADY TOO LATE.

- OIL IS ALREADY A MAJOR CAUSATIVE FACTOR IN THE GEOPOLITICAL CRISIS CENTRED IN THE MIDDLE EAST.

- THERE IS NO POSSIBILITY THAT THE CONVENTIONAL AND LIMITED MINDSETS PRESENTLY IN CONTROL OF THE PLANET'S ECONOMIC DESTINY WILL PAY SUFFICIENT ATTENTION TO THE MEDIUM-TERM CONSEQUENCES OF OIL SHOCK WAVES. BY MEDIUM-TERM WE MEAN THE NEXT THIRTY YEARS.

- IN REALITY OF COURSE WHEN YOU CONSIDER THAT WE ARE TALKING ABOUT THE MOST SUDDEN AND MOMENTOUS CHANGES IN THE WORLD ECONOMIC STRUCTURE THIRTY YEARS IS REALLY NO TIME AT ALL.

- THE PRIMARY POLITICAL AND ECONOMIC POWERS WILL BE FOCUSED ON TRYING TO PROP UP THE COLLAPSING SYSTEM.

- THE SYSTEM WILL REALISE, ALL TOO LATE, THAT THE TIME TO DEVELOP SUITABLE ALTERNATIVES TO MAINTAIN THE CURRENT FINANCIAL INFRASTRUCTURE HAS ALREADY RUN OUT.

- THE FACT THAT OIL IS A FINITE SOURCE IS ALREADY RECOGNISED BY THE WORLD'S LEADING PETROLEUM ENGINEERS AND PETROLEUM EXPLORERS.

- THE EVIDENCE FOR THESE "FACTS" IS READILY AVAILABLE TO THOSE WHO WISH TO STUDY THE PUBLISHED ACADEMIC SCIENCE.

- PEOPLE WILL WONDER WHY, SINCE THESE FACTS ARE READILY AVAILABLE, NOTHING MUCH IS BEING PUBLISHED IN THE MAIN MEDIA COMMUNICATION CHANNELS.

- THERE ARE PROBABLY A NUMBER OF REASONS FOR THIS LACK OF INFORMATION AND ANALYSIS.

- THE PRESENT PLANETARY POWERS CAN ONLY THINK IN SHORT SUSTAINED BURSTS ABOUT THE PRESENT CRISIS AND ONLY IN EVEN SHORTER BURSTS ABOUT THE VERY SHORT TERM. IT IS VIRTUALLY IMPOSSIBLE FOR THEM TO PLAN AND THEREFORE TO THINK BEYOND THE NEXT ELECTION.

- AS A RESULT WE LIVE IN A WORLD GOVERNED BY PEOPLE WHO ARE UNABLE TO PROJECT VERY FAR INTO THE FUTURE.

- FACING THE REALITY OF THE OIL SHOCK WAVES AS THEY FIRST START TO REVERBERATE AND THEN START TO THUNDER AND STORM THROUGH THE EXISTING FINANCIAL STATUS QUO WILL NOT BE EASY. IN FACT IT WILL BE RATHER DISTURBING AND THUS MOST POLITICIANS AND INDEED MOST PEOPLE WILL FALL INTO A STATE OF DENIAL.

- OUR PRESENT POLITICAL SYSTEM WILL REACT, IF THEY BOTHER REACTING, WITH DISBELIEF AND SCEPTICISM.

- MANKIND PRESENTLY IMAGINES ITSELF TO BE THE HIGHEST INTELLIGENCE ON THE PLANET.

- MANKIND IS SOON TO BE DISPOSSESSED OF THIS ARROGANCE THROUGH THE RE-MANIFESTATION OF THE INEVITABLE AND NATURAL INTELLIGENT SELF REGULATING SYSTEMS OF NATURE.

- INITIALLY THE "STAGNATION" AND "DEFLATION" CAUSED IN THE WORLD ECONOMY WILL INITIATE GREAT CONCERN. EVERY METHOD THAT HAS PREVIOUSLY BEEN TRIED TO STIMULATE THE GLOBAL ECONOMY WILL BE TRIED AGAIN.

- THE COMING SERIES OF OIL SHOCKWAVES WILL START TO UNDERMINE CONFIDENCE IN THE EXISTING FINANCIAL STAUS QUO. BUT SIMULTANEOUSLY THERE WILL BE AN INCREASING NUMBER OF PEOPLE WHO WILL RECOGNISE, APPRECIATE AND ENJOY THE EXTRAORDINARY OPPORTUNITIES PRESENTED TO US BY THIS CRISIS TO DESIGN THE

ARCHITECTURE FOR A NEW ALTERNATIVE
ENERGY MODEL.

- THE WORLD WILL DIVIDE INTO TWO DISTINCT
SIDES. ON ONE SIDE THERE WILL BE THOSE
WHO INSIST ON USING MAN'S INGENUITY,
WEALTH AND INTELLIGENCE TO MAINTAIN THE
STATUS QUO AND CREATE SIMULTANEOUSLY A
DIRECT FUEL SUBSTITUTE FOR OIL SO THAT
THE PRESENT GLOBAL TRADING MODEL CAN
BE MAINTAINED.

- ON THE OTHER SIDE THERE WILL BE THOSE
WHO WILL CONSIDER THE CRISIS TO BE AN
OPPORTUNITY TO REDESIGN A LOW ENERGY
SUSTAINABLE LIFESTYLE FOR THE PLANET'S
MULTITUDINOUS AND MULTIFARIOUS
INHABITANTS.

- THE POLARISATION BETWEEN THESE TWO
DISTINCT WORLD VIEWS WILL CREATE THE
NECESSARY FRICTION WHICH IN TURN WILL
CREATE THE NECESSARY FUSION FOR
ALTERNATIVE ENERGY SYSTEMS TO DEVELOP.

- THE MOST IMPORTANT ENERGY OF
CAPITALISM, ITS GREATEST VALUE, AND ITS
ONLY REAL ASSET, IS IN THE DEVELOPMENT OF
TECHNOLOGY.

- WHEN OIL/GAS IS FINALLY DEPLETED THE
ONLY ADVANCED ENERGY SYSTEM AVAILABLE
TO US WILL BE BASED ON HARNESSING THE
EXCESS POWER OF THE SUN, THROUGH LIGHT,
WIND (CAUSED BY THE WEATHER) WHICH IS IN
TURN CAUSED BY THE SUN, AND WATER.

- IN OTHER WORDS OUR ENERGY WILL COME
FROM TURNING THE PRIMARY ENERGY OF THE
SUN INTO SECONDARY ENERGY FOR HUMAN
USAGE.

- THIS SIMPLE FACT WILL REORIENTATE HUMAN CONSCIOUSNESS BACK TO THE FOUR BASIC ELEMENTS.

- THE RESOURCE CRISIS WE ARE ABOUT TO FACE IS NATURE'S WAY OF RE-EDUCATING OR RATHER, ACCELERATING THE EVOLUTION OF HUMAN CONSCIOUSNESS.

- FOR THE FIRST TIME IN HISTORY THE COLLECTIVE CONSCIOUSNESS OF EVOLVING HUMANITY WILL BE AWARE OF ITS EFFECTS ON THE ENVIRONMENT.

NO 19 BUS IS A METAPHOR FOR THE JOURNEY WE ALL HAVE TO TAKE INTO THE FUTURE.

Before we proceed further, the definition of the word oil, as used in this book refers to conventional or regular oil. There are various other alternative sources of oil, such as heavy oil or oil extracted from tar sands or shale. These sources of oil have very different characteristics to conventional oil. They will not affect the date of Peak Production which will occur between now and 2010. Conventional oil can best be understood as easily accessible oil which is particularly suitable for making into petrol, kerosene and many other products. Non-conventional oil, such as polar oil, deep-sea oil, oil made from tar and non-gas liquids add another 10% to world oil production. Thus the daily world consumption of oil is 76 million barrels. This includes the 10% of non-conventional oil.

A barrel of oil is equivalent to 42 U.S. gallons.

THE TRUE STORY OF THE WAR AND OIL

Oil Shock Waves

Trying to imagine what the world will look like in a few years' time is much easier than you might imagine. All we have to do to see what the future holds is follow the patterns of the past. When I started writing The no 19 bus back in 1998 my research clearly indicated that the world was about to face a major crisis. Most specifically an energy crisis. This energy crisis would be caused by growing insecurity in our oil supplies. In 1998 I foresaw a war, starting in 2003 in the Middle East, in Iraq. I did not imagine, back then in 1998, that my predictions would be quite so eerily specific but perhaps, in retrospect, the scenario presently unfolding was not difficult to imagine.

All my research has led me quite clearly to the conclusion that oil production upon the planet Earth is about to peak. Indeed it may already have done so. It is a subject of *massive* importance for a number of different reasons.

Oil, from which we get petrol and diesel, is the lifeblood of the world's transportation systems and the backbone of global world trade. It provides ninety-seven per cent of the fuel for the western world's combustible transport systems. It is a finite source. Oil is no longer being made. What oil the earth possesses was made millions of years ago during a very specific geological period of global-warming. The most important question is:

How Long Will Oil Last?

To answer this question we first need to know how much oil is left on the planet. As you might imagine, there is no *single specific* and undisputed answer to this question. Oil companies say one thing, governments say another. But if we turn to the scientists and engineers who have access to the most accurate and dispassionate information, we will find that virtually all of the world's leading oil petroleum geologists are almost universally agreed. There are about one thousand billion barrels of oil left upon the planet. This *includes* all the reserves we know about and all the oil that we are likely to find by more exploration. For the purposes of understanding the nature and importance of oil shock waves the *accuracy* of this figure is not critically important. If there is a little more oil then the oil shock waves will be *less* severe. If there is a little less oil then the shock waves will be *more* intense. The principle of oil shock waves and their effects on the global economy will not change. This essay will illustrate, through the most comprehensive science available, the present world endowment of oil.

Just to give an overview, here is a chart which describes the total world endowment. The bars behind the black line represent the oil that we have used so far. The blue bars after this line represent the known total oil reserves and the little yellow bars tagged on the end represent the oil that we are likely to find.

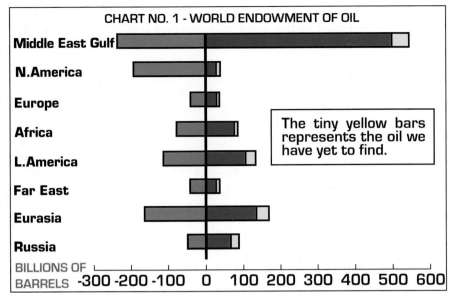

CHART NO. 1 - WORLD ENDOWMENT OF OIL

Middle East Gulf
N.America
Europe
Africa
L.America
Far East
Eurasia
Russia

The tiny yellow bars represents the oil we have yet to find.

BILLIONS OF BARRELS   -300 -200 -100 0 100 200 300 400 500 600

Look at this graph: imagine the long blue line in the Middle East reserves is a petrol station. The tanks are nearly full. Now look at the N. America blue line. the American petrol station is nearly empty. America uses ten times as much oil than all the Middle Eastern countries put together. America needs to fill up! It is not difficult to understand why they need to fill up in the Middle East.

During the development of the Industrial Revolution we used oil at an increasing rate of knots. Between 1800 and 1900 we used only a few billion barrels. Since then we have spent the money in our oil bank at an ever-increasing rate. Over the last hundred years we have used up *almost exactly* half the world's oil. At the *present* rate of consumption which has been *increasing* every year we will use up the other half in twenty-seven years and six months. This is based on the premise that industrialising countries like China and India will greatly *increase* their use of oil. A former UK Minister of Energy predicted recently that demand would rise by 50 per cent by 2020.

In fact *we cannot continue to use the oil up at an increasing rate.* We will quite soon only be able to use it at a *decreasing* rate. The technical and scientific reasons why this is so are presented in this essay. We are not going to "run out of oil" tomorrow, or next year or indeed for many years. What will happen is that at a certain point, called "**Peak Production**", we will have *less and less* oil to use every year. After Peak Production the rate at which we can pump oil out the Earth begins to slow. This is far and away the most critical point to understand. The Earth's oil tanks are not designed like the petrol tanks in a car which can be depleted at exactly the same rate until they are completely empty. There are a number of technical and scientific reasons why this is so which will be explained in more detail shortly.

Between 1950 and 2003 we used nearly one trillion barrels of oil. Presently we are using oil at the rate of:

26 billion barrels of oil per year.

Which is equivalent to: -

76 million barrels per day

Which is equivalent to: -

150,000 litres per second

[A barrel of oil equals 42 US gallons or about 160 litres.]

Economists and ecologists generally come from both *ends* of the spectrum. But there are *also* two types of ecologists who also come from both ends of the spectrum. On one side there are those who want to reorganize the ecology of the planet according to their own plans. Then there are those wish to learn *what it is the planet wants of us.* The first type of ecologist/conomist wants to create a new sustainable model whilst still maintaining or even increasing the input and output of energy. This mindset makes *man* the most important component. In fact we need to realize that the Earth is designing the only possible economy for man. It is up to us to learn how we can live off the interest of the Earth without destroying the capital. New methods of technology and production will not in themselves be sufficient to achieve this balance. A very simple but intuitive understanding of the natural science of the planet indicates that the most intelligent present course of action would be to design a society where the members use a lot less energy. This will have the effect of slowing the whole process of life down. Slowing down needs to begin firstly as a process in our minds and then it will be reflected in our actions and then we may be able to begin to harmonize with the Earth's natural rhythms once more. Astonishingly and perhaps paradoxically this means we will *become a great deal more when we do a great deal less*. We are presently addicted to the idea that we need to do more in order to survive whereas in fact the opposite reality is true. We will need to do a great deal *less* if we are to survive.

An extract from no 19 bus the novel;
Volume Two - 2003
Alex De'Ville

The Beatles were in full swing and pot, heavily garnished with readily accessible, guilt-free sex, was on every liberal-minded young boy's mind. They frequently got drunk and often stole the key to Lord March's well-stocked cellar where they made themselves sick on the best vintage port.

They were caught once. Lord March threatened to send Alex home but in the end they were grounded for the week-end and none the worse was thought of them afterwards. In fact at dinner, a few days later, the jovial Lord March brought the subject up himself.

"So what did you think of my '39 port?" he asked Alex.

"Not bad!" replied Alex. "A touch syrupy. I think I preferred the '33,"

If we don't actually increase the rate of oil usage but just continue to use it at the **same** rate, we will use the world's total oil endowment in about thirty-eight years. America, with one twenty-fifth of the world's population, uses over twenty-five per cent of the world's oil. Some people may imagine that having twenty or thirty, or possibly as much as forty years' worth of oil is such a long period of time that we don't need to worry. Many people suggest that alternatives, such as hydrogen, will take over as oil declines. In the next chapter I illustrate how this blind optimism is profoundly misplaced, unscientific and is leading us towards a dangerous complacency. Peak oil is the point at which we can no longer pump oil at the same rate. After peak oil the amount of oil available for mankinds use is reduced year by year.

From the point of peak oil every year there will be less and less oil available for mankind to use. The decline is inevitable. The only question is **when** will the decline begin and how will we adjust to this decline? If we act now, dramatically and sharply, we may be able to conserve our existing supplies of oil for a hundred years or maybe even more, but if we continue to travel on our present course, eventual decline may be delayed for a few years but when the crisis hits, as it surely will, it will simply be that much more severe.

As I write it is March 2003. Last week gas prices in the US jumped forty-one per cent in one single day. Oil has jumped to nearly $40 per barrel. Petrol prices have risen forty per cent in America and nearly fifteen per cent here. America's strategic stocks are down to a thirty-year low. American oil company stocks are down to about two weeks. Later this month America will invade Iraq, ostensibly to get rid of Saddam Hussein and liberate the Iraqi people. *Is it merely a coincidence that Iraq has the second largest reserves of oil on the planet?* In fact, Iraq has about fourteen per cent. Saudi Arabia, with twenty-five per cent, is the only country with more.

Saudi Arabia is just next door to Iraq. These two countries alone have over forty per cent of the world's remaining oil reserves. Fifteen of the nineteen suicide bombers who brought down the World Trade Centre were from Saudi Arabia. What is less known is that these suicide bombers wanted US military forces to withdraw from the Middle East, specifically from Saudi Arabia, the spiritual home of the Islamic Prophet Muhammad. The terrorists also demanded that America give the Arab oil states thirty-seven billion dollars to repay them for oil which had been *'forcibly'* sold to them at less than market value.

If America withdrew unilaterally from the Middle East and stopped financing and militarily supplying Israel, the terrorists would stop. But we **never hear**, however, in the West, what the terrorists' demands actually are. Terrorism is portrayed in the West as a group of religious fanatics, evil psychotic fanatics, intend on destroying the 'Free Democratic Western World'. In fact it's a lot more about 'oil' than you might imagine, as the following essays will illustrate. The 'terrorist' demand that the US takes their military out of the Middle East is given no consideration whatsoever by the US administration. On the contrary, as we all know, they are planning to invade Iraq. In fact these plans have been brewing for years. American military forces are very much **in** the Middle East. They are getting ready to invade Iraq and Tony Blair, quite against the will of the majority of British people, is going to take us to war with them.

Although by now many people will have become aware of the oil issues surrounding the war, it is unlikely that many really believe that oil is the over-riding motive. Well just read on, absorb a few of the relevant scientific facts and then make up your own mind. Apparently the Middle East plan formulated by America is to 'liberate' the Iraqi people from their monstrous regime and take out, or rather take over, all the oil wells and manage them for the benefit of the Iraqi people. That may be so but the **only** certainty is that the US will get its hands on Iraqi oil. Actually taking over the oil wells will be militarily speaking very unproblematic. All the oil wells and pipelines in Iraq are easily accessible and unprotected, in the middle of the desert but protecting the oil pipelines from saboteurs, local freedom fighters/anti-Western terrorists will not be so easy.

Unfortunately, to justify an invasion, US and British forces will simultaneously have to take over Iraq's main economic, social and political functions. The governments of America and Britain will insist they are taking over the oil for the benefit of the Iraqi people, and that when the Iraqis have been 'liberated' by a number of cruise missiles and cluster bombs they will be giving the oil back to the Iraqis. This may be the case. We have yet to see. In either event it is unimaginable that the US will not retain control of the management of the oil fields and dictate the price and the means whereby the oil is sold. The pre-war hype and the critical state of world oil supplies have made the price of oil rocket up to $40 a barrel. Oil traders are hoarding oil and speculators are driving the price up. This kind of oil price volatility is a very good opportunity to make money. No doubt when the war against Iraq is over, probably quite quickly, the oil price will sink back down again. No doubt the stock exchange, presently at its lowest ebb for four years, will shoot back up. This kind of volatility is here to stay and in fact it can only get worse – even after America manages to appropriate Iraqi oil.

After the war is over the Americans will, no doubt try to get Iraqi oil flowing onto the market very quickly, for America is desperate for more oil. Whether they succeed or not remains to be seen .In fact it is so desperate that it recently rescinded the prohibition of searching for oil in its national parks. There is a beautiful park in Florida called the Big Cypress. Most of the trees are over two hundred years old. It is regarded as a national monument. Permission has now been granted to bore over a thousand exploratory seismic boreholes. These are small holes down which explosives are set. The company doing the drilling believes that there may be up to twenty-five million barrels of oil under the park. That may sound quite a lot. In fact it would keep the world supplied with oil for about eight hours and would keep America going for just thirty-two hours.

Most people reading this will not be aware that an oil crisis is approaching. Thinking about today is hard enough. Planning this year and next is difficult. To contemplate an entirely altered energy/economic reality in the next five to ten to fifteen years is virtually impossible. We still fill up our cars on demand. We go flying wherever and whenever we want and we order heating oil for our homes through a simple telephone call. Many people also like to point out that we have had 'oil shocks' before, specifically in the 1970s, and that nothing happened then. A lot of people think we just need to do more exploration. Most of these opinions are held without knowledge of any detailed analytical research. People think, quite naturally, that if this crisis were so imminent then surely our governments would be aware of it and

A Reader's Comments: -

"Everyone feels alone sometimes. This is a book about loneliness. 40 people each in their own separate universes being inexorably drawn together into the web of life. It is an astonishing achievement and certain to make us all think about who we are; why we're here; but, most importantly perhaps, where do we all want to be?"

A Reader's Comments: -

"Mankind carries the seeds of its own destruction but also the secret of survival and eventual recovery as long as it exercises common sense, sticks to kiss, and makes brave decisions. The forces of declining oil supply, global trading, international terrorism and imperial ambition are the familiar ingredients of this doomsday scenario, but the reader is not hurried towards a dramatic climax by means of a conventional plot. The reader can pursue a somewhat eclectic journey that will provide a range of different and contrasting experiences of life."

*An extract from no 19 bus
- the novel;
Volume Two - 2003
Chloe*

Chloe was trapped by one single recurrent memory. One single moment in time. It was a moment in the past, the present and the ever-foreseeable future. This memory liquidised time and frothed it up into an unbearable mixture of poisoned, vicious gases that choked all of Chloe's senses. The sensation of the suspension of time was overwhelming, complete and total.

Every living moment of every living minute of every long drawn out day was vibrating fiercely with the image of the death of her baby girl, Claire.

----

*An extract from no 19 bus
- the novel;
Volume Two - 2003
Chuck Sackville*

More than this, Chuck just loved the pulsating , throbbing sound of the oil surge in the pipelines.

The explosion, the first explosion, was quite muffled, as if it had been some way in the distance. Chuck's first thought was that a wellhead had blown out. Then he thought - Terrorists!

Flashes of blue and yellow light nearly blinded him. This was a bomb!

---

would be doing something about it.

In fact the American Government is very aware of the situation and they **are** actively doing something about it. They are shortly to take control of Iraq's oil reserves. In fact governments are all too aware that there is an oil/energy crisis brewing.

Much of the information about the impending oil crisis comes from Dr C.J. Campbell, one of the world's leading petroleum geologists. In 1997 he published a book called **The Coming Oil Crisis**. His book was taken very seriously. So seriously, in fact, that on July 7th, 1999 he presented a paper to the House of Commons All-Party Committee. It was entitled 'The Imminent Peak of World Oil Production.'* These are the main points that Dr Campbell made to the House of Commons: -

- **The world has now been thoroughly explored with the benefits of new understanding and high-resolution seismic surveys.**

- **About ninety per cent of the world's oil has now been found.**

- **I think that a price-shock around 2001 is inevitable and will trigger a stock market crash.**

    [You need to remember that this was a report to the House of Commons in 1999.]

- **America will vie for access to the Middle East. More missiles can be expected.**

- **I think it is absurd that the management of the world's supply of its most important fuel should be left to a few feudal families in the Middle East.**

There is a growing awareness that this report to the House of Commons has been seriously suppressed and that the extraordinary importance to our future economic wellbeing is being ignored by the government. Instead, they are pursuing their own short-term aims. Why do you imagine the issue has not been taken up by the government energy departments and by the media? The answer is very, very simple: -

FEAR

The consequences of running out of oil, of world trade disappearing and the world financial architecture collapsing is simply too ridiculous. It simply can't happen! It won't be allowed to happen! No government will let it happen! It would be ruinous to their election chances.

Anyone interested in looking at the whole paper can download it from The No 19 Website: - no19bus.org.uk

C.J. Campbell's book The Coming Oil Crisis is available to order through the above website or direct from the publishers.

Anyway *that* all happened back in 1999. Four years later, mainstream media and politicians still have not *properly addressed* the subject. Much of the reason for this is that politicians, business and the media pretend to be separate but in fact they occupy, with a few rare and special exceptions, the same identical limited mindsets. The elite run the world on our behalf according to the golden rule of power. Don't worry the people if you can avoid it.

Politicians/business/media know just one thing for certain. Capitalism is all about confidence. The illusory confidence generated by the so-called successful invasion of Iraq is making the Stock Exchange leap upwards one last time. Starting to even *discuss* the effects of major oil shock waves could undermine what little confidence there is presently in the system. Unfortunately this 'closed' mindset is leading us towards possible disaster and that is why it is absolutely essential that as much pressure as possible is brought to bear upon this critically important subject. The irresponsibility of our government is quite shocking. One can only imagine that it is trying to protect its short-term future. When these facts are more fully appreciated by the public at large, it will become clear that the real motives for going to war were quite different to the motives declared by the US and UK governments.

What is very hard to realise is that the transatlantic twins "Blair and Bush" *are not fully conscious* of their real motives. Self-awareness and the development of spiritual philosophy; the ability to recognise the true origin and intent of one's motives is very difficult but, perhaps more importantly, such an itinerary is not top of an ambitious politician's daily agenda. Indeed, in many respects, the successful development of a modern day politician simply requires single-mindedness and complete unquestioning faith in oneself and one's opinions. Natural intelligence and self-reflection can actually be a hindrance to gaining political office.

In a few years, perhaps even sooner, it will become more and more apparent to more and more people that the "primary, deepest motive for war in Iraq was to control Middle East oil." The issue of oil is also intimately mixed up with "world order" and "economic stability". It's part of the power game. As it happens, America is probably willing to pay for Iraqi oil but unfortunately it doesn't have ready access to it nor, in these uncertain times, can the reliability of its supply be guaranteed – unless, of course, you are running a pro-American puppet administration. It is absolutely essential, at least for the *very short-term*, up until the next presidential election, that America controls oil in the Middle East. It is also essential to the very short-term health of the American economy. Don't laugh! In a year or two, when **everyone** begins to realise that the US, in particular, went to Iraq for the oil, this will become the accepted position. It is unbelievable, in fact quite extraordinary, but in a few years the American government, the America media and American business will have convinced *most* of the American people that the American government *did the right thing* by invading Iraq. Which will actually leave Americans in something of a quandary. Will the growing minority of the American population, (the ones who are becoming incearasingly ashamed of their administration) be able to influence the majority?

The effect of the invasion will occasion many more terrorist attacks in the region and America will use these attacks as an

The price of jet fuel has doubled in less than a year. It is estimated that war and terrorism could deepen the airline industries' losses to $10 billion or even more.

"Without help, all of the big network airlines in the US are heading for bankruptcy within the next two years", says Samuel Buttrick of U.B.S. Warberg, a major Swiss bank.

In February 2002 the price of jet fuel rose from 60¢ to more than $1.20 gallon. The airline industry says that it loses up to $200 million a year for every *extra cent* added to the cost of fuel.

*An extract from no 19 bus
the novel;
Volume Two - 2003
David Sadleigh*

Sheila's small, piercing eyes stabbed greedily from amidst the sagging folds of her face as she plundered the plateful of food in front of her. With breathless anticipation she wriggled around like a jelly trying to fit into a mould. She started shovelling great forkfuls of food into her mouth. It was the first time for several hours that she had looked at something other than the TV screen. She gobbled and chortled as she fed. There was an American daytime soap on the digital television. The programme was about young girls who wanted to take up stripping as a career. Most of the young adolescents were accompanied by their mothers. One particular adolescent was dressed in black PVC including a micro-skirt that entirely failed to cover her knickers.

"Ain't she a fucking sight!" said Sheila and she flicked her fork towards the TV, scattering lumps of potato and onion over the walls and duvet as she spoke.

STOP PRESS: 21-06-03

Paul Wolfowitz the Deputy US Secretary of Defence stated today to a meeting of Asian Business leaders that Korea was not Iraq. The reason he gave for invading Iraq was *OIL!*

excuse to convince the American electorate that their continued presence in the Middle East oil fields is essential for maintaining security. As terrorist attacks become more frequent in the Middle East, America will use them as a justification not only to their continued presence but to an *increased* presence ..." It's called 'spin'. When you 'spin' something you 'twist' it around. Looking up the word in the Oxford English Dictionary reveals:

'Spin: An act or spell of spinning. The capacity for being twisted or spun.'

The ability to twist something is the ability to distort it. Perhaps you also noticed that interesting little word 'spell'.

'An act or spell......of spinning.'

As we all know, a spell is something we cast. It's a magic trick, an illusionist's sleight of hand. It is designed to hide something from someone else or, in other words, to delude them. To create delusion. This is the present act and art of politics. Mostly, they don't know they're doing it. Tony Blair was forced to cast spells over the British electorate and forced to 'spin' the media to dance to his tune because, otherwise, he could not have taken up the reins of power. His ability to create mass psychosis and carry most British people to war, even when the vast majority don't want him to, illustrates perfectly Tony Blair's awesome power to weave a 'spell' and then cast it over the population.

In fact spin is a part of every salesman's patter. It's even a part of each and every 'story' we tell each other. Putting a 'gloss' on things and making them appear in the best possible light, and preferably to our own advantage, is natural.

It is obvious to many of us that much of the Islamic world lives in a society that is *suppressed*. But is our society so much better? Many of us are coming rapidly to the conclusion that we are living in a society that is *manipulated*. Either way we end up with a distortion of the truth.

The act of spinning or spelling is of course firmly attached to the power and intent of human language. Indeed words need 'spelling' correctly or they will not work. The only real difference between ordinary folk spinning yarns or telling stories is that the effects of their 'trickery' do not generally have world-shattering conclusions. In other words: WAR. The ability of politicians to "spin" what they present to the world makes them much more effective in the real, practical, day-to-day affairs of humdrum life. Politicians get to decide what we should think. We are being taught to react like circus animals to the ringmaster.

Spiritual philosophers, on the other hand, get to wonder, constantly, what on earth we're all doing it for! Politics and self-reflection are like the two antagonistic poles of a magnet. They are incompatible. Spiritual philosophy and self-reflection, however, are mutually attractive but the problem with spiritual philosophy, as it becomes more and more internalised, is that it becomes further and further removed from the practical day-to-day economic realities of ordinary life. That is why we need both to function. It is also the reason why nothing much will change overnight. Politicians are very unlikely to turn into spiritual philosophers. They will not suddenly begin to question or analyse their motives. They will not disappear for long periods of self-reflection [unless, of course, they are voted out of office]. It is very unlikely that many members of the British Parliament will be reading this, **even though every one of them** has been **individually** sent a copy. The war in Iraq is not going to disappear off the political landscape. The U.S. and the U.K. will get bogged down in a civil war. This will come as a surprise to Tony Blair and George Bush. The mayhem will act as a magnet to the worlds terrorist's. As it becomes more and more obvious that the war is creating chaos and anarchy, the imperial spin-miesters will have to spin harder and harder to maintain their false justifications.

Of course, by now, it may be apparent that what you are presently reading has its own 'spin.' Perhaps it is even trying to weave its own private spell. I make no apologies for this state of affairs, since it is natural, inevitable and unavoidable. I believe that the **primary motivation** behind this particular bit of spinning is to try and spin so hard we reach the still point in the centre. [This still point is a very good vantage point from which to determine the numerous different directions from which creation is simultaneously flowing and exploding.]

The Americans are shortly to take control of fourteen per cent of the worlds oil reserves in Iraq. They will also, geographically speaking, be in a position, to control the whole of the Middle East oil producing region. A region that just happens to control over fifty per cent of the worlds remaining oil.

One of the main purposes of American foreign policy for the last twenty years has been to try and break the 'Opec' cartel which is run by Saudi Arabia. Controlling Iraqi oil will give them a huge leverage in international oil markets. After the war the price of oil may start to collapse. This may provide a short-term boost to the beleaguered world economy. If America can start to produce Iraqi oil at the rate of five, six, or even seven million barrels a day there may be a glut of oil for two or three or maybe even four years. The only real effect, however, will be that the inevitable decline in production will be put back a few years and, thus, when the decline arrives it will be that much sharper. I have fully illustrated the effect of American requisitioning of Iraqi oil in some graphs that follow. If the freedom fighters/Jihad warriors/terrorists manage to destroy the Iraqi oil infrastructure, the situation will get that much more critical that much sooner.

The world's leading oil experts, the ones that study these issues for a professional living, are unanimous in their conclusions. Oil production will peak soon and thereafter the life blood of the consumer capitalist economy and the world's fossil-fuel transportation power systems will move into permanent decline. Ordinary people tend not to agree with the expert view. Why I wonder? Is it because the effects of a continual oil shortage/ energy crisis and the consequences for our complex industrialised economies are almost too much to think about?

Politicians and much of the public are burying their heads in the sand. I don't blame the public – for they haven't been present-ed with the facts. I do however blame the politicians for their short-term views and their dangerous inability to plan for the future. Some people will also feel that what they are presently reading is just 'one view' among many. I challenge you to ignore it at your peril. For those who want to look for themselves, just type in 'oil crisis' on the internet and you will be astonished at the response. In the last two weeks alone there are over 500,000 more entries.

A Reader's Comments: -

"The number 19 bus pulls no punches. Through the medium of 40 individuals all the important social, economic and political issues of our time are explored in minute detail. A masterpiece."

A Reader's Comments: -

"Young people will love this book. It is so brash and bold and chaotic but yet it gives faith in the future. But old people will love this book too. It gives them faith that their past has not been a waste of time."

Most commonly of all, people generally hold the view that alternative energy sources will be found. Hydrogen, in particular, is quoted. In fact the idea that hydrogen, as a combustible liquid fuel, will step into the breach and seamlessly and painlessly provide all our needs is presently a myth. The American government's main scientific research department has already rejected a 'hydrogen economy', both in technical terms and economic costs. It may be a fuel of the future, and I, for one, very much hope it will be, but it is not coming in time. If we had started planning and organising an alternative hydrogen economy twenty-five years ago, we might have had a chance. We didn't! And now it's already too late. The science of a hydrogen economy is still at the basic research stage.

However, this is not all doom and gloom – for reasons that I hope will become much clearer as we progress. The advent and development of 'Alternative Energies' is technologically possible and most of these new sources of energy will have a much more benign effect on the environment. Unfortunately they will not replace oil directly. We are approaching the end of hydrocarbon man. He's got another thirty or forty years to run at most. The last period, however, will be fraught with enormous changes. We are not going to just suddenly 'run out' of oil at some distant point in the future but oil is about to start *declining in availability* to a very considerable degree. This has never happened before. True there have been oil shocks but they were just hiccups on an endless expansionary path. In fact one doesn't even need to postulate a decline in oil availability to foresee major problems ahead. For the last fifty years or more industrial man's advancement has been directly related to the *increasing* availability of fossil fuels – particularly oil and gas. The growth that is so totally essential to Western economies is based on *increasing* availability. So even if oil availability levelled out we'd be in a spot of bother. To put it blithely! Oil is set to decline and the repercussions may be overwhelming. The **main point** is that declining oil production will not be even. The moment world demand for oil is just fractionally more than actual production, then market forces, designed by the capitalistic financial economies of the West, start to kick in.

So, is the coming oil energy crisis a doomsday scenario? Not at all. In fact it may be quite the opposite. It may finally give us the opportunity to ask ourselves what kind of society, what kind of world and what kind of local community we want to live in. It might spell disaster, indeed it will spell disaster if the world chooses to ignore this problem in the vain hope that it will go away, but it might lead, in the end, to a much more sustainable, enjoyable and less stressful world. But more of that later. What follows is "Part Two" of the 'Oil Shock Wave'. This is quite scientific. You do not need to take all this information on board and you certainly do not need this information to enjoy your **literary adventure** on The no 19 bus. I include it because there are those who will be interested in the basis for this research and the scientific evidence for these conclusions. Woolly theories may keep one cosy but there is nothing like cold, hard, scientific facts to illustrate reality.

Oil is a hydrocarbon. In other words, a mixture of hydrogen and carbon. The hydrogen gives us fuel; the carbon is generally a waste product and disappears into the atmosphere as gas. Oil was formed during an intense period of global warming many millions of years ago. In 1980 a geochemical breakthrough allowed petroleum geologists to determine very accurately which 'source' rocks were likely to contain oil. **The planet has now been thoroughly explored for oil deposits and quite thoroughly exploited**. About seventy per cent of our oil goes on transportation. The rest goes to industry and heating for our homes. In the Western industrialised world our basic transport and freight systems, cars, vans, trucks, lorries, planes, boats and ships are ninety-five per cent dependent on fuel derived from oil.

There have been several major recessions since the Second World War and each of them has been preceded by an oil shock wave.

What follows is a very brief synopsis of the world's oil situation. Oil is being pumped out of the ground at roughly 75 million barrels per day. There is however very little additional pumping capacity left. The beginning of 2003 has already experienced a mini oil shock wave. Prices have leapt up in the last three years by nearly three hundred per cent. There was a mini oil shock wave in 2000 that caused an economic recessionary ripple around the world. In 2000/2001 the price of oil increased, and the world actually used *less* oil in 2002. Then the oil price stabilised slightly. The situation is now much more critical. The oil shock wave we are presently experiencing in March 2003 will certainly be more prolonged and more severe. It is, almost certainly, going to plunge the world eventually into another mini recession. This recession will lead to reduced oil usage and will temporarily reduce the price. The fluctuations in price will be very dependent on the volatile military situation building up in the Middle East. There may even be a mini boom in 2003/2004 as Iraqi oil comes on stream and the financial markets start to gamble on a standard economic recovery pattern. Any little boom will be very short lived because any boom will start to put pressures on the oil supply system and then there will be another oil shock wave. Each time an oil shock wave hits us it will hit harder and each time there will be less room to manoeuvre out of it. There will be increasing geopolitical uncertainty. It is certain that this will lead to greater volatility in the oil markets and financial markets. Such volitiliaty will impact the development and growth of the world economy.

So far, the political response to these foreseeable oil shock waves is primitive, ignorant or, as in the case of America, down-right barbaric and dangerous. However, controlling Iraq's oil and the Middle East will simply allow Americans to consume oil at their present profligate rate for just a few more years. It is estimated that Iraq holds between ten and fourteen per cent of the world's oil reserves, amounting to around 100 billion barrels. Even if all these reserves were recoverable it only amounts to four years world use. The fact is that the *longer* we delay facing up to the crisis the *worse* the ultimate crisis will be.

Oil is a legacy left by the planet to help mankind along his evolutionary path. It is a legacy that we are spending faster and faster. It will run out for it is not being renewed. When our 'inheritance' is spent it will be spent. We have one endowment. The search for oil has been going on for almost 150 years and during this time almost everything that there is to know about the geological conditions responsible for oil formation has been learnt. The international oil industry has explored every corner of the globe. You can see this fact graphically illustrated in the series of charts that are to follow shortly. Most major oil companies have stopped exploring.

Indeed, it was in the rough and tumble relationships portrayed upon the silver screen that Debbie found her most constant and loyal companions. The more she watched, the more her scattered marbles concentrated on the flickering electronic screen, the more the information coalesced into another alternative, much more satisfying world: a world that at times was as bad as hers, indeed a world that at times appeared even more miserable and emotionally desperate.

An extract from no 19 bus the novel; Volume Two - 2003 Desiree

"Right then," said Desiree, "in you go," and, as she spoke, she opened the door to a small wardrobe. Gerald stepped inside. He was a small, portly fellow with his clothes off. A sagging, middle-aged paunch flopped on his miniscule willy, reminding Desiree of the decorative tiles in the loo. Submissively he held up his arms above his head and put them either side of the sturdy wardrobe rail. Desiree snapped shut some metal handcuffs around his wrists.

"Oh thank you, Desiree!" he exclaimed very politely.

"All right ducky?" she asked sweetly.

"Fine, fine," said Gerald.

*An extract from no 19 bus
the novel;
Volume Three - 2003
Emily*

The boy birds were always popular, whoever they were. Most of them were teased mercilessly and with good reason. To such mischievous feminine fairies, men are but silly children to be scolded or taught various small but important lessons. Occasionally to be admired, very rarely to be praised. In this enchanted world, boys were only invited into the songbirds' inner circle on the condition that they left behind their rather small and silly male egos. Thus the girls, the foxglove between the daisies, danced their way delightfully and distractedly through their privileged existences: The swallow darting mischievously between her sparrows.

----

*An extract from no 19 bus
the novel;
Volume Two - 2003
Gill Gale*

Gill studied her latest letter. It was from a new loan company. About a year ago she had seen one of those beguiling adverts on TV: Overcome by debt? Yes, oh yes, she was! The company promised to reduce all debts to one manageable monthly payment. How? Gill didn't really worry about that. They were a finance company properly licensed by the

The world's leading oil geologists have identified all of the prolific oil basins on the planet. The bulk of what remains to be found lies in ever smaller fields within the established provinces. **Estimates naturally vary of how much more** oil there is to be found but *they do not vary very much*. Indeed there is a fairly general consensus on this matter. We have so far discovered, used up, or 'put' into reserves about ninety per cent of the world's oil.

Clearly one of the critical elements in any analysis of the world oil situations depends upon the amount of reserves currently held by the oil-producing nations. However it is clear to most analysts that world reserves of oil may have been grossly over-stated for political reasons. Just look at the following table. This chart shows the Opec reserves.

Chart No. 2
ORGANISATION OF PETROLIUM EXPORTERS

THIS IS 'DECLARED' RESERVES IN BILLIONS OF BARRELS

	ABU DHABI	IRAN	IRAQ	KUWAIT	SAUDI ARABIA	VENEZUELA
1980	28.0	58.0	31.0	65.4	163.3	17.9
1981	29.0	57.5	30.0	65.9	165.0	18.0
1982	30.6	57.0	29.7	64.5	164.6	20.3
1983	30.5	55.3	41.0	64.2	162.4	21.5
1984	30.4	51.0	43.0	63.9	166.0	24.9
1985	30.5	48.5	44.5	90.0	169.0	25.9
1986	31.0	47.9	44.1	89.8	168.8	25.6
1987	31.0	48.8	47.1	91.9	166.6	25.0
1988	92.2	93.0	100.0	91.9	167.0	56.3
1989	92.2	92.9	100.0	91.9	167.0	58.0
1990	92.2	92.9	100.0	94.5	257.5	59.0
1995	92.2	88.2	100.0	94.0	258.7	64.5
2003	92.0	88.0	112.0	94.0	267.0	64.5

Take a look at the figures that are highlighted in red, and then the figures highlighted in green. For instance, in Kuwait in 1984 reserves are stated as 63.9 billion barrels. Suddenly next year in 1985 reserves had jumped to 90 billion barrels. One would be forgiven for thinking that this 'jump' in reserves was because lots of oil was found but this is not the case. Look again at the chart. Every single Opec country has an anomalous jump in its reserve figure. Saudi Arabia was the last to jump in 1990. The reason for this falsification of reserves is actually to do with the apportioning of Opec quotas. These quotas were apportioned according to the members stated reserves. The **more** oil a country had in its stated reserves, then the **larger** one's quota. Ironically this unnecessary greed and consequent falsification may provide the very perfect fulcrum, the final balancing factor as to whether or not technologically advanced humanity will survive the oil crisis.

Kuwait started the game first and then all the other countries did likewise. At the time the world was awash in oil anyway so no one really bothered to question whether this 'Oil' that had **newly arrived on the reserve list actually existed**. Some new oil had been found, but not much. It is now becoming clear that these 'spurious' reserves are distorting in a rather critical manner the possible amount of oil available for mankind's use. It makes a staggering difference to the calculation of how much oil is actually left in the Middle East. When you add up all these anomalies the difference is **over 300 billion barrels.**

But the story doesn't end there. Now look at all the figures in blue. Notice anything odd? The reserves don't change! In 1989 Saudi Arabian reserves were stated as 167 billion barrels, then a huge jump in 1990 to 257 billion barrels. Then no change. **Reserves for Saudi Arabia in 2003 are still almost the same as they were in 1990 at 267 billion barrels.**

There are only two possible ways to interpret these figures. From 1990 to 2003 Saudi Arabia didn't sell any of its oil reserves. This is obvious nonsense. Or the **exact** amount they sold was replaced by new oil finds. This is also rather absurd. Some oil has been found – but it appears that the reserves are massively overstated. Half of Saudi Arabia's oil is found in just two fields: The Ghawar, the largest oil field in the world, and the Safiniya. There have been no **huge** new finds in Saudi Arabia for twenty years.

One theory is that if the Western world knew the real state of affairs, **that there is less oil than we imagine**, then it may run off and develop alternative sources of energy leaving the Middle East with unsold oil. But this is probably more nonsense.

If you take the total reserves of Opec, as stated before they were falsified, you end up with these sums:

Stated Opec reserves in 2003 equalled 800 billion barrels.

If you now take off the 300 billion which have been falsely reported, you reach a new total of 500 billion barrels.

If you then take off gross production between 1986 and 2003 – about 100 billion barrels – you end up with a reserve total of just 400 billion barrels plus, of course, what they have actually found during this period.

Most experts agree that eighty to ninety per cent of Opec's reserves were discovered by the mid-Eighties. So it adds up to, maybe, another 100 billion barrels. That is being generous. Thus it is actually quite possible that Opec only has 500 billion barrels of oil left for production and not 800 billion as stated in the statistics.

These 'facts' are well known by the American administration and these 'facts' have been discussed by the Pentagon. However, Governments and oil companies are very reticent to discuss these facts or make them public. Oil supplies/reserves have been falsified for politcal advantage but shortly the falsification will become physically obvious. We will have physical oil shortages.

Now look at this: A cutting from the Financial Times, Tuesday November 5th, 2002. **The stated reserves for Opec are 800 billion barrels.**

government and they were on TV so that must make them bona fide. They probably had sources of cheap finance... just like...well. It didn't really occur to her to analyse the small print the fees, the insurances, nor the length of time this 'rolled up' loan would be for.

A Reader's Comments

"The no 19 bus is very hard to prepare for because it holds you in complete suspension as if it was a going nowhere and yet everywhere simultaneously."

The world's largest insurance company reports that three times as many natural catastrophes are occurring now compared to 30 years ago.

Volume Three - 2003
Graham

Graham was getting rather unsettled about the mysterious processes of his mostly misunderstood life. Did it have any purpose? Was life supposed to have a purpose? Or was it just a process of random freakishness cunningly designed to cause the most irritation? At forty, the outcome of his life seemed certain. It was going to drift into perfect oblivion.

Volume Three - 2003
Hubert Elloneurf

In his first year at University Hubert discovered, unsurprisingly, that he particularly, indeed exclusively, liked to hypnotise women. Bit by bit, whenever he could find a female willing to submit herself to his hypnotic charms he began to introduce some sexually explicit and erotic suggestions. Then in his fifth year, whilst finishing his PhD, Hubert was asked to leave university.

Dr Hubert had thought at first that he had managed to get Madeleine into a deep hypnosis only to find, as he was removing her trousers, that she awoke with a great grunt and grabbed him by the balls. This rather surprised him, particularly as her gesture was not

First, here is a bar chart which was published as part of the article.

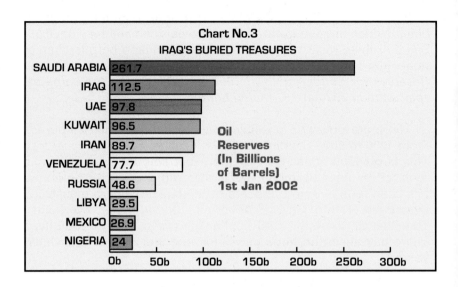

The bar chart came with this accompanying text:

"Oil groups poised to pick over the spoils of Iraqi battlefield

The White House has tried to distance itself from perceptions, particularly in the Middle East, that its possible war against Iraq is about oil. But for international oil companies winning access to the riches under Iraq's soil in a post Saddam Hussein era, is a rare opportunity. Oil majors are finding it increasingly hard to meet their production targets and Iraq's vast oil fields offer potentially huge awards. The country's reserves: 112 billion – according to the US energy information administration – are exceeded only by Saudi Arabia's. Saddam Hussein and the sanctions imposed against his regime have prevented large scale investments and long term contracts. But with the US apparently committed to toppling Mr Hussein these obstacles could soon disappear. If they do, industry specialists see Iraq becoming the focal point of the oil world's next "great game."

With no clear US blueprint for a post Hussein era and international unease about a possible war, oil companies are cautious about showing overt interest in Iraq's oil riches. Yet some companies have had contacts with Ahmad Chalabi, head of the Iraqi National Congress, an opposition group favoured by the Pentagon.

"No company in the US or UK wants to be viewed as being too far ahead of the politics on this," says Raad al-Kadiri, an analyst at the Petroleum Finance Company. Lord Browne, the chief executive of B.P., raised eyebrows last week when he called for a "level playing field" in a post Saddam Iraq. But just how big the stakes could be for these companies could depend on whether Iraq stays in the O.P.E.C. cartel. If it leaves the cartel its huge reserves could be set for rapid exploitation. According to Muhaammed Ali Zainy, senior economist for Global Energy Studies, Iraq could raise output from about 2.8 million barrels a day now to 7 or 8 million barrels per day over the next seven years."

[End of Article]

Note the date: 5th November 2002; 5 months before the Iraqi Invasion.

This article speaks for itself. Pretending that the US is not interested in Iraqi oil is a sham and a lie but it is being cleverly concealed from the general public. The media, particularly in America, makes virtually no mention of Iraqi oil. One wonders why until one realises that the media is owned and run by people with direct links and access to the American administration.

Presently the world seems to be peopled by eternal economic optimists with the kind of mindset which simply says: -"What's the point of worrying? If we are running short of oil we will go and find some more!" Well let me give you an analogy.

*You're on a very long car journey in unknown territory. You're not low on petrol, at least not for ordinary conditions because you've got about **half** a tank full but you don't know **where** or **when** you will be able to fill up. In this circumstance, quite naturally, any intelligent person would give some consideration to the problem so that **one's reserves don't run down to critical levels.***

Now here is the world oil situation. The world oil is in a big big tank called the Earth. The Earth's oil tanks are almost exactly half full. So why worry?

Well the human race is also on a long journey into unknown territory and presently the only reason we can continue to take this journey is because of our vast daily supplies of oil. **About 150,000 litres per second.** Wouldn't it be **wise** therefore to consider where the energy is going to **come from** to continue our journey? Presently the industrialized countries are journeying relentlessly forward without considering what will happen when the Earths oil tanks can no longer produce at this prodigious and unsustainable rate.

What will happen when the Earth's oil tanks are unable to pump out the oil at the rate we need to sustain our oil-energised consumer lifestyles? Are you one of those people who **hope** alternative energy will make a miraculous appearance?

Hope is **the** important word in this context because in this situation optimism alone will not suffice. We need facts. Analysis. Intelligent thinking...and...above all we need transparency and honesty. Perhaps that is why I am seriously troubled by the situation that is developing because I do not see our political leaders having many of these attributes.

So, **please**, don't take any of the information that is being presented to you at face value. Investigate the scientific evidence for yourself – surf the Web. This is a source of information that is readily becoming more available.

Fortunately it is getting increasingly hard for governments to monopolise information or to hide information, vital information, from the public. On the Web you can investigate oil reserves/ exploration, country by country. You will find literally hundreds of thousands of essays and academic information about the subject of oil depletion from the world's leading academic experts. The only thing you won't really find is anything that enables you to put all the different pieces of the jigsaw together. I hope this invitation to take a journey on the no 19 bus will perform that function. **The issue is not just about having a bit less oil to go round.** It runs far deeper than that. In fact just having a little bit less oil every year wouldn't matter very much at

aggressive but sexually explicit. They ended up bouncing around the floor, literally, since Madeleine liked to do somersaults whilst having sex. It was a novel experience but did not last long as Madeleine's physical exuberance was rather too much for him and he eventually ended up, one rainy Saturday afternoon, locking himself in a kitchen cupboard whilst Madeleine cart-wheeled naked in the therapy room begging for more.

Worldwide forests are shrinking by over 10 million hectares a year.

That is an area the size of Portugal.

It may be better to think of eco facts as merely eco thoughts. Science has begun to blind us with so many contradictory statistics we are not certain what to believe any longer. At this point it is much better that we reserve judgment on the facts so presented by science and technology and return to more time at proven methods of understanding such as common sense and intuition. We may find that hidden in these forgotten qualities lies the secret to developing a more balanced and harmonious relationship with nature and resultantly with Our Environment. Maybe the 21st Century still has a lot of evolving to do.

all if it wasn't for the reason that oil is the blood of our advanced industrial societies. Oil depletion *will* impact every area of economic life.

The world's leading petroleum geologists tell us quite definitively that oil will start to run out shortly at the rate of about three per cent per year. They do not, because they cannot, tell us the repercussions this will have on the world economy. How such a situation, such a critical situation, could develop is truly astounding.

The oil situation is critical enough if world oil reserves are about one thousand billion barrels. If they are substantially less, then the time frame to change the structure of our energy use is also substantially less. American appropriation of Iraqi oil will only staunch the Western economy's financial haemorrhage for a few more years. Could it be time to wake up to reality? **We are using it up at over two billion barrels a month**. A month is not very long. If we use this oil up at our present rate of consumption, there is about thirty-eight years left of oil. But if you've been following this argument you will have realized that we can't continue to use up the Earth's remaining oil at the *same rate*. We can only use it at a *declining* rate. We are not about to run out of oil. We are about to have a little less of it every year.

Just to illustrate the total stupidity of the idea that we can use it up at the same rate, here is a graph.

Graph No. 1.

The Government Fantasy Graph.

Graph No. 1

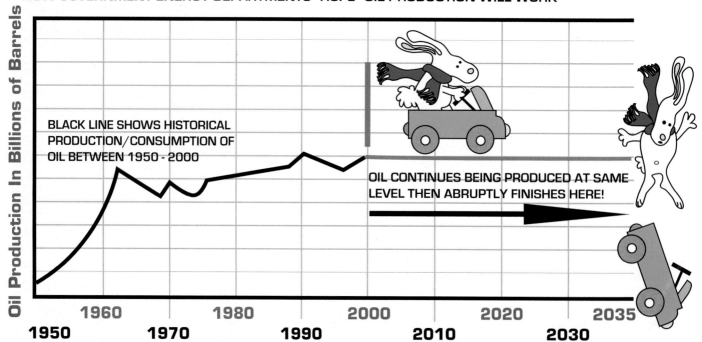

HOW A GPAPH MIGHT REFLECT THE "IDEA" THAT WE HAVE 35 YEARS WORTH OF OIL LEFT, OR : - HOW GOVERNMENT ENERGY DEPARTMENTS "HOPE" OIL PRODUCTION WILL WORK

Oil Production In Billions of Barrels

BLACK LINE SHOWS HISTORICAL PRODUCTION/CONSUMPTION OF OIL BETWEEN 1950 - 2000

OIL CONTINUES BEING PRODUCED AT SAME LEVEL THEN ABRUPTLY FINISHES HERE!

1950   1960   1970   1980   1990   2000   2010   2020   2030   2035

AS YOU CAN SEE, THIS GRAPH SIMPLY ENDS UP NO WHERE: IT'S LIKE A CARTOON REALLY. IT HAS ABSOLUTELY NO FOUNDATION TO REALITY. THE NEXT GRAPHS AND CHARTS WILL SHOW YOU VERY GRAPHICALLY THE REALITY OF THE OIL SHOCKWAVES WE ARE ABOUT TO FACE...

This is important because **this** graph is the one that government spokesmen believe can be reality!! In this scenario, oil is pumped out at the same rate for the next thirty years or so, which means, of course, that we don't **really have to start worrying about it now.** Then there simply isn't any more oil! You don't need to be a mathematician to understand this graph. Saying there is thirty-eight year's worth of oil left is statistical nonsense. It is as stupid as asking the question: How many apples are left and getting the reply three bananas. There is shortly going to be less and less oil to use. **Meanwhile**, Western industrial economies are being designed to use more and more of it.

Hamish McRae, senior economist at the Independent Newspaper, recently said: "In another fifteen years or so the **present** comfortable supply/demand ratio will become much tighter." Where does he get his facts from? The world oil supply, as of today, is **already** tighter than it has ever been. It is of course the standard 'underplay' of the importance of the topic we are discussing. Hamish goes on to say, "All the projections show a world becoming more dependent on oil and gas, and the US particularly so. On a ten or even a twenty-year plan they may well be right. But on a longer time frame I suspect they will be wrong. THE OIL PRICE WILL NOT SOAR AWAY and destroy global growth because we will find ways of managing with less of it."

In one respect he is right. We will certainly have to find ways of **using** less of it because we will **have** less of it.

What Hamish fails utterly to comprehend is the economic repercussions to global society and global trade. But then he's only a senior economist so how could he be expected to understand! Hamish continues: "Within the next couple of decades it will become clearer which energy technology is likely to supersede petroleum. It may be fuel cells, it may simply be conservation." Poor Hamish! The above passage is entirely typical of the conventional economic complacency surrounding this vital subject. Hamish finally states: "Nor do I believe it is sensible to assume that revolution (in Saudi Arabia) would lead to a US invasion to secure the oil fields. Quite aside from the practical, moral and legal objections, the entire history of the oil business is doing deals with awkward governments." I wonder, Hamish: Will the practical, moral and legal objections stop the US and the UK invading Iraq?

What is becoming increasingly obvious, day-by-day, is that oil is at the centre, the very epicentre, of the conflict in Iraq but it is IMPOSSIBLE for the government to admit it because all MORAL credibility for the war would be destroyed. Indeed the moral credibility of our whole political system would be called seriously into question.

Hamish is right about something else. We are using oil at a faster and faster rate and if we use it faster and faster then it will run out even sooner. In fact the US and Europe are beginning to stabilise their oil consumption and, in some cases, to reduce it but, meanwhile, the Far East is increasing its usage and China is dramatically increasing usage. Four of the world's major manufacturing companies are engaged in building (or providing) factories in China for conventional cars that use petrol-burning combustion engines. It is estimated that they will soon be producing six million cars a year and that by 2020/2025 China will be using as much oil as the United States. Only they won't, of

---

Volume Three - 2003
Ivor Ramsbottom

Mostly, Ivor Ramsbottom just cruised Hampstead Heath. Casual sex was still a buzz and knowing that he was probably infecting half-a-dozen young men every week with Aids was just his last gasp at making life meaningful. He lived only to make some impression in the tidal wave of self-nausea that constantly over-whelmed him.

His one really intense desire, his one passion, was to bring as many people down to his own state as possible.

"Two people fucking on the back seat of the Corsair whilst a monkey drives the car," said Ivor. That will make a great advert.

"A monkey!" exclaimed Ray Dorling.
"Absolutely brilliant!" He paused and then he thought again. But why was it brilliant? Then he knew! Because it was different! A monkey driving the car in the desert, with two people having sex on the back seat. Brilliant! Brilliant imagery! The monkey driving sedately down the highway. The petrol gauge never moving, endless desert. Sounds of sex in the back seat and then back to the petrol gauge. Wow…wonderful.

The Economist Magazine, March 15th, 2003:

"Mr Raymond, the head of Exxon Mobil Oil Company (the largest oil company in the world), was recently asked about renewable energy. He dismissed it as "a complete waste of money." Mention at your peril the possibility that hydrogen will be the fuel of this century just as oil was that of the previous one.

Strangely, Mr Raymond may know what he is talking about, since his company has investigated the economics of hydrogen fuel quite deeply. Mr Raymond insists that the costs of manufacturing hydrogen fuel, which is not a primary energy source, and developing the infrastructure to support fuel-cell powered cars are just simply too high. He forecasts that, even on the most optimistic assumption, green technologies will only lower the demand for gasoline in the next twenty years by a mere 5%.

At another interview, when asked about oil depletion, Mr Raymond went apoplectic and started to talk about conspiracy theories."

course, because the oil simply doesn't exist! It is a source of complete and utter wonderment, if not downright bewilderment, how these 'intelligent' corporate car makers could be so ignorant of the imminent demise of their basic fuel source.

No. We can't use it up faster and faster. There is something called Peak Production. This is the point at which the earth can no longer pump oil at the same rate. The rate of production declines. Peak Production is estimated to occur any time soon but certainly no later than 2007/2010. We will then have to use less and less oil each year, for the simple reason that we can't get more and more oil out of smaller and smaller oil fields. One doesn't have to be a genius, or even an oil scientist, to realise the importance of this matter. It doesn't matter if you are an oil company executive or the President of the United States, a capitalist or an anti-capitalist, a Jaguar driver or a Ford Fiesta driver. The facts are becoming indisputable. This may be the first time that you have recognised the significance of the oil issue. I can assure you it won't be the last time. Oil shortages are just around the corner, literally. Around the corner may mean tomorrow, next year or not, perhaps, for ten years but my intuition tells me we are rapidly approaching a critical point in the very near future. The precise time scale is not in fact actually the most important point. The deeper I analyse this subject the more obvious it becomes that we are failing to **anticipate** the problems. I have come to the conclusion that this failure to anticipate is quite natural and understandable. The faith now invested in man's technical and financial ingenuity is unshakable. In fact so is **my faith** in man's ingenuity. But the problem arises because no one, so far, at least as far as I can tell, has really connected all the inter related pieces of the global jigsaw. It is so complex it is almost beyond comprehension. Politicians do politics, economists do economics, ecologists do ecology, oil petroleum engineers do oil. One could continue this list which describes increasing specialization for a long long time. But what happens when we start to put all the pieces of the jigsaw together?

Generally speaking the history of politics and world management in particular does not give us much room for hope or optimism. Politicians universally hide crisis or bad news hoping that either the crisis will simply go away or it can be dealt with later. The issue of oil depletion is presently tucked away in the **distant** future. At least as far as ordinary political timescales are concerned. When crisis looms governments often try to distract us with other issues. The war in Iraq is over militarily but the agony inside Iraq is only just beginning. The **real** issue of why we went to War is being buried amidst the 'red herring' called Weapons of Mass Destruction. The real issue is oil. When will we face up to it?

So how soon is this crisis coming our way? In the very short term it will depend primarily on how fast the US can take over Middle East oil fields and bring increased oil production on stream.

We use 26 billion barrels of oil a year. We are now finding less than 6 billion barrels a year. **But most oil majors are now cutting back on exploration**. What's the point of exploration when they know there isn't much more to find? Shell recently slashed its exploration departments. BP has given up stated production targets and, instead, has bought up fifty per cent of Russia's third largest oil company. Now it is rumored that Shell is about to invest up to six billion pounds in another major Russian oil company which incidentally happens to own the world's largest reserves of liquid gas [LNG]. Could they know something we don't? Might they want control of the world's largest liquid gas production facilities because they know oil is going into decline?

The major oil companies are not really looking for oil any longer. They are merely consolidating their financial power over the remaining oil fields.

The oil wells we **are** finding are quite naturally smaller and smaller. Just recently the British press got quite excited over the biggest so-called "find" in the North Sea, called the Buzzard Field. [Actually it had been known about for some years.] Revised estimates now suggest that this wonderful huge find, the biggest in ten years, could contain up to 500 million barrels. This mega-sized field will supply the world with oil for seven days. Yes, seven days!

A Boeing 747 jet travels five miles on one barrel. [That's 42 gallons of fuel]. That is one barrel every 40 seconds. Or about 4/5 litres per second. There are tens of thousands of "recreational vehicles" or "R.V's" in the US. Many of them are the size of coaches. They do about 4 or 5 miles to the gallon. Oil gobbling-guzzling juggernauts do twenty thousand billion miles a year across the globe just to get our food on the table.

If the facts presented to you are even vaguely correct, you will be wondering why on earth (literally) we don't know more about it. Is it a government conspiracy? I'm not a great lover of conspiracy theories. More often than not a so-called conspiracy is simply deluded people working in ignorance of the facts. The Opec quotas were based on 'reserves' and then these reserves 'jumped' suddenly. They jumped, not because the Opec countries had found more oil, but because having higher reserves enabled them to have a higher production quota. It has been suggested that Opec has grossly overstated its oil reserves because it does not want America or Europe investing in alternative and renewable energy technologies. It is also suggested that Saudi Arabia and the Arab oil-producing countries want the US and Europe and Japan to remain heavily dependent on Middle Eastern oil for the next ten years or so. At that point the Middle East will then control perhaps sixty to seventy per cent of the world's reserves. At that point the Middle East would be able to hold the US and the rest of the world to ransom and they could demand virtually any price they like. Black gold would be more like black diamonds. Other conspiracies suggest that maybe America would, by then, have taken military control of the Middle East.

Whichever way you look at it, it is a recipe for geopolitical ferment. The Arab Muslim world will soon control the oil destiny of the West and, with it, its economic success or failure unless the Americans take over all the Middle East oil fields. I don't know what you think but, personally, I believe it is unlikely the Americans will be particularly happy leaving their economic destiny in the hands of Arab Muslim oil nations. Just wait for the next episode. It would be ludicrously funny if it were not so desperately serious. Millions will die in this unnecessary geopolitical oil posturing and we may be among them for it is certain that this boiling discontent will seep towards us all like a wall of evil.

Volume Three - 2003
Jack Smith

Jack checked his watch. He had to be at the opera in Glyndebourne in half an hour. The helicopter was already warming up on the front lawn waiting to whisk him to the opera in about five minutes. The five-minute trip would cost about £1500 but then it was only a business expense! Jack had started with nothing and he had found making the first million was by far the hardest. The first billion came much more easily. The next ten billion seemed effortless. Now the momentum was unstoppable. Making money was no longer a problem. Hiding it, however, was getting to be a bigger and bigger headache. Jack and Aidan had no clear idea what to do with their enormous piles of cash. Until Jack thought of oil. The real black stuff. Not just trading in oil or oil futures or oil company shares but actually buying and storing the black stuff itself. In 2001 the price of oil was less than fifteen dollars a barrel. It simply had to go up soon. Big time.

A Reader's Comments

"When it is time a vision will arise. This is a remarkable literary adventure, and now we all have the opportunity to join in."

Volume Three - 2003
Jacqueline Hyde

Jacqueline went to the scullery and collected a dozen or so vases. None were quite large or tall enough for the sunflowers. It had been the children who'd insisted on planting them ever since they had been hypnotised by the endless summer fields of sun flowers in Tuscany. Eventually she picked up some very tall, thin, elegant flutes and placed one sunflower in each. The sweet peas were easier. One little vase for each bedside table. She hesitated with the roses. They were too delicate, too early in the summer. She leaned down to inhale their bouquet. It was so subtle. She sat down, overwhelmed. The morning was nearly gone and all she'd managed to do was clutter up the kitchen with flowers!

Volume Three - 2003
Jasper Hyde

Whilst Jacqueline was arranging the flowers and listening to Clarissa talk about her various charity projects, Jasper, her husband, was on his way to the House of Commons. There was something about the sombre grandness of the architecture that appealed to him.

There is an alternative. It just happens to be unpalatable to economically advanced global consumers and vast international corporations. It means doing less, buying less and consuming less. The reason this is so unpalatable is not just because we are addicted to shopping but because vast continuous consumption is essential to keep the global economic juggernaut on the road. Slowing down our consumption quite drastically would make a great deal of ecological common sense but could lead to economic catastrophe. To keep the present system up and running we need to do more, work more, spend more, consume more, travel more, eat more and play more.

The trouble is we have created, or rather more accurately been exploded into a **world driven by desire**. The human planetary consciousness is on hyperactive. Amidst this intense activity and business it is getting increasingly hard to appreciate the pleasures of reflection and silence. The Western mind is on 'fast forward'. Pressing the pause button is presently unthinkable. Maybe it's just the way it was ever meant to be. It certainly makes for a fascinating creation as long as you can view it with a certain degree of detachment. Ah I forgot! In order to be detached you need to have pressed the pause button. I get the feeling we will just go round and round until Mother Nature herself simply presses the 'stop' button. Oil depletion may just be nature's way of making us slow down.

It may be that there is a divine collusion in all of this. Why? Because in order for humanity to survive this particular evolutionary round we will probably have to use the existing remaining fossil fuel endowment to create an alternative energy/economic system. In order to create this system we will need to **co-operate** with, rather than **annihilate,** the Arab Muslim world; and swap/trade/exchange our future technology for their remaining oil.

There may **presently** be little chance of working together with the Muslim world rather than against it but maybe a severe oil shock and a growing consciousness of these vital issues amongst ordinary people in western democratic societies could force political change. It is very easy to blame today's politicians but we have to remember that **we put them there**. If such political change could be rapidly effected the very worst of this crisis could be averted. Then we might find that, through this divinely enforced collusion, we will discover that Muslims in general, and Arabs in particular are, curiously, simply human beings, much as we are: harbouring the same hopes and fears, the same fates and beliefs, the same passions and desires for themselves, their families, their communities, their countries and the world beyond that. In fact many people, and perhaps most particularly Americans, would be astonished at how open, how gentle and how sociable most Muslims are. But of course when we talk in language like that we are describing ordinary Muslims and ordinary Arabs and ordinary people like us. Unfortunately the world is not being run by ordinary people. It is run by people whose blood is throbbing with the heady pleasures of power.

Frankly I don't believe that the Governments of the US and the UK, in particular, will be able to keep the electorate ignorant about this topic for much longer. Tony Blair may well be trying to forge a place for himself in the history books, but it may not be quite the one he imagined. He is probably just about to meet his own personal political Waterloo.

Serious, honest questions need asking, urgently. But asking serious, honest questions is not a habit politicians have got into. Prevaricating, dissembling, spinning: These are the habits of the politicians who confound us daily with their false economic optimism and their shrewd manipulation of the truth.

We're at the midnight soul of man. The evening light has gone. There is still a long, dark road to travel to the dawn but it will surely come - one way or another. America and the UK will, no doubt, do their best to try and cover up this 'coming oil crisis' but they can only 'cover up' the problem for so long. It is estimated that in the coming war to 'liberate' the Iraqi people, America will use over a billion barrels of oil. Enough to keep the twenty poorest countries in oil for years!

Now the issue presented here is oil depletion. But running out of oil is only the beginning of the story. Oil is the blood in the body of capitalism. When we run out of blood, then the 'body' begins to suffer. Whether or not we can create a new type of blood for our body will depend on so many things. One thing is for certain: Change is on the way, at last. Oil shock waves will reverberate through the world economy and through the world's global financial systems. The effects will be profound. In the next essay I examine the World Economy and discuss how prepared it is for these shock waves but first we're going to dig a little deeper into the scientific and academic studies which corroborates all this data. Oil is about to peak. Soon there will be less and less of it for our daily use. Are we prepared? Are you prepared?

Some of you may be thinking that all this information doesn't really concern you personally. You'd be very wrong to assume that. This information *concerns directly and critically every single human being on the planet*. We are going to have to change our lifestyles, dramatically and quickly.

This is not, I realise, a pleasant piece of information to pass along to my fellow human beings. It is not information I find very palatable myself. I happen to share a little plane with a few friends and my fun and games in the sky could well be curtailed if the oil shock waves are allowed to develop with such intensity that the oil price explodes into the stratosphere. As it happens, personally, I'd be happy to give up cars altogether because I no longer find driving on these seriously congested roads any fun at all. I should, however, like to help develop a solar powered/bio diesel motor glider. However if I am to achieve this personal little dream I will need to live in a technologically advanced society that is still functioning financially.

Some way or another we will all have to share what little oil is left and prioritize our usage. There will be no clear consensus on what our society's priorities should be. My own preferences are very unlikely to find universal acceptance. I would like to see oil *hugely reduced in usage* for any industrial, commercial or transportation uses. I would preserve it mostly for fun: motor racing, go karting, flying [little planes only] Motorcross, maybe some road touring for vacations, a few motor boats perhaps? Well perhaps not. Sailing would be preferable. Petrol is highly explosive and ideal for high energy, high compression combustion engines. Bio diesels and alternative gentler energies need to be introduced for our day to day local transportation uses.

It had seen, or rather it had lived through, the intimate affairs of state for some one hundred and fifty years and watched dozens upon dozens of Prime Ministers come and go. It had overseen scandals, dramas and wars and somehow it remained above them all like a great, watchful father. Various ministers and members came and went, lived and died. Some achieved great office and were then quietly despatched by the great equaliser. Some achieved nothing. A few achieved notoriety and were remembered not for their political successes but for their frailness of character. Some ended up immortalised in bronze monuments. A few ended up (the storytellers amongst them) in cheap, brick prisons. In the end it did not matter very much. Wise ministers or just foolish minstrels, wily diplomats or lying, prevaricating knaves. In the great hotch potch, each one had their own particular drama to unfold. 'Not even the grand and famous can escape the fate that awaits all mankind', thought Jasper as his well-worn leather shoes clapped noisily against the soft stone floor.

The 'red' cap on top of this graph indicates what might happen to oil production if the U.S. also appropriates the oil of Saudi Arabia.

At the very least we should all become aware of those activities that have high-energy use. War is a very high-energy use. Transporting unnecessary food and flower products on air freight planes is pretty ridiculous. Constantly making expensive energy-consuming packaging and then burying it is not only energy intensive, it's bloody stupid.

This graph indicates that the world is just on the verge of Peak Production. This graph also illustrates the effect that American appropriation of Iraqi oil will have on this peak. It will delay it for just a few years. The US administration is absolutely desperate to buy some 'Oil Time'. A few years of increased production will lower the oil price and give the economy a chance to revive just before the next US election in about two years.

GRAPH NO. 2 - WORLD OIL PRODUCTION SCENARIO

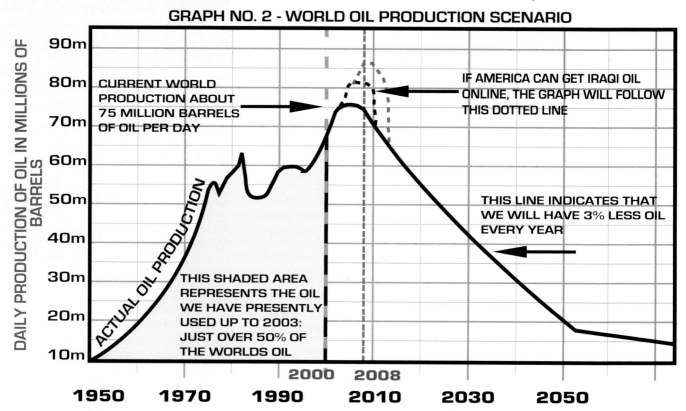

DAILY PRODUCTION OF OIL IN MILLIONS OF BARRELS

90m
80m
70m
60m
50m
40m
30m
20m
10m

CURRENT WORLD PRODUCTION ABOUT 75 MILLION BARRELS OF OIL PER DAY

IF AMERICA CAN GET IRAQI OIL ONLINE, THE GRAPH WILL FOLLOW THIS DOTTED LINE

ACTUAL OIL PRODUCTION

THIS LINE INDICATES THAT WE WILL HAVE 3% LESS OIL EVERY YEAR

THIS SHADED AREA REPRESENTS THE OIL WE HAVE PRESENTLY USED UP TO 2003: JUST OVER 50% OF THE WORLDS OIL

2000   2008

1950   1970   1990   2010   2030   2050

IT IS IMPORTANT TO REALISE THAT THE THEFT OF MIDDLE EASTERN OIL WILL HAVE THE EFFECT OF INCREASING OIL TERRORISM WHICH WILL CAUSE A COLLAPSE IN OIL PRODUCTION. EVEN WITH THE BEST SCENARIO IMAGINABLE (FROM BUSH/BLAIR POINT OF VIEW) STEALING MIDDLE EASTERN OIL FIELDS WILL ONLY LEAD TO A VERY TEMPORARY INCREASE IN OVERALL WORLD OIL PRODUCTION. PHYSICAL LIMITS, OIL WELL EXHAUSTION AND THE INEVITABLE DEPLETION BUILT IN BY NATURE WILL EVENTUALLY IMPOSE STRICT LIMITS TO PRODUCTION.

SOURCE: FOR BLACK LINE ON GRAPH - CAMPBELL/LAHERRE

A Reader's Comments

"It takes a very bold man to predict the near-term future. The number of possibilities are so endless but yet I sense an intuition from this book which deserves our attention."

Present oil production is 75 million barrels a day. Iraqi oil production might increase this to 82 million barrels a day. We may even experience a few years of increased oil availability, lower oil prices, a stock market rally in 2003/2004 and a slight increase in world gross industrial production but other factors, like terrorism or any number of unforeseeable geo-political events may affect this temporary boomlet. If America takes over the Saudi Arabian oil fields we may even follow the red line up to the top of the graph. [just follow the dotted red line] If this

For those who wish to pursue the published academic literature on the ubject of oil depletion the best place to start is a book called "The Coming Oil Crisis" by C.J. Campbell. You can order copies of this book direct from the publisher On www.multi-science.co.uk Dr Campbell is universally regarded as the world's leading authority on these matters. A new book by him called "The Essence of Oil and Gas Depletion." Is also available from March 2003 (ISBN No. 0 906522 19 6) from the same publishers.

happens when we reach the top of the graph we won't just fall down the mountain we will be plunged off the cliff edge into the precipice. A few years ago I anticipated that America would invade Iraq but I projected, and I still hope, that America can be thwarted in its geo-oil-political ambitions to commandeer Saudi Arabian oil as well. The top of the black dotted line is the point at which the whole of humanity will have to make a stand and say, Enough is Enough. No more. Let us make do with what we've got.

The total amount of oil on the planet was about two trillion barrels. We have used, to date, about one trillion barrels and we are using it up at the rate of 26 billion barrels per year. There is, therefore, about one trillion [1000 billion barrels left], although much of this will be unusable, difficult to access or in increasingly small fields.

Graph 3. This shows 'The Ultimate' - so called because it also includes all the oil we have yet to find, but I have also added some interesting information to it.

Try to take a little time with this graph. It may just be the **most important** graph you will ever have seen. In particular there is one coloured line, the green line, [which is the only really important one] because it is the only line on the graph over which we still have some influence. In other words, there is still time to change the **shape** of this line.

Graph No. 3 represents the pattern of actual oil production and consumption from 1945 to 2001 and the **projected** production and consumption of oil from 2001 to 2050.

Human ecological history has not yet been written since it is a story that has only recently begun. Since 1950 the average human consciousness assimilates about 1 million times more information than previously.

Highly connected Western brains probably assimilate 10 million times more visual, aural and cortical stimulation than people born just 50 years ago.

GRAPH NO. 3 - A CONVENTIONAL PRODUCTION SCENARIO PEAKING IN 2007

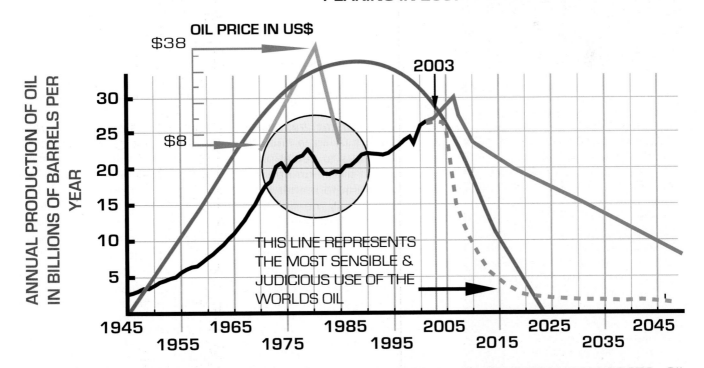

THE ORANGE LINE SHOWS HOW PRICE HIKES MIRROR PRODUCTION COLLAPSES: OIL PRODUCTION ONLY SLIPPED FROM 22.65 BILLION BARRELS IN 1979 TO 19.2 BILLION BARRELS IN 1983 - A DIFFERENCE OF ONLY 15%. HOWEVER, THE OIL PRICE CHANGE WAS FROM $8 TO $38 - A RISE OF 475%! IF A SIMILAR PRODUCTION LOSS AFFECTS PRICES IN THE SAME WAY BETWEEN 2007 & 2012 OIL WILL GO FROM $25 PER BARREL TO $118

"The world may be running out of energy but this book doesn't. This is not a standard Armageddon novel. It doesn't even specify an end to the world. On the contrary there is a sparkling new future within our grasp. But will we have the courage and the wisdom to grasp it?"

On Graph No. 3 the red line (called a bell curve) illustrates what oil production would have been like if it had been entirely uninterrupted by political, economic events or the randomness of oil wealth and oil wells. In other words, it's a kind of perfect mathematical projection. Since in life, of course, nothing is perfect and therefore not perfectly predictable, the manner in which we use up the remaining oil will not exactly parallel this perfect mathematical reality.

The line in black shows *actual* oil production until 2001. The line in green shows just one of many possible depletion curves. It is called "possible" because it cannot be precisely known in advance. All sorts of geo-political events or unforeseen oil discoveries could change the plot of this curve. We might, miraculously, even manage to use less oil!

The circle in yellow centred around the 1970-1980 period represents the first 'Oil Shock Waves'. Without these oil shock waves the black line would probably have traced the path of the red line much more closely. But, as you can see, around the early Seventies the oil production figures suddenly slumped and the worst post-war recession was induced.

Economic expectations and the need for growth requires the black line to keep going ever onwards and upwards. As the previous chart, number two showed, the effects of the Iraqi war and American appropriation of Iraqi oil may well steepen the curve, simultaneously delaying the inevitable moment of peak production and simultaneously causing a more precipitous crisis in a few years' time.

No one in the oil industry disputes that this graph – up to 2001 – is an accurate reflection of established scientific data because up until 2001 of course *the graph* is established as a *fact*. What is in dispute, or put more pleasantly, what we all have to decide, is the shape of the green line. The imminence of decline is inevitable. The manner of the decline is yet to be determined.

So why are there no government plans to deal with it? Since this information is now readily available, *how is it possible that the government has plans to triple the amount of airline passengers flying in and out of the UK?* How is it possible that, simultaneous to depletion of oil, we are planning to double the amount of traffic on our roads in the next twenty-five years? It doesn't seem to matter how many times one asks this question. There is simply no satisfactory answer coming from the powers that be. But let's keep on asking the question. The stock answer, the easy answer, is of course that we will come up with some-thing else. Some 'alternative energy'. I deal with that issue in the fourth essay. Just for the moment however it is necessary to

There is another more technical book called "Hubbert's Peak – The Impending World Oil Shortage" by Kenneth S Deffeyes, published by the Princeton University Press. The book is based on the work of M. King Hubbert who predicted in 1956 that US oil production would peak in the 1970s. No one in government or even in the oil industry believed him. Fifteen years later, in 1971, he was proved right. As it happens, the peak of American oil production didn't matter that much because there were plentiful amounts of oil available elsewhere in the world and America could afford to pay for it. It was during this time that the US administration started to befriend Saudi Arabia and Saddam Hussein. [Since then, of course, they seem to have lost one good friend and one might be forgiven for wondering when they might lose their other.] Hubbert used a scientific and mathematical analysis to produce something called Hubbert's Curve or Peak. It is because of his science that we can now be assured that world oil production is about to peak.

repeat, until you sick of hearing it, *that there are no readily accessible liquid fuels, like oil, available either now or in the near future*. We are going to continue with oil usage until the status quo cannot be maintained and there is a crisis. Alternative fuels are available and coming on stream quite rapidly but they won't fill the void left by oil.

In other words, what we really have to contemplate is how to use a lot less energy. Oil at about $25 a barrel is incredibly cheap. It is equivalent to about 15 cents or 10 pence a litre. (Most of the cost of UK petrol, as we all know, is tax). Alternative sources will not be anything like this cost and they simply cannot be got ready in time in the quantities required by Western industrialised societies.

Hoping that alternative energy might come on stream just in time is another stupid, silly, dangerous game governments use to play down the importance of this issue. A misinformed, popular optimism for alternatives simply allows politicians to put this political hot potato on the "back burner".

As if the problem with oil shortages for transportation systems wasn't a big enough problem, there is another issue that does not get sufficient coverage. Oil is the base chemical for over 500,000 everyday products. Yes! Half a million everyday things. The main uses of oil, other than for liquid combustible fuels, are: -

1. **Fertilisers.**
2. **Pesticides.**
3. **Chemicals. This includes bleaches, ammonia, etc.**
4. **Plastics.**
5. **Pharmaceuticals. Over sixty per cent are derived from oil.**
6. **Inks and printing materials.**
7. **Dyes for clothes and for paper.**
8. **Clothing fabrics (nylon, polyester, viscose etc.). Over eighty per cent of the clothes sold in cheap clothes shops comes from oil.**

These products represent the 'raw base material' for over fifty per cent of the world's manufacturing industries. Here is a sub-list of those products, just for fun. It describes, in no particular order, just a few of the everyday items manufactured from oil: - Saccharin, roofing paper, aspirin, hair colouring, heart valves, crayons, parachutes, telephones, bras, transparent tape, antiseptics, deodorant, tights, car interiors, air-conditioners, shower curtains, shoes, floor wax, lipstick, sweaters, running shoes, fleeces, bubblegum, car bodies, tyres, house paint, hairdryers, guitar strings, computer cases, pens, ammonia, eyeglasses, life jackets, rafts, insect repellent, fertilisers, movie film, film for still camera, all digital discs and tapes, ice chests, loudspeakers, footballs, combs, linoleum, fishing rods, rubber boots, car tyres, water pipes, vitamin capsules, electrical sheathing and insulation, motorcycle helmets, fishing lines, petroleum jelly, lip balm, antihistamines, golf balls, insulation, glycerine, computer ribbons, trash bags, rubber cement, cold cream, umbrellas, wax paper paint brushes, hearing aids, compact discs, cassettes, bandages, artificial turf, cameras, other items about which neither you nor I have a clue, but thanks for reading the list anyway, shoe polish, cooking utensils, tape-recorders, stereos, plywood adhesives, bonding chemicals for chipboard, TV cabinets, toilet seats, car batteries, candles, refrigerator seals, carpets, vaporisers, solvents, nail polishes, denture adhesive, balloons, boats, dresses, clothes of all sorts

Goldman Sachs, the world's biggest merchant bank, thinks we may be facing the biggest shock in oil market history. They quote the fact that American oil stocks are at their lowest since 1975 and they also point out that Opec has less spare oil production capacity to fill the gap. In 1990, when Iraq invaded Kuwait, Opec had a spare capacity of six million barrels a day but now, in 2003, the spare capacity is less than two million barrels. Over the past three decades oil prices have jumped sharply on four occasions: In 1973 after the first Opec embargo, in 1979 after the Iranian revolution, in 1990 after Iraq's invasion of Kuwait and in 1999/2000. On each of these four occasions, the hike in the oil price led to a global recession.

A Reader's Comments: -

"This is a story that seeks to illustrate the damage we are inflicting on the world through our environmental vandalism, not through doom-laden prophecy but through an amazing pot pourri of personal experiences. It will be surprising if anyone fails to find resonance in at least some of these distinctive human portraits"

Volume Two - 2003
John Peacock

John Peacock loved the smell of Brussels sprouts, particularly on a wet November day when the autumn mists mixed with the hot stink of his new diesel lorry. He had worked hard as a driver for more than eight years in order to save the deposit on his first big truck, a Scandia fifteen tonner. Since then, every day for six days a week, he had loaded up his truck with the local Bedfordshire produce: potatoes, cabbages, tomatoes, horticultural products and box upon box of Bedfordshire's most popular vegetable, the Brussels sprout, or sprog, as it was affectionately nicknamed.

from artificial fibres, clingfilm, storage boxes and, of course, not forgetting rubber bands, gasoline, diesel, fuel, kerosene, heating oil, asphalt, motor oil, jet fuel, marine diesel, butane. Oh, and most surgical hospital tubes, gloves and vital medical equipment.

Any industry that works with or manufactures or uses these products will be affected. How many people and businesses will be affected? That, at least, is one question which is relatively easy to answer. Every single business and every single person will be affected by a shortage of these items.

When confronted with theories about the imminent decline of oil availability many people respond with the proposal that we should simply drill for more oil.

The next graph shows that drilling for oil is almost complete. This graph shows that the number of oil wells drilled peaked around 1980. Since 1980 the number of new oil wells being drilled has fallen precipitously. *Most exploration for oil is now complete*.

By 2015 we will only be finding one barrel of oil for every ten that we use. Or maybe even less. The last big spike around 2008/2012 represents the desperate and probably futile attempts that will be made to drill for more oil. This will happen when the world is *really getting desperate* but it will not succeed. **It will be an act of faith and hope versus the sound seismological science of the oil exploration engineers.** The number of oil wells drilled peaked in 1980 but world discovery actually peaked in 1962. If you look at 1980 one can see that a vast amount of new oil drilling yielded very little result. That is why drilling for oil peaked. It was no longer economic to drill more and more oil wells for less and less oil. We are presently finding one barrel of oil for every five we use and this ratio is declining rapidly. It is estimated that in ten years we will only be finding one barrel of oil for every ten we use.

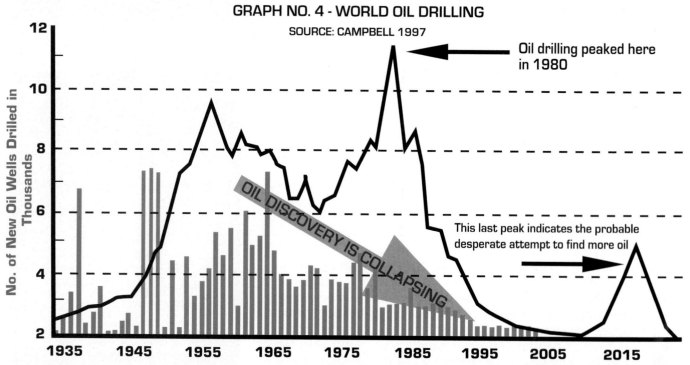

GRAPH NO. 4 - WORLD OIL DRILLING

SOURCE: CAMPBELL 1997

Oil drilling peaked here in 1980

This last peak indicates the probable desperate attempt to find more oil

OIL DISCOVERY IS COLLAPSING

No. of New Oil Wells Drilled in Thousands

THIS GRAPH SHOWS THAT THE NO. OF OIL WELLS DRILLED PEAKED AROUND 1980. SINCE 1980 THE NO. OF NEW OIL WELLS BEING DRILLED HAS FALLEN PRECIPITOUSLY. MOST EXPLORATION IS NOW COMPLETE. BY 2013 WE WILL ONLY BE FINDING ABOUT 1 BARRELS OF OIL FOR EVERY 10 WE CONSUME. THE RED BARS REPRESENTS THE ACTUAL AMOUNT OF OIL DISCOVERED.

Since 1980, the number of new oil wells drilled has fallen precipitously. British Petroleum has given up doing any more exploration and drilling. Instead it has bought a Russian oil company with established major reserves. However, most economists, or what is termed flat earth economists, simply believe more exploration will occur when there are shortages! Here's Hamish McRae again: "In any case in the short term there are alternative supplies and instability in Saudi Arabia would stimulate exploration in every other corner of the globe." Well, Hamish, I'm afraid it won't. Oil majors are packing up their exploration and leaving what few oil wells remain to be explored to tiny exploration companies with far lower costs and overheads. The majors need major oil fields to make it financially viable.

There are no major oil fields left to find.

An Extract from an interview between Jean Laherre, one of the world's leading Geo-Physicists and Dr Campbell; One of the World's leading Oil Geologists: -

LAHERRE:
"Can you explain the evidence for the coming peak [in oil production]?"

CAMPBELL:
"It is fairly obvious that before you can produce oil you have to find it. Countries often have several cycles of discovery as different geological trends are opened up. You can correlate them with production cycles after a time lag, at least in countries producing at capacity. Peak discovery occurred in the 60's and is about to be reflected in production, which in World terms will peak around 2000."

When the fuel protests really started to heat up, on 2nd September 2000, he was up there, up front, galvanising support and urging others to do the same. That was when he met Sven, a petroleum engineer from Uppsala in Sweden, who explained to him, quite convincingly, that oil was likely to reach peak production in the next year or so and that in the next few years there could even be actual world oil shortages. He showed John some fairly convincing literature which quite clearly seemed to suggest that the planet Earth had probably only enough oil to last another forty years or so, but that serious supply problems could occur much sooner. It was, in his opinion, too precious to waste. Our usage must change and, indeed, the whole 'trading' infrastructure of the world must change. John had never come across 'alternative ideas' before, but he was just at that point where he was open to new ideas. One thing was for sure, the protesters were united in one thing. They all felt that the government was completely out of touch with people's genuine sentiment. The strength of support coming from the public was unprecedented, even though many of them were being very inconvenienced.

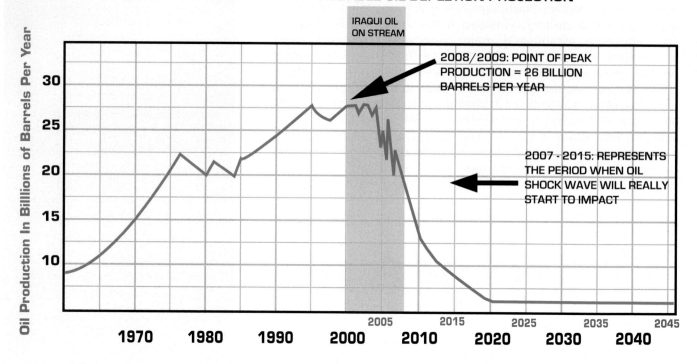

GRAPH NO. 5 - PROBABLE OIL DEPLETION PROJECTION

IRAQUI OIL
ON STREAM

2008/2009: POINT OF PEAK
PRODUCTION = 26 BILLION
BARRELS PER YEAR

2007 - 2015: REPRESENTS
THE PERIOD WHEN OIL
SHOCK WAVE WILL REALLY
START TO IMPACT

Oil Production In Billions of Barrels Per Year

30

25

20

15

10

1970 1980 1990 2000 2005 2010 2015 2020 2025 2030 2035 2040 2045

I call this the "probable" oil depletion projection because I have built into it political ignorance, stupidity, oil wars, and a general lack of preparation and foresight. *Thus it leaves only a very remote possibility that the crisis could be anticipated and its effects ameliorated by a little foresight.*

When oil production peaks sometime between now and 2010 the fall off will be intense. The World economy will contract. Just to give you an idea: If production drops between ten and fifteen percent between 2010 and 2015 [as it is projected to do] then in order to compensate we would have to bring to an *entire halt* the *whole world tourist industry.* All the planes and cruise liners, cars and trains that carry tourists. All the restaurants, hotels and all tourist attractions.

This is the scale of change we are talking about in a time span of only five or so years! Needless to say it won't just hit the tourist trade but all world trade.

The global economy will sink at the fastest rate ever seen in the history of industrialization. The World economy will contract severely and dramatically reduce its consumption of oil.

This will be the first really major oil shock wave.

We may avoid actual physical shortages or we may not. That remains to be seen. What *is* certain is that the oil price will rocket and then a few years later as supply and demand change their ratios the price will probably collapse. Speculators will no doubt see this as an excellent opportunity to drive market sentiment and makes tons of money. Little will they realise that they are driving the final nails into the coffin of capitalism.

The next oil shock wave is the Tsunami. The Tidal Wave. A few years after these shock waves oil production will collapse permanently. Never to recover to previous levels. We will survive, probably, but in what kind of shape?

Graph No. 5, on the previous page, represents a probable oil depletion projection for 2003-2050. The red line represents the history of oil production to 2003. The green line represents projected oil production thereafter. The green line peaks about 2003, which indicates world peak production. There are two main points to make about this graph.

In graph number three, the green line, which also showed projected oil production/consumption, was quite smooth. In other words it just fell away evenly. In reality, of course, life doesn't have nice smooth curves. Life is unfortunately a bumpy road, at times, sadly, rather jagged. There will be numerous little peaks and troughs and some major peaks and troughs.

On this graph the most critical point occurs between 2003-2007 and about 2013. *This is the period I deal with in my novel, the no 19 bus, in volumes seven through to ten.* It will be a critical moment in human history and it is just around the corner. Politicians and economists may try to convince us it won't happen. They are not lying – not consciously. They are merely ignorant and possibly a bit deluded. It cannot be avoided. It can, at best, be only temporarily delayed. The biggest possible change to this projection would occur if America appropriated Saudi Arabian oil and began massive oil pumping projects but, as repeated so many times, this would only delay the inevitable peak production point by a few years. *Then the fall off would be even more serious.*

Governments are simply putting off acknowledging the problem of oil energy depletion and shock waves. When they do finally wake up it may be too late. The public is, however, becoming increasingly aware that a problem is standing on our doorstep waiting to come into our homes. It would be nice to think that a political leader will react in time, with wisdom and common sense, but the lessons of history teach us otherwise. Part of the problem is that governments are unable to cope with the size of the problem. It is coming from so many different angles at once.

54

Volume Four - 2003
Johnson

"I've been quite lucky!"

"Lucky?" enquired Lady Lambert, biting her lower lip but finding her unquenchable curiosity too much even for her.

"A little bit on the lottery", said Johnson rather quietly.

"Well, jolly good for you!" said Lady Lambert, her voice just swerving off in a pang of violent, iridescent envy. It was an unpleasant feeling, one with which she had been unfamiliar for most of her life but recent financial disasters, particularly with Lloyd's insurance and the collapse of her farm, had made more common. Lady Lambert's immediate thoughts were that the lottery was unfairly discriminating towards the lower classes. Surely it was much more important that they had the money to repair the roof on their three hundred year old manor house than that the plumber should have a brand new Mercedes!

Later that afternoon Lady Lambert's daughter, Angela and Johnson spent several hours down the cellar together. It was the strangest experience of his life. It was as if she had been born to be a plumber's assistant. By the time the afternoon was over, she had rearranged all his tools in

In this scenario, during the period 2007 to 2013, **world oil production will collapse by between ten per cent and fifteen per cent**. It doesn't really matter if the lower estimate is correct, the crisis is still very real and very acute. A ten per cent drop would be desperate enough. In fact, any drop at all would be desperate because the price will start to fluctuate wildly. Actual shortages, which are forecast to occur around this time, will deal a deadly blow to the world's industrialized economies, unless we start to get prepared now! Well don't worry, *I can promise you one thing for certain.* We won't start preparing until it's **too** late to prepare.

The new parameters of post-peak production will create a very different market place. If you remember from Graph No. 3 [on page] with the yellow circle: when production collapsed in 1975-1980 the oil price went from $7 to $38. This represented a production drop of just 2 billion barrels. The oil shock wave coming in 2008-2013 will represent about 6-10 billion barrels. This drop will come simultaneously with a huge increased demand from China which is presently designing an enormous automobile industry with the help of American and German car giants. The competition for oil will be really intense. More wars? It would be quite comical if it weren't so bloody serious. The oil shock waves are, unfortunately, unavoidable. All we can do is prepare for them, batten down the hatches and hope to reduce the intensity of the shock waves by a more judicious and careful use of a depleting source. We will seriously need to reorganise and the sooner we start, right here in West Sussex, the less of an impact the decline will have. [There is no point in waiting for politicians. They are *too far* behind the mind curve on this one. They will spend the next few years in denial then in panic and finally in capitulation]. Since reducing oil supplies will severely impact the economy, what it actually means is that we will soon have to redesign economic and financial architecture to suit a *shrinking* economy. Up until now, mankind has designed many new features to the world's industrialized economies but it managed to do so because there were *huge increases* in the amounts of fossil fuels available for its use.

This time we will be faced with the prospect of re-designing new energy and financial architecture whilst simultaneously facing energy shortages.

No one is in a position to work out exactly what all this means but it is obvious to anyone who gives it even a modicum of thought that it's not going to be easy.

No one likes to be the bearer of bad tidings. Throughout history bearers of bad news often had their heads chopped off. I sincerely hope, however, that there are sufficient numbers of enlightened people who will see the coming crisis in a much more positive light. The balance will be difficult to achieve. Oil energy is required to keep the economy going. The political and business resistance in adapting to a shrinking economy will be severe in the extreme. *We are going to have to design how to live with a virtually permanent recession*. We are going to be forced to dismantle industry which is energy intensive; cars, planes, steel and aluminum making, travel by fossil fuel-powered vehicles, etc. and replace them with low energy industries that, of necessity, will have to be local.

The end result is, of course, no bad thing but how will we cope with the transition? That remains to be seen but I have forty characters in my book, their lives described between 2007 and

2012 and each of them, in their own particular way, is learning to cope. Indeed, some of them have never been happier in their lives. We are about to face a wonderful challenge.

Just to emphasize the point, here is a blow up of a graph highlighting the period 1975-1980 when we were hit with the first real oil shock waves. The oil price fluctuations correlate very clearly with the peaks and troughs of oil production. Between 1975 and 1985 the oil price climbed from $7 to $38. Simultaneously, production/consumption collapsed from 22.6 billion barrels in 1979 to about 19.3 billion barrels in 1982. Simple maths. Less oil, higher price.

THE FIRST OIL SHOCK WAVES

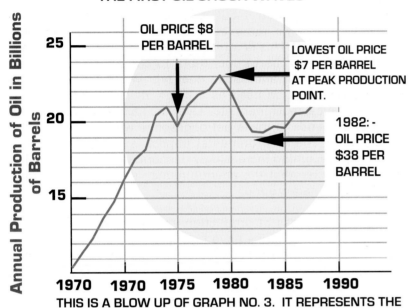

THIS IS A BLOW UP OF GRAPH NO. 3. IT REPRESENTS THE FIRST OIL SHOCK WAVES.

NOTE: THE OIL PRICE FLUCTUATIONS CORRELATE VERY CLEARLY WITH THE PEAKS AND TROUGHS OF OIL PRODUCTION. WHEN OIL PRODUCTION COLLAPSES IN 1982 THE PRICE WENT INTO ORBIT

The first world recession occurred around 1975. **No one** regards this as **coincidental**, by the way. The effect of oil price on economic growth is well established. This recession was long and deep. Anyone remember the three-day week? There was another oil-related recession in 1989/1990 that was related to the Gulf War. Then another mini global recession was induced by the mini oil shock wave in 2000. This could be considered the *'shudder'* just before world peak production. Capacity limits were being breached. In the very short term we are probably going to see great volatility in the oil markets - volatility that can only get worse in the next few years.

This information must be distributed as a matter of the utmost urgency. The longer we leave recognition of oil depletion the more desperate the future will become. In the next essay I will discuss the state of the world's financial readiness to deal with the imminence of oil shock waves.

One argument that is now being expressed by economists is that the oil depletion scenario I have described will not happen because we will start to use another type of oil called shale or tar oil. It is perhaps worth dispensing with this myth. Shale or tar is more of a solid than a liquid. As we all know tar is thick black treacly stuff that makes bitumen and asphalt for roads and roofs. In its natural state shale tar is mixed up with sand and

the proper order, wiped the handles of all his wrenches and spanners, and even sandpapered some of the glue off his old chisels and screw-drivers. By four o'clock in the afternoon the boiler was fixed and the heating back on. Lady Lambert was in ecstasy.

A Reader's Comments

"How can I describe this extraordinary concoction? A rich assortment of characters drawn from the widest range of ethnic, educational, social and economic backgrounds pursue their distinctive and evocative separate existences until fate brings them together on a bus journey as the world faces apocalypse."

A Reader's Comments

"I just asked myself: Where on earth could all these people come from. Then I looked around the railway carriage I was in at Victoria Station and I realised that was where they'd come from. These characters, these passengers on an innocuous number 19 bus are surrounding us daily. They may appear as perfect strangers but in fact they already exist inside us."

Volume Four - 2003
Jo

Jo was distracted from these thoughts by a gorgeous young blonde with tight white leggings painted down her legs and up and around her mouth-watering arse. She was clearly upset and in a hurry. She had a huge, black shoulder bag, the weight of which was pulling down a small, white T-shirt and revealing the best part of a perfectly proportioned boobie. Jo whistled under his breath and promised to himself that, when the bastard De'Ville had paid his bill, he would also treat himself to a nice little tart. He had recently noticed a new card in the telephone box near his home: "Gina – new in town." There was a photograph underneath on which was written: "This is the real me." It was a bad black and white photocopy of a shadowy Amazonian woman with superhuman thighs and breasts more brilliantly pointed than the iron railings that he was tearing out for the bastard De'Ville. As soon as he had some spare cash thought Jo, he'd pay Miss Amazon a visit.

Jo threw some larger lumps of bricks into the back of the all but crippled truck. One particular lump caught his attention. An old rusty iron railing was still impaled in the masonry. He bent the railing

many toxic chemical by products, sulphides in particular. Tar and shale oils are more like coal than oil. They are certainly oil products but they have to be **mined** rather than **pumped**. There are several major tar deposits in Canada and Venezuela. The US also has major shale deposits. Tar oil is usually near the surface and is strip mined. This means vast volumes of it are ripped off the surface of the Earth and moved by the largest lorries in the world into huge vats where the oil is boiled up to 500 degrees centigrade to separate the tar from the sand and other impurities. The waste products are then dumped. The volume of the dumped products is actually greater than the original volume of tar sand that was mined. This is because the heating process increases the volume. This is a simple law of physics. Heat expands and cold contracts. The liquefied tar oil is now processed and sold on. It can be refined into petrol but it is very expensive as all the pollutants need to be removed and the oil, being so viscous, needs to be thinned. This is achieved by reacting the liquefied tar oil with hydrogen. [There's lots more to come about hydrogen later in the essay on alternative energy]. When the tar oil has been purified it can be used as a heavy diesel oil for ships or heavy mechanical machinery etc. Over the next decade or so, the mining of tar sands to make petrol/gasoline will become a hotly debated issue. The environmental impact is apalling, but in a world that is becoming increasingly desperate for petrol/gasoline it is quite possible that the environmental issue will be pushed further into the background.

During the process of production vast amounts of water are required. Tar oil operations have been started and abandoned in many countries in the world including the US and Australia. They have been abandoned because of the economic cost. It is now assumed that as conventional liquid oil declines and the price goes up tar oils will become profitable again. The Alberta tar sands operation in Canada mines about 27,000 tonnes of the stuff every year. I use the word tonnes specifically because this product is really a solid and is sold by **weight** rather than by **volume**. Clearly only liquids can legitimately be sold by the **barrel**. **Interestingly enough just recently the US geological survey added tar and shale oils to its estimate of oil reserves. Indeed just recently the technical term tar _sands_ has been changed to tar _oil_.** This is even more interesting when you realise that tar sands only contain 10-12 per cent tar oil and 80-85 per cent sand and other impurities. Cynics suggest that these references were altered to make the world oil reserves look less serious. Many flat-earth, flat-headed, non-thinking economists are quite convinced that our energy problems can be solved by tar sand extraction. As I will shortly show you this view is nonsense and dangerous nonsense at that.

The largest tar oil operation is presently in Alberta, Canada; a multi billion pound operation employing ten thousand people. It produces about 200,000 barrels of oil **equivalent**. The word equivalent is used because when the word oil is used it can be added to international planetary oil inventories. The estimates of total reserves of shale and tar oil vary enormously, mostly because much less seismic work has been done. However it is widely accepted that it is a vast amount running into many billions of oil equivalent. In fact two tonnes of tar sand have to be processed to create one barrel of oil. One does not have to be a genius or have a degree in oil engineering to recognize that this process is energy intensive. In some instance it has a net loss. In other words, more energy is put into the process than is eventually created by the process. This should make anyone instantly think: why bother? The answer of course is that even though there is a **net** loss of energy the **end product** is more desirable. i.e. fuel oil for lorries and ships etc. In actual fact the **dollar cost** of producing a barrel of this stuff is not actually the **most important** factor, though conventional economists would have us believe that it is the **only** factor. Presently it costs about $15 to produce a barrel of tar, and many more dollars to refine it into usable fuel for cars etc. The conventional economic mindset therefore believes that as **soon** as the price reaches $25 a barrel or so the production operations will become profitable. If oil reached fifty dollars a barrel conventional economists simply assume that production could be increased ten fold or even a hundred fold! But the economic argument is not the most important one. There are other limiting factors of **far greater consequence** which cannot be overcome simply by **more** financial investment.

Presently the Alberta tar sands produces about 200,000 barrels of oil equivalent. This represents only 0.38 per cent of world oil production. To produce this amount it needs millions of tonnes of water. In fact it needs nearly four barrels worth of water to create one barrel of oil. Even as I write there is a huge local disaffection growing amongst the local people of Alberta because they are already beginning to experience water shortages. As much as 26% of Alberta's underground fresh water is being used in oil recovery and this in a country that has the second largest water reserves (per capita) in the world. Once more one doesn't have to be a genius to understand the consequences of water shortages. If shortages are occurring when production is running at 200,000 barrels per day what on earth will those water shortages be like when they try to produce just twice as much? Let alone ten times as much! It is another perfect example of how economists live in a narrow world dominated by the idea that the power of money can solve every technical problem. Economists assume that production from the tar sands will grow exponentially once shortages show up in the liquid fuel supply. In other words billions upon billions upon billions of tons of shale/tar/sand/oil will increasingly be mined to satisfy our ever increasing desire to import and export all sorts of unnecessary stuff around the globe.

An oil shockwave coming around 2007/2008/2009 will start to reduce the availability of conventional liquid oil supplies by about three per cent a year. The possibility that non conventional tar oils could bridge this gap is simply wishful thinking on a massive scale. When oil reaches peak production and the availability starts to decline by three per cent each year then there is only **one** alternative for humanity. **It will have to use less and less of it**. Using less and less will have an enormous impact on the world economy. Between 2007 and 2012/2013 the world may well have to cope with a supply that has dwindled from roughly 80 million barrels a day to about 64 million barrels a day. This is at a time when energy consumption is forecast to increase!!

Shale tar oils will not be able to make any impression at all in this deficit. As the essay on alternative energy conclusively shows pure hydrogen liquid fuels are not going to come charging to the rescue. Presently the world's political masters, economists and the transnational corporations are trying to find ways of making the world economy grow. They will need **lots of energy** to make this growth happen and there is shortly to be less energy. Over the next few years a great deal of economic voodoo will be preached by the power elite. Their faith in the markets and money to provide technical solutions will be tested

backwards and forwards and backwards and forwards with a kind of manic energy.

Eventually, it snapped jaggedly at the end. Jo picked up the rusty old railing and threw it at his truck. It missed the back of the truck and shot up inside one of the scaffolding poles that Jo had used to make up the sides of the truck. Jo did not even notice where it had gone and, since he could not be aware of the future, he could have no idea of the extraordinary role this old iron railing was to play in life's unfolding drama.

China has formulated a plan to turn itself into an automobile economy. Volkswagen, General Motors, Toyota and a dozen other world car manufacturers are investing in new plants. At their anticipated rate of increased production by 2005 China will need over 80 million barrels of oil a day.

This is more than the whole world presently produces in a day!

At the Johannesburg World Summit on the Environment in September 2002, Tony Blair was one of many thousands of ministers attending. He was given two minutes for his speech. During this speech he stated that it was very important to get all Third World countries more involved in international trade. Increasing world trade with Third World companies took up the first minute of his speech. He was quite passionate about it. It was, he stated, "the only way to get millions out of poverty." For the second minute he said the next most important thing was to reduce carbon dioxide emissions and to stabilize global-warming. Mr Tony Blair did not explain how increasing the number of huge container ships running back and forth from the First World countries to the Third World countries would simultaneously reduce carbon dioxide emissions. It is probable that he has been to the same Harry Potter film as Patricia Hewitt, the Environment Minister.

to the limits. It will come as a great shock to the power elite that some of the biggest, **indeed the biggest problems facing humanity do not necessarily have a financial solution.** It is clear to me that we are shortly to divide very clearly into two distinct camps. The power elite, the capitalists, the wealthy bankers and economists will do absolutely everything within their power to maintain the status quo. They will not recognize that they may be jeopardizing our long term future. The power elite do not regard the environment as something to be respected. They regard it as a nuisance and as such they will find ways to deal with its annoying habits. What is clearly impossible for the power elite to consider is a radical change of lifestyle but this is going to be forced on us quite soon and what the power elite **thinks** will not really be that relevant. The physical realities of energy depletion will not be reversible through technical or economic solutions imposed from the top downwards. As time goes and the international energy crisis becomes more acute **the ability to deny that there is a problem** will of course be removed. **Presently** theories such as the ones I and many reputable oil engineers are expounding can be refuted. But the time will come when the facts cannot be disputed because the crisis will actually be upon us. We will actually be in the crisis rather than **anticipating** it. By then of course it will be too late to do much about it. The choices that will confront us will be severe.

Naturally most people in the wealthy western world will be firstly determined and then desperate to preserve as much as possible of their highly developed and sophisticated consumer lifestyle. Whether they, perhaps I should say we, can do so will depend on so many inter related factors. In the next essay I will analyze the state of the global economy and its major financial structures and determine whether or not it is ready to deal with the energy crisis which is about to descend on it. Some of the information may well be frightening and I imagine that one's first reaction will be denial. How could we have got ourselves into this state? Why couldn't we have been more aware of the impending crisis sooner? The reason is quite simple. Oil is the blood inside the body of capitalism and the wealthy western world. We simply cannot believe that we are shortly to be deprived year by year of the very blood that sustains our lives in the manner to which we have been so accustomed. The only parallel I can think of is our attitude to dying. We know it is going to happen but we will do **almost anything not to dwell on its inevitability**. Naturally many people will assume that my calculations and my conclusions could be in error. Some people will think that I'm being unduly pessimistic. In fact this is not the case. I see oil depletion as an essential cycle in man's next evolutionary journey. This will become clearer as these series of essays progress. Like everyone else, I do not relish the crisis that is likely to develop but I refuse to put my head in the sand and not think about it. Over the last five years my predictions for the future have proved quite accurate. When I started writing the no 19 bus as a novel I foresaw many of the economic developments that have since occurred. You might be forgiven for wondering why I have been privileged to have these insights whilst the conventional political and economic masters of our planet did not share the same insights. The reason for this is also simple. I am prepared to look into the future without prejudice. One might remember that the word prejudice means pre-judge. I have made an enormous commitment to try and see the unfolding of human evolution from the longest and deepest possible perspective. These essays are based on the best possible academic science that I can find but science is not infallible.

My *conclusions* however are based on meditation and intuition liberally dosed with common sense. Everyone will come to different conclusions even when presented with the same information. I do believe however quite *passionately* that once the evidence I present is subjected to the *deepest* and most *dispassionate* scientific scrutiny available then the *seriousness* of this matter will become obvious. At this point humanity will be left with a number of choices. We can try to carry on as we are doing and steer ourselves towards possible oblivion or we can change course and prepare ourselves to embrace a new world.

Finally, I would like to conclude this analysis of oil depletion with some geopolitical data that you may find interesting. The map you are about to see shows, in many ways better than words ever can, the strategic importance of oil and its role in the world's hot spots: Iraq? Saudi Arabia? Afghanistan? Chechnya? Familiar names to all of us and they are all related, quite distinctly, to war, geopolitical posturing and oil.

I call this map the 'Arabian Sea of Blood' for fairly obvious reasons. I **defy** anyone to look at this map and not recognise that blood is being spilt for oil. All the red lines represent oil flows and oil pipelines, most of them, except for the ones in Iran, newly proposed by the Americans over the past ten years. The pipelines that were planned by the American oil company Unocal in Afghanistan, didn't materialize because of the Taliban but the oil blood will soon start flowing from Iraq.

One third of the world's shipping is oil tankers.

One of the biggest Saudi Arabian oilfields is called The Manifa. It is a huge field and is included in Saudi Arabia's reserves total. However the oil is unusable as it is polluted with heavy metals and hydrogen sulphide.

There is no technology presently in place to remove these contaminants. The Manifa oil basin is still on Saudi Arabia's list of reserves, however.

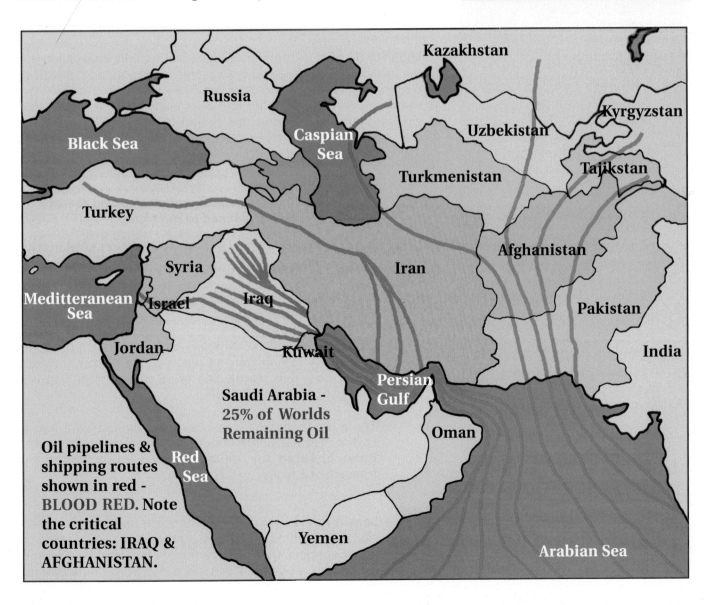

Book Two
Kaptain Krazy

When he reached the age of twelve, Kaptain Krazy developed an overwhelming urge to share his rather individual dress sense with someone else. Anyone would do really, just as long as he was noticed. Eventually, one bright summer's afternoon, Kaptain Krazy skipped school for the umpteenth time and dressed very demurely in a long, green emerald skirt, a delicately woven lace blouse and a Chinese silk waistcoat. To complete the ensemble he wore some bright red high-heeled shoes and a small black French beret. Once he had dressed and inspected himself thoroughly in the full-length mirror he sat down to apply, quite vigorously, his mascara, eyeliner and lipstick.

---*Meanwhile*---

Mrs Morgan flicked from one item on the clothes rail to the next. Behind the rail the Kaptain knelt in exquisite anticipation. Then, quite unannounced and with one great leap of faith, he hurled himself in front of Mrs Morgan. Her reaction was not what the Kaptain had expected. He had craved praise and recognition for so long that he had expected Mrs Morgan to clap her hands in delight

The US needed to secure Afghanistan to try and gain access to oil in the Central Asian states, which happen to surround the world's "second largest reserves" of oil in the Caspian Sea. [In fact the Caspian is not living up to its potential]. An 'Oil War' has been going on in Afghanistan for over twenty years. On Christmas Eve 1979 (when the Western world was distracted by consumer utopia) the Russians invaded Afghanistan. They were resisted by Afghan tribes. The Afghan tribes were then supported with billions of dollars, rocket launchers, machine guns, grenades and various other military equipment by the Americans so that the Afghans could fight the Russians with American weapons. America hoped that the Afghans would defeat the Russians and eventually, after ten years of war, they did.

Unfortunately, the country descended into anarchy with different warring tribal factions fighting each other. Then the Taliban arrived and tried to impose order on chaos. For some years the Taliban were supported by the US administration. Many major US oil companies, like Exxon Mobil and Unocal negotiated with the Taliban directly. ***In fact a Taliban delegation actually went to Washington.*** Eventually, however, Taliban fundamentalists were severely criticized for their treatment of women. This eventually became a major political issue in Washington and so the US administration retreated from their support of the Taliban. During this volatile period, Osama Bin Laden was being supported by the Americans. But when Osama discovered what Russia and the US were really doing in Afghanistan (i.e. trying to look after their oil interests) he apparently, but perhaps not unsurprisingly, grew somewhat disillusioned and changed his mind about America. He even began to distrust its motives. Osama came to the conclusion that the Americans (at least the CIA, the Pentagon and the State Department) were without honour. They never fought their own wars. No American soldier had ever been killed in this twenty-year Afghan war. During this period the Americans didn't get their own troops directly involved in battle they simply financed any convenient opposition.

This is where the oil pipelines and oil shipping routes were/are planned to run from:

♦ Kazakhstan through Kyrgyzstan through Tajikistan through Afghanistan through Pakistan to **New York**.

♦ From Iraq to Israel [via Jordan, if the Americans can buy them off] or else by sea.

♦ From Iraq to the UK: A thank-you from the US for going to war. A few million barrels a day will come in very useful now that North Sea oil is rapidly declining and world shortages are looming.

♦ There are, apparently, no pipelines planned from Iraq to France, Germany, Russia or China, the four countries who ***most opposed*** the unilateral war concocted by the transatlantic twins.

Everyone is now aware that the Americans have a vast military superiority. They will no doubt pick off the Iraqis like cherries off a tree. I don't suppose they will even blink. But of course ***most*** of the terrorists who caused 9/11 actually came from ***Saudi Arabia.***

The blood ships, the oil blood container ships will soon begin to flow out of the Gulf. The blood/oil ships are real. They are literally ancient sarcophagi, or coffins if you prefer, carrying the ancient fossilized remains of our ancestors over the even more ancient oceans where they will be sacrificed upon the altar of progress, by man, in order to gas up the atmosphere a bit more.

So the next country to find oil spilling for blood will probably be Saudi Arabia which has, according to its own reserve estimates, 267 billion barrels of oil. In fact Saudi reserves are not publicly declared. They are regarded as a State Secret. Saudi Arabia is virtually the only country in Opec that consistently under produces its quota. It does this to try to provide a 'balance' of oil supplies.

Because Saudi Arabia controls so much oil it is called the swing producer; it holds the oil balance in its hands. Iraqi oil will not increase world production for very long; four or five, maybe six or seven years at most. Ironically we may ultimately all benefit from this short window of opportunity that Iraqi oil is providing. We now have a few more years in which to prepare.

Fifteen of the nineteen terrorists who blew up the Twin Trade Towers in New York with stolen civil passenger planes came from Saudi Arabia. They are dissident Saudis of course. The real ruling family is the Saudi dynasty with King Fahd as its head. Just for the moment King Fahd and the US administration are quite close allies but King Fahd knows he cannot hold the Americans to ransom with an oil price. Over the last twenty years the House of Saud and America needed to work together for a stable oil price because it was in their mutual political interest. Most of the revenue from Saudi oil over the last twenty or thirty years has been reinvested in American infrastructure, property, company shares and vast amounts of military weaponry. Weaponry is America's biggest export. Bigger even, in dollar terms, than Hollywood. There are about thirty thousand in the royal Saudi family and at the last count fifteen thousand of them were princes. Each member of the Saudi royal family has an average income well in excess of one million dollars a year. Meanwhile the illegitimate Saudis, the ordinary Saudis, are simply aliens in their own country. Mostly the other tribes act as servants to the Saudi royal family. They are very badly paid but for many years they were very well looked after medically and socially. Recently however the country has become entrenched in its own deep financial problems. It is actually hugely in debt, mostly to the Americans and mostly for American weapons.

I imagine the American administration's ultimate long-term plan is to take over Saudi Arabia and possibly the whole of the Middle East. The powerful Jewish lobby in the US administration will then try to winkle out the Palestinians. Perhaps they will kindly offer to make them a new home somewhere else, just like the US and Europe so kindly did for the Jews after the Second World War. They might well suggest popping all the Palestinians into Iraq. This should also have the effect of bringing all the terrorists in the world together into one central area. I imagine the Americans, rich and vibrant from their valiant victory in Iraq, could just about manage to hold off the terrorists whilst they very proudly provided the Western world with much of the Blessed Hydrocarbons. When all the oil was just about gone the US would have developed its own hydrogen economy and then it could use all its spare nuclear weapons to finally blow the Arabs off the face of the Earth.

and exclaim: "Oh! How wonderful!"

Mrs Morgan's reaction, however, was quite violent. She began to shudder and, bit by bit, her huge body started convulsing. The Kaptain tried to smile at her but this only seemed to make it worse and panic and confusion overcame Mrs Morgan until finally her legs wobbled horribly and then she shrieked. The Kaptain's unexpected intrusion into Mrs Morgan's small and comfortable world was unprecedented. As Kaptain Krazy moved forward to reassure her, Mrs Morgan thrust out her hands in front of her and pushed him back-wards. He collapsed over a pile of old hat-boxes. His boyish legs stuck out from the emerald green skirt and splayed out, revealing his well-developed boyish anatomy. Mrs Morgan stared at the Kaptain's willy in complete disbelief. Then she began to laugh.

"What on earth are you doing John?" she said, giving him a hand up. "I didn't know that you liked dressing up."

"I... I ..."stumbled John incoherently.

Mrs Morgan eyed up John warily. "I quite like dressing up, too", she said coquettishly.

Four of the main ecosystems on Earth :- forests, range lands, fisheries, and crop land are in serious decline and depletion. The rate of destruction is increasing daily. Over half of the world's range land is over-grazed and deteriorating into desert.

Unpleasant data, I have always thought, should be taken with a nice cup of sweet tea and biscuits. The scenario does not have to unfold like this, does it? If enough people wake up to the fact that we actually have a **wonderful democracy** here at home then **we can change the system in time**. For all the dreadful, virtually seismic, fault lines in present day party politics we should be very grateful, that at least in the UK, free speech is still free speech.

Joining with each other to formulate a thirty-to-fifty year plan could be quite exciting. It would be a grand new adventure for us all to take together. We cannot presently stop the blood for oil. All we can do is pray for everyone's soul; for those who play this game of blood and vengeance **will** have to pay the price in **their** souls.

It is a good map I think. It gets to the basics and then beyond. Now here is a hard one. To stop the rivers of blood we need to stop the rivers of oil. We all use this blood. Every time we put a petrol pump nozzle in our cars we fill up on the fossilized remains of our ancestors. They are helping us get about. Perhaps they have got us running about a bit too much and its simply time to try and develop a less frenetic, less frantic lifestyle. For the moment of course the political will for a complete dismantling and restructuring of our economy does not exist. The need for change will be denied initially, then resisted.

Only when the oil shock waves become more frequent and simultaneously increase in intensity will the need for change, finally, become apparent.

Of course, nearly everyone during the course of reading this essay will probally have thought we've had "oil scares" before: We've had oil shocks before and then the situation settled down. Indeed we just went out and found more oil. Unfortunately, this **is** <u>true</u>. There have been many false alarms and many false alarmists.

Why is it different this time?

The oil shocks of the 1970's were political. This time they are imposed by nature. The symptoms will manifest in similar ways but the causes are entirely different.

This is the "peak" of the cycle: The science is more accurate, because most of the planet's oil has already been located. Yes, I know the boy cried wolf once too often; but as we all know, when the boy cried wolf for real one day and no one bothered to listen a catastrophe occurred.

PROSPECTS FOR THE GLOBAL ECONOMY

Is It Prepared For The Oil Shock Waves?

Oil shock waves will send shudders through the global economy. All of the world's recessions since the Second World War have been preceded by an oil shock wave. We are presently (March 2003) experiencing another oil shock wave. The oil shock waves we have experienced so far were based on a number of geopolitical factors - but the end result was the same. The oil price went up. The economy (as measured by gross domestic production GDP) went down. There is a fairly accurate correlation between the degree to which the oil price goes up (and for how long) and the depth of the resultant recession. In all previous oil shock wave-induced recessions, however, the market adjusted to the price and though the price of petrol etc went up, at times quite dramatically, we never actually ran out petrol. The oil shock wave currently reverberating around the world is in this category. Temporary shortages will lead to a price increase, the increase will lead to reduced economic activity and reduced economic activity will lead to a reduction in oil usage which stabilises, temporarily, the system. The oil shock waves which we will experience in the near future (from 2003 and for the next few years) will probably take the same form.

Quite soon however the shock waves will be qualitatively different. We will reach a point where price adjustments will not stabilise the market. There will be actual shortages. It is of course difficult to predict exactly where the price will peak. Informed experts estimate that all buyers will continue to buy at anything up to $80 a barrel. Thereafter they may stop buying because they may not be able to make a profit reselling. The oil selling price is always geared to demand but the market is always distorted by speculation. The main effect will be volatility. The oil price will play YoYo just like the stock exchange has been doing for the past few years. Only the *trend* will be *forever upwards*. Oil producing countries may decide that it is better to have a huge oil price and lower production, even if this means that the world economy will lurch deeper into recession. At this point shortages, actual *physical shortages*, will occur.

The effects on the general economy of the world, in the United Kingdom, in Sussex in Ditchling and on petrol prices at the garage at the end of my road will be quite acute. **Everyone will be affected**. How long before we experience actual physical shortages is anybody's guess. Mine is .... well, you have to read the no 19 bus to find out. There are so many different factors involved. No one can possibly know the specifics of future changes because fortunately the future has been designed to be mysterious and unfathomable. But though the specifics are unknowable the major trends are not. Oil price volatility combined with an ever increasing tendency for the oil price to rise will have a dramatic effect on the foundations of the global economy and on our local ones. Actual oil shortages will **intensify** the situation but it will also have the benefit of focusing our attention much more clearly on the crisis.

Volume Four - 2003
Krsna

Krsna had been born in Rajasthan, deep in the land of the Indian Sikhs.

Krsna was quite worried about Western consumerism and materialism. He was a natural ecologist but, yet, still a firm believer in the British Empire and its colonial past. Krsna forgave England its quirkiness and its general pomposity, even its imperial past, because it had given him the chance for an unimaginably fine life. He was, ironically perhaps, one of the very few truly proud Englishmen left. Without the British Empire he would never have had an English education. He would never have learnt English or had the opportunity to study engineering at university. On his few visits back home to India he was enormously saddened by the lives of his relatives. Almost without exception, they struggled pitifully as farmers or civil servants, barely eking out a living. He was aware that they had a richness of human relationships which seemed forever to compensate for their lack of material security, and he never ceased to marvel at how generous they were with what little they had to share. He found it odd that the Indians remained, for the most part, cheerful and

The impact of the present oil shock wave has already had dramatic effects and it isn't just oil. *A few weeks ago, in February 2003, gas prices jumped forty-one per cent in one day in the USA*.

Oil at today's spot prices on 1st March 2003 are nearing $40 a barrel. A few years ago it was less than $15. Gasoline prices in March 2003 in the USA have gone up forty per cent.

This volatility will have an impact on the global financial economy. Oil is its lifeblood. It is the essential energy inside the system. It keeps cars on the road, planes in the sky and ships on the sea. It fuels factories and heats our homes. It is the most basic raw cost of all manufacturing production.

Most people are aware that the global economy has been in the doldrums for a few years. Since the mini oil shock, in fact, which occurred in the year 2000. Most people today are expressing concern over the future of the global economy. Japan has been in recession for ten years with interest rates at zero. Germany has just moved into recession and growth in the US is 'stalling'. On 5th May, 2003 the UK economy was reported to have stalled. Gordon Brown is estimating growth this year of 2.5%. Meanwhile the Confederation of British Industries reported ZERO growth for the first quarter of the year.

The debt mountain built up over the last fifty years of credit explosion cannot be made much bigger. The creation of money and wealth in society has largely been an act of self confidence and much of that confidence is about to expire. In order to counteract the downturn, the US, Europe and the UK will try to lower interest rates further but lowering interest rates is going to fail, ultimately, to stimulate the economy back to growth. The stock exchange has already had three bearish years and may well have few more when the economic impact of oil shock waves start to reverberate around the world economy. Economists say it can't happen again but I'm not sure where they get their reasoning from. No, I've just remembered, I **do** know where economists get their reasoning from. From the past.

All predictions, indeed any prediction of where the economy is headed, is flavoured by the nature of one's desires and preferences. Economists universally **want** economic growth. They want to see gross domestic product (GDP) up. Year, after year, after year. It does not matter that such a philosophy ultimately defies both the laws of nature and the laws of physics.

Economists like to talk about sustainable growth but this is a contradiction in terms. The only possible sustainable economic model is one in which everything is in a cycle. In other words everything is being recycled. Fortunately, ultimately, all systems are self-correcting because all systems have an inborn mechanism to seek equilibrium.

Global consumer capitalism is past its sell-by date. Why? There is not enough **excess energy** left in the system (i.e. oil) to sustain it on its present course. Let me stress that I'm not anti-capitalist. That would represent a very narrow view. My understanding is that the whole global economy will be forced, largely against its will, to make fairly urgent modifications to its modus operandi. The decline of oil may well bring an end to many of the worst excesses of consumer capitalism and global world trade. Inevitably we will all be forced to look much more carefully at the resilience of our local economies. Presently it makes "economic" sense to ship lambs from New Zealand, mangoes from India and carnations from South America. Of course it does not make environmental sense but, up until the present time, the importance of the **economic factors** has always outweighed the **environmental factors**. The wheel is now beginning to turn. The turning of the wheel will definitely have major implications for the way in which we live. Many ecologists have wanted the wheel to turn and have been exhorting governments, politicians and international corporations to take into account the effects of their activities on the environment. They have had a great deal of success highlighting the failures but virtually no success in getting them to change their ways. Now the changes will happen because of intense economic pressures.

The present global economic framework encompasses virtually every human being on the planet. There is no opt-out. Everything is connected to everything else. It is a simple law of economic relativity. Apart from a very few tribal cultures, everyone every day is required to be part of the money system and the money system is now a global framework. None of us can operate outside this framework. If this framework were to suddenly collapse the consequences for our economic, social, bodily and psychological welfare could be disastrous. During the events ahead therefore it will be important to develop a transitional economic framework. Unfortunately, we will not really start working on this alternative framework until we have a *proper* crisis in the present one.

Many people are concerned, naturally and properly, that their pensions are being steadily eroded. The UK stock market (the FTSE) is currently being held up by the equities held by insurance and life companies. That is, in other words, your and my pensions. If the pension funds take the money out of equities (i.e. shares) then the stock exchange will fall further. This could create a negative downward spiral. The economy will deflate and everything will fall back just a little bit further.

At the same time, in order to stimulate the flagging economy, our 'prudent' Chancellor of the Exchequer is busily borrowing great wodges of money from all of us in the form of Treasury bonds which are also held by pension and life companies on our behalf. Meanwhile every month the forecast for the United Kingdom's economic performance is being re-evaluated downwards. Tax receipts are dropping like a stone. Government borrowings are up. Interest rates are down. The amount of consumer debt is up. Stock exchanges are going down then up; then up and down; then really down and then back up a bit, on a day to day basis. Corporate indebtedness is going up. The price of oil is going up. Then it's going down again. The economy is going down. No, hang on, it's going back up...House prices are starting to tumble. It's enough to make one a bit seasick. The good news is that just before any system decides to move into the next dynamic system it shows signs of stress. In the financial system this manifests as volatility. In fact the 'volatility index' has recently broken all known records. Breaking out of the chrysalis and becoming a butterfly is not easy.

In the next thirty years mankind will have to dispense with its present economic model and create the architecture for an entirely new one. The timescale, or rather the time frame for this to take place is extraordinarily small. In order for the new global economic framework to be built we will almost certainly have to

accepting of their difficult circumstances, whilst the English middle classes, swamped with wealth and feather-bedded in continual material comforts, only found room to complain. He was most deeply saddened by the demise of the English character, swamped by cheap TV and tawdry magazines and the general selfishness of thoughtless consumerism.

In the new energy system that mankind will have to devise in order to preserve some of his technological advantages there will need to be a subtle interchange of knowledge. It will no longer be enough to think as individuals. We will need to interact collectively and consciously as a community. This change will not come about through political means or political expediency. It will come through the planet putting pressure on every system simultaneously.

Volume Four - 2003
Lao Tzu

Lao Tzu sat by the side of the Thames. Battleship grey water churned like great waves of wet cement around the keel of a small barge. Lao looked into the water, trying vainly to seek some deeper meaning to his life. He wanted desperately to see pure, crystal-clear water. To have something that might remind him of the purity of his childhood back in China. His mind was muddy, like the water flowing past him, and his whole being frothed up into an overwhelming greyness.

--

Activity dulled Lao's depression. For the next twelve hours or so he would dance the cooks' dance amidst the clatter of china and cutlery and stainless steel, amidst the solid thwack of cleavers on the chop boards and the sharp, catatonic babble of Cantonese. There was barely time to think. He tried to draw a deep breath but it only made everything worse. He resorted to taking small snatches of breath through his mouth whilst trying not to actually smell anything. Lao tried not to look or to think or to feel or to smell because when he did, all he saw was the relentless feeding frenzy of life devouring life. In the early hours of the morning he wrote poetry.: -

use the remaining fossil fuel energy systems in such a manner that they create the basis for alternative renewable systems. The most important thing is not to panic. Panic could sink the ship permanently.

Strangely, yet wonderfully, if we weren't about to have an oil supply crisis we probably wouldn't be about to have a world economic crisis, and if we weren't about to have a world economic crisis (and if there was sufficient oil to carry on for a number of generations just as we are) then we would have a far more devastating climactic global warming crisis! Take your choice! Not really: your future, our future, is already being shaped by events beyond our immediate control. We can't stop this ship sinking; we can only organise a sensible and panic-free evacuation.

Most fortunately the forthcoming events are outside political control. Recent events have made it clear to many people that politicians are the worst people to be in charge of geopolitical events and the world economy. America may try to cure temporarily the world's economic woes by appropriating Iraqi oil and taking over the rest of the Middle East but common opinion, common sense and intuition indicates that the US war in Iraq will just create more geopolitical instability and crisis. The world economy is on the brink of an abyss. This is a positive thing. From this juncture we may be able to initiate some real and fundamental changes. Continuing as we do, cosmetically fiddling with the same system, will no longer work but that is, of course, exactly what conventional political mindsets will do, at least for the present.

In 1997-1998, when I started writing about 2003, I predicted most of the events that have since taken place. So what of my predictions for the economy by 2007? To really find out you have to read The no 19 Bus, but here is the fascinating bit. By writing about the future one tends to influence it. For instance, if I were to tell you that I'm coming to rob your house on Friday 27th April at 7 o'clock then the likelihood of the robbery taking place is naturally far less. Writing about the future can act as a warning.

The main reason for writing The no 19 Bus the novel, and portraying the future through the lives of *people* is very simple to answer. **People** are **much** more important than *things*. People are not just economic units, they are living, breathing, intelligent, conscious, emotionally-charged, spiritually challenged souls. Presently, however, people have become helpless economic digits in a global financial numbers game.

It would be natural for most people to wonder why, if there is to be a crisis, more is not known about it. Why isn't the coming oil crisis being discussed in government, in business, and in the media? The reasons are numerous but the main reason is probably simple disbelief. Much of what I am predicting is regarded by mainstream politicians, businessmen, economists and the media as aberrant amateur rubbish. I am not surprised at this reaction. In fact I expected nothing less, but may I, in turn, illustrate the extreme ineffectiveness and downright laughable predictions of mainstream economists. In 1999, just as the new year turned, the world's leading one hundred economists predicted that by the end of the year 2000 the New York stock exchange (the Dow) would be up by an average of about ten per cent. In fact the Dow reached its all time peak on the 15th January 2000 at 11,722. Not one of the economists predicted that it would be down. Then, at the end of the year 2000, the same one hundred economists predicted that (yes, you've guessed it) the stock exchanges would be higher! They were all one hundred of them comprehensively wrong. At the end of 2001 the same process repeated itself, this time there were one or two dissenters but over ninety-five per cent predicted that by the end of 2002 the Bear market would have come to an end and the stock market would be on its way back up. It didn't happen. They were wrong again. The same scenario is unfolding in 2003. In June the stock exchange has just recovered to last year's closing levels. Where will it go from here? It's all a matter of confidence. Now the war is over and oil prices have stabilised at about $25 a barrel many people are optimistic that growth will return. For the moment let us hope that the mainstream economists are right.

Over the last three years the stock exchange has gone down by fifty per cent. So why, I wonder, does anybody ever bother to listen to mainstream economists? If you asked a hundred horse tipsters for three years in a row to give you a good winner and not one tip proved correct, would you not give up in despair and trust your own hunches? The reason for their appalling record is actually quite simple. Their predictions are, to a large extent, a reflection of their desires welded to their optimism moulded to their projections. In other words, economists, naturally, always want to "talk" the economy upwards. They are all too aware that the biggest single factor in economic decision-making and economic growth is confidence. As economists, their job is to "talk" the economy up. Fortunately, I'm not a professional economist so my analysis was not prejudiced by the same influences. I am an amateur economist and a professional ecological thinker. This platform allows me to take a much more detached view of the inner processes of the system. The system is presently coming under immense and unprecedented pressure from numerous directions simultaneously. The main systems that will be affected affect us all.

What follows is a brief analysis of the major global financial structures in play in the world economy at the moment. All these structures are intimately related.

Stock Exchanges Equities and Shares

For global capitalism to function money has to move around quickly. For companies to grow they need to invest and so they sell shares in their 'prospects'. For capitalism to prosper profits need to continually increase. Standing still is not good enough. When shareholders invest in companies they hope and generally expect to make money. The share value of companies needs to continually increase in order for investing individuals and companies to make money. The faster the value of companies goes up, the faster investors make money. The most prolific increases in share values happened just a few years ago, in 1997-1999, when telecom companies and new internet style companies started up. The worldwide web, the internet, had really only begun in 1993. The rise in their share value was meteoric, literally defying, for a little while at least, the basic laws of physics and, of course, commonsense. As we all know, they crashed back to the earth with the same spectacular speed that they had been propelled towards the financial heavens. Back in 1999, many economists were predicting a totally new economic world. They called it the new paradigm. Recessions, they told us, were to be a thing of the past. Some economists were talking, quite literally, of the Dow Jones index reaching 30,000. A year

In the old days
Before the slavery
Before clock time
The ten thousand things
Rose and fell
Regardless
Little silver fish
Were one thing
The great river
Was another
The water was constant
Now The ten thousand things
Have multiplied

They do not rise and fall
They are constant
They do not come and go
They are always here
They are deafening
And the little silver fish
Are dead.

Two thirds of the world's fisheries are being over-fished. Over 8000 fish species are in danger of extinction.

This represents one third of all fish in the sea.

After the first phase
of the war in Iraq is
over confidence will
return to the
markets. If there are
no catastrophic geo
political
interruptions the
economy will enter
another temporary
growth phase. This
will result in the
stock exchange
rising. As it rises
small investors will
be lured back into
the market. As the
momentum builds
even those investors
who suffered very
badly in the last
three years will
return to the
market. Bonds will
lose their allure as
shares start to rise.
Companies will feel
more confident and
will start to invest.
Confidence in the
system is self
reinforcing.
Investors will not
want to miss the
boat. Consumers
will continue to fuel
a spending spree
whilst their house
prices are racking up
double digit growth.

later the American economy caught a cold. A sniffle really but the boom times were over.

There is a story, possibly apocryphal, about Rockefeller in 1929. He was then the richest man in America (on account of oil). He remembers that he decided the Stock Exchange was probably at its zenith when his shoeshine boy started to give him tips about shares. Sure enough, shortly thereafter the stock exchange crashed. I also remember 1999 very well. At that time I advised everyone I knew to get out of stocks and shares. Why? Because the Stock Exchange was due for a terrible fall. How did I know that? In America vast numbers of people were beginning to trade shares on a daily basis. They were actually called day traders. At one point I remember watching an interview with two seven-year-old children. They had their own share investment group. Their respective parents had given each of them $5,000 to invest and in less than a year they had turned it into $30,000. They were not being advised on what investments to make. It was up to the seven year-olds to decide themselves. They fully fulfilled the adage that making money in this environment was child's play. At the same time, millions of Americans, and some British people in particular, were beginning to speculate on a daily basis in shares. Often, in fact more often than not, on borrowed money. These day traders bought and sold shares all day long, sometimes keeping them for only a few hours before selling them. Most of them are now bankrupt.

You could say nothing much has changed. The chance of making a quick effortless buck is very enticing and many banks and other financial corporations drew day traders greedily towards their sticky ends. But just as vast numbers of small private investors piled into the American market, the professional 'canny' investors were beginning to pile out. They had seen the writing on the wall. The chairman of the Fed in the US, Alan Greenspan, famously called it "irrational exuberance." There is perhaps another description that better suits this behaviour: "unwholesome greed". Lots and lots of the little people got badly burnt. Since then, of course, vast numbers of wealthy private investors have sold out and, as a result, the share and stock indexes have declined by about fifty per cent.

Unfortunately, however, not everyone can bail out. Pension and life companies, in particular, who hold the lion's share of the world's traded equities, have to hang on to most of their share investments. We all know the result. Pension funds are collapsing and pension deficits are increasing. Rolls-Royce, for instance, is presently valued on its balance sheet at more than £1,300 million but its pension deficit alone is actually £1,700 million. In other words it is presently **technically bankrupt**. However, due to the various manipulations in pension accounting, Rolls-Royce continues to trade. Why? Because just as equities have collapsed by fifty per cent, so the reasoning goes, they will probably go back up fifty per cent quite soon, and perhaps even more. The Post Office, BT, and in fact most major British companies have vast pension fund deficits amounting to over £45 billion.* Virtually everyone within the banking and equities market believes that the bull market will return eventually, solving the pensions equity problem. In the meantime we are told not to worry. But what if the stock market doesn't go back up? What if

---

* STOP PRESS: Latest business survey: August 1st 2003 puts U.K. company pension deficits at over 300 billion pounds.

the system is being continually hit by a series of increasingly short, sharp oil shock waves? Then there won't be many pensions left at all. The same pattern is developing throughout the industrialised world. France has recently seen national demonstrations and protests as the government tries to address the issue. The problem can only get worse because simultaneous to energy shortages and deflation the number of old people as a proportion of the population is growing very rapidly.

Over the last ten to twenty years the Stock Exchange has ceased to function in its traditional way. Originally the function of 'stock' or shares was to allow lots of ordinary people to invest in larger corporate enterprises. Energy companies, oil companies, car manufacturing companies, plane manufacturers, etc. were enterprises that could not be created or run by a single entrepreneur. Lots and lots of people needed to be involved, both in the company itself and in its financing. Today most 'stock' holding is purely speculative. The day traders, holding stock for just a few hours, in some cases literally minutes, are only the most acute examples but, in fact, vast numbers of investors are constantly buying and selling shares on a daily basis, hoping that, in the various volatile movements, they are able to make money. *On an average day the total volume, in money terms, traded worldwide in financial transactions, shares, bonds, currencies, etc. is almost equal to the entire manufactured product of the world in an average year!*

Money is now just a commodity. The stock exchange is essentially a casino, and investors are primarily professional gamblers. It is a recipe for eventual disaster but the resilience of the system is quite breathtaking. It's all about confidence. What happens when confidence in share and stockholding disappears? Where does the money go? Over the last three years many individuals and institutions have withdrawn money from equities. What do they do with it? The answer is invest into different, safer financial instruments, such as:

Bonds

What are bonds? Specifically what are corporate bonds? Well, unlike shares, they offer a fixed return. For instance, if Ford Motor Company in the US wants to raise money it may make a bond issue of say $5 billion for five years at five per cent interest rate. This means it will sell to investors a promise to pay them five per cent per annum and then in five years it will give them back their original investment. Bonds, especially in highly rated companies, are generally considered much safer than equities, but the reward, the five per cent, is fixed. Whereas equities can go up they can, of course, go down. Over the past few years many investors have opted for the relative security of the corporate bond market. It's a safe investment as long as the company doesn't go bankrupt. Unfortunately companies do go bankrupt sometimes, quite often in spectacular fashion like Enron, World Com and Marconi.

Although bonds don't go up and down in value quite like shares they can still be traded and their price can change. For instance, to take our above example, the Ford Motor Company issuing five per cent bonds over five years. It may be that after two or three years the five per cent interest Ford is paying looks like a very good rate of interest, so bondholders may sell the bonds at a profit for someone who is looking for a safe five per cent rate of interest. Alternatively, the debt rating on the

Most people will feel that the worst of the world economic slowdown is behind them. Personal debt will steadily increase. Increased growth will put pressure on the hydrocarbon energy supplies. There will be another energy crunch and another mini-collapse. Then the cycle will repeat itself until it destroys itself from the inside out. There is presently a very limited awareness of these cycles within the mindsets of those who could break out of the cycle. Although it is very hard to recognise we actually need this destructiveness within the system. We must allow it to destroy itself. We will serve nature's needs most intelligently by standing back. Or standing under. There is absolutely no need to be aggressive. Gentleness will generate success.

Volume Five 2003
Mark and Anita

The next day the weather cleared and the helicopter trip was back on. Mark still felt obliged to go, even though he had decided not to join the oil company after all. The flight was exciting, the weather was rough and, beneath them, the great watery mass swelled as if huge, grey, piteous sea monsters were rising and falling over one another in an eternal tangle of unconsummated love-making. Above, the rotor blades thrummed with energy. It was a strange yet wonderful mixture of man's infernal mechanical energy and the Earth's great natural eternal synergy.

After discarding their helmets and sorting out their luggage, Mark followed a man down four long flights of metal steps. They were descending through a massive iron gantry. Around him machinery hummed and massive generators thumped vigorously.

Everything was vibrating; even the iron hand rail shimmered gently under his hand. Eventually Mark found his room, or rather his steel cell. The room was small, just big enough to turn around in. A single bunk bed was fixed between two walls and underneath there were

company may change. Very safe companies which issue bonds are given what is known as an AAA rating. These bonds tend to offer lower rates of interest because they are regarded as the safest. If, however, the financial strength of the issuing company deteriorates then the bonds will be considered less safe and, as a result, in order to sell them, a higher rate of interest will have to be offered. Credit ratings go from AAA all the way down to what are called 'junk bonds'. The name speaks for itself. Junk bonds, just like goods at a jumble sale, are cheaper to buy but offer very high rates of interest, at least while a company stays in existence. There are billions upon billions of junk bonds in existence in the market today. In the event of a large number of corporate collapses, it would be the junk bonds that would collapse in value first. Thus, though bonds are generally safer than equities, they can change in value according to how well the company is doing. For those looking for the safest haven of all, you have to turn to treasuries.

Treasuries

Treasury bonds are considered to be the safest form of investment because they are issued by sovereign governments who are not expected, ever, to default. Naturally, treasuries issued by the US, Europe and, still perhaps a little surprisingly, Japan, are regarded as the safest of all. Countries however do occasionally go bankrupt and default on their debts. Russia, in the 1990s, is the main example and Argentina is the most recent one. Treasuries are basically the means by which governments borrow money from people and from financial institutions. Because they are generally regarded as perfectly safe, they offer very low rates of interest and often over very long periods of time; up to thirty years in fact. Just presently the US is issuing treasuries at an unprecedented rate of knots to cover its massive budget deficits and its war in the Middle East. Indeed, so is our delightfully prudent Gordon Brown. The US administration is optimistic that it will be able to pay off these debts when the economy races back into top gear and growth resumes its relentless upward momentum. There is presently no precedent in the twenty-first century for any major country to default on treasuries and, indeed, as long as there is continual upward momentum in the economy and continual growth, the likelihood of sovereign default on treasuries and government 'gilts' is minimal. However, though it doesn't have a precedent, the event is not impossible. Treasuries are still regarded as the 'safest bet' but they get the lowest rate of interest.

Derivatives and Hedge Funds

The financial world is now very complex. For investors who want good returns on their money but want to minimise their risk a number of equally complex financial instruments have been created. The most popular of these is something called a hedge fund. You may or may not be familiar with the terminology but those of you with a financial memory may recollect a hedge fund called Long Term Capital Management which, in 1998, almost brought the world financial system to the point of meltdown. It had accumulated billions upon billions of unrepayable debt through taking a variety of speculative positions in the market. In the end, the US federal government and various banks bailed them out because the consequences of seeing them go under were too horrific to contemplate. Since 1998, however, hedge funds have proliferated. It's quite difficult to describe precisely how hedge funds work. They are frequently run (like long-term Capital Management) by Nobel prize-winning mathematicians and scientists. They are probaly best described as 'global financial bookies'.

If you want to look a little deeper into their definition we could take a glance at the Oxford English Dictionary. Here a hedge is described (apart from being a row of bushes) as a barrier, a limit, defence or means of protection. Specifically involving betting. It also means third rate, paltry, despicable and rascally. It further defines the word hedge as "to secure oneself against a loss by entering into contracts which balance one another, and it also means to go aside from the straight way, to shift, shuffle, dodge and generally dissemble. All these definitions are probably appropriate. They describe the function of hedge funds perfectly. In the uncertain and dangerous financial waters in which most of today's speculators are currently swimming (drowning?) they can make a lot of sense. It's simply a matter of not putting all one's eggs in one basket for fear they might all break at once. Unfortunately for long-term Capital Management, that's exactly what happened. Everything started to go in the wrong direction at the wrong time. It shouldn't have happened but it did. It defied all the odds but then that is why we have odds - in order for them to be defied. A similar strange phenomenon has been happening in the world economy for some years now. When the phenomenal bull years of the market took place in the late Nineties and American GDP roared away like a runaway tiger, inflation, according to conventional economic theory, should also have risen and then interest rates should have risen to rein back in the runaway inflation. None of this happened. Inflation remained subdued and interest rates remained very low. It is almost certainly because the world financial systems are running out of 'energy' to sustain their desired "continual growth phase."

Hedge funds are designed essentially to try and minimise risk and maximise profit. Some have been incredibly, breathtakingly successful. George Soros, the billionaire hedge fund investor-cum-philosopher, made a fortune for himself and his clients out of the most successful hedge fund of all time: the Quantum Fund. George, if you remember, is the one who took a huge bet on the British pound coming out of the European exchange rate. In fact he has been, at times, accused of being the architect of the pound's downfall. He has since been mostly forgiven because, ironically, even though no one wanted it at the time, coming out of the European exchange-rate mechanism was the best thing for the pound and the British economy, at least in the short term.

Hedge funds make various bets on the expectation that they will go in different directions and hopefully balance one another out. They are designed primarily to limit risk just as a bookie might lay-off a large bet with another bookie. A form of 'stop-loss'. Hedge fund managers are currently the most successful (in financial terms) of all money managers in today's financial markets. They thrive on volatility, things going up and down like a yo-yo, and fortunately for them there has been lots and lots of volatility in the marketplace. As I write, literally, the Iraqi war has probably begun an economic disaster but yet the stock exchange is racing ever upward. Up about twelve per cent in about a week. Now here is a short-term prediction. It's a war rally on a war cry from the hurting investors and it won't last. The fundamentals will eventually return. Fortunately, human institutions, like stock markets, will be humbled by the natural, inevitable constraints imposed by nature.

some drawers. There was a tiny, stainless steel hand basin in the far corner underneath the steel riveted porthole. Mark threw his bag up onto the bunk bed and immediately went to the porthole. He could see very little as it was already beginning to get dark and the waves seemed a long way below him. Everything was hard and metallic and brittle. Everything was utilitarian and engineered. As he settled himself down in his small, steel cubicle it reminded him of many cheap sci-fi movies, for which he had a particular fondness. Below him the drilling machine and the pipes burrowed down past the choppy surface of the sea, through the cavernous stillness of the ocean's fathomless being and down, down further until the drill broke apart the Earth's ocean floor, splintering rock and shattering the sea bed, pushing and penetrating like some determined, manic worm plunging deep into the heart of the Earth and then sucking up the oil from the arteries and veins into which it had penetrated like a hypodermic needle.

Mark's anger was left for the way people treated the Earth and the way people treated each other. He could not bear to watch much news coverage on TV and he seldom, if ever, looked at newspapers. He found an episode of EastEnders so emotionally distressing he could not sleep. For some completely inexplicable reason he felt responsible for all the horrible things that were happening in the world and, simultaneously, a helplessness. He understood the strange irony of his feelings. He was intelligent enough to realise that in his own simple life he was not adding to the catalogue of human misery but, at the same time, he was bitterly and deeply aware that he was doing nothing constructive or useful towards making the world a better place.

He regarded his gardening as an extension of nature's maintenance programme. He was a servant of the organic world. He was not sure where his awesome helplessness came from. He did not understand why man's soul seemed dissatisfied with the simple qualities of life. He did not understand the religious fanaticism or the frenetic schisms with which the majority of men seemed endowed, nor the passionate desire for sexual gratification and financial success. Most significantly of all, he did not understand why the people in the world around him seemed incapable of understanding the horror of the world they were making.

Secondary Debt

Secondary debt is much simpler to understand than hedging. To give you an example: Mrs G from Woking owes £3,000 on credit cards, £3,000 in bank loans and £4,000 on store credit cards. Most of them are non-performing. In other words, she's finding it very difficult to pay them off. Because she's always late in her payments she is now being charged fantastic rates of interest. In some cases she is being charged compound interest. In other words, Mrs G is now paying interest on the interest. She is in pretty desperate straits and is wondering what on earth she could do. Fortunately she sees an advert on daytime TV. A very friendly and clever finance company assures her that they can sort out her financial problems, reduce her outgoings dramatically and even leave her enough for a nice holiday to Barbados. It sounds very attractive and Mrs G applies. Her £10,000 of accumulated debt is lumped together (consolidated) into one long term loan, often over five years or more at a much more acceptable rate of interest, **perhaps fifteen per cent**. She is now paying only £400 per month for five years. She also added an extra £1,000 to the loan to take that well deserved and much needed holiday in Barbados. [Mrs G felt it was essential to escape all the dreadful stress that occurred as she was getting into debt.] Unfortunately, Mrs G finds that Barbados is quite expensive. This however is no longer a problem. All her credit cards are now empty and just lunging at her ready to get her back into debt. Mrs G promises herself that she will only use the credit cards whilst on holiday in Barbados. When she gets home she will mend her ways. Unfortunately, after Mrs G gets home, she begins to find that finding £400 a month is, after all, quite hard work. To cheer herself up she starts to buy herself some nice little outfits from the shops on her store cards...and the story continues.

Secondary debt, i.e. buying people's primary debt and rolling it into longer and longer loan periods, is fantastically big business and is growing at a phenomenal rate. In fact it's growing so fast that last week (early March 2003) British Airways was dropped as one of the country's biggest hundred companies and in its place there entered a company specialising **exclusively** in secondary debt.

Speculative capitalism, especially secondary debt systems in their present pernicious form, is the most obnoxious method ever yet invented to insure that wealthy people can take financial advantage of poor people. Secondary debt is, almost exclusively, geared towards the lower end of the social economic spectrum. A recent survey estimated that twenty-five per cent of UK households had 'some' difficulty with domestic debt and this is in an era when we have the highest employment in history and the lowest interest rates. The fact is, in order to keep major western industrial economies on the move, it is essential to keep people in debt. If people are consuming, and thus simultaneously in debt, they will have to work that much harder. (Advertising helps a lot. Advertising is a highly developed psychological weapon aimed at fuelling people's desires).

The explosion of general credit over the last twenty years is truly astounding and every year the credit limits are pushed forward. In fact these days, in many 'finance' deals on houses and cars, you will now find 'cash-back' programmes. This means that after you have borrowed the money for the car they will also lend you a £1,000 or more to use for some other purpose. Credit repayments for furniture are often deferred entirely for three, or even four, years. Ford in America is so desperate for car sales it is offering up to six years interest-free credit! Credit and store cards are ever more available and young people with considerable disposable incomes are increasingly targeted. The degree of competition between credit cards has never been so intense. Virtually all of them offer zero interest introductions for a few months but then the interest rates revert, on average, to about eighteen per cent per annum. Citizens Advice Bureaux are besieged with debt problems that have spiralled out of control.

Secondary debt companies are the fastest-growing financial sector. They roll over debt and simultaneously roll up the problem a little bit further into the future. It is not pessimistic or irresponsible to suggest that this practice is merely creating a time bomb of mountainous debt. You can only roll up debt for so long before it starts rolling back on you. The reduction of interest rates to historically low levels only puts back the fateful day when the domestic/private debt mountain will have nowhere further to go but backwards. It is a debt bubble, just like the equity bubble. It is simply waiting for the appropriate moment to explode. That moment may not, in fact, be that far-off for the simple reason that most of this secondary debt is secured on property and property may well be just coming to the end of a little bubble of its own.

My house, my home.
Or my financial piggy bank?

We all know what happened to house prices over the last few years; they haven't just gone up, they have rocketed into the stratosphere. In some areas in London and the south-east they have doubled in a little over three years. This has happened whilst, simultaneously, the stock exchange/equities have gone down equally dramatically in those same three years. House prices have inflated at about twenty-five per cent a year and yet inflation has been at an historical low? What on earth is going on? Bankers and economists will tell you that a house is an 'asset' and should not therefore be included in the general retail inflation index. But what is the inflation index based on? Generally inflation is based on about a thousand everyday items and services. Food is a big part of it, alcohol, cigarettes, general services like plumbers and builders, petrol and consumer goods like fridges and cookers and microwaves. Most strangely of all, the cost of the most important thing in your life, your home, doesn't appear on the inflation index.

House prices have risen in value for a number of reasons. There is a shortage of houses compared to demand but mostly they have risen because historical low interest rates have made houses affordable, even though they are fantastically expensive. All that is also probably about to change. We may not yet get an immediate housing price collapse but, even if house prices simply level off, it will have a dramatic effect on the country's economic growth. Why? Because presently six per cent of domestic consumption, which represents seventy per cent of the total UK economy, has been created by people re-mortgaging and making equity withdrawals against the increased value of their house. This six per cent represents many billions of pounds pumped into the economy. Equity withdrawals are running at historic highs and represents nearly seven per cent of personal disposable income. In essence people are using their inflating house prices to pay for their consumption.

Can the U.S. go bankrupt?

Just over two years ago, in 2001 the U.S. federal surplus was predicted to be over 500 billion dollars: two years later the *reality* is somewhat different. In 2003 the U.S. federal deficit was projected to be 455 billion dollars [only 4 months previously, in February 2003 the deficit was projected to be only 340 billion dollars].

Thus in just two years the difference is over 950 billion dollars.

The U.S. Governement believes it will get itself out of this financial hell hole because growth is going to come zooming back at over *4% A YEAR!*

If the U.S. Government cannot get its federal deficit under control it will have to keep issuing more and more debt to finance the repayment of bonds that are due.

If people and institutions begin to feel a little uneasy about buying government debt then the U.S. will have to offer higher rates of interest to entice them to buy. Higher interest rates? Coupled with deflation?

- A bizarre situation but perfectly understandable: we are beginning to reach the beginning of the end of the line: we cannot create any more money. We cannot borrow our way out of resource shortages.

Volume Five - 2003
Michel

Michel looked adoringly at Peter as he lay asleep in bed. He always seemed most peaceful when he was asleep. His face relaxed just a little and the strained creases in his forehead melted away. Michel's heart was bursting because Peter was dying and there was nothing that could be done about it. Almost every night now Michel had to wipe away the hot and cold beads of sweat. Peter's temperature oscillated like a yo-yo. AIDS was such a terrible thing. A waste. Lovingly, Michel pulled up the bedclothes around Peter's neck and plumped up his pillows.

It took many months before the two of them developed any kind of relationship. Peter, once gregarious, had been forced by his disease to become a loner. Michel suspected, indeed he knew intuitively, that Peter had AIDS, months before he told him. The night he did tell him, in a restaurant in Camden Town, Michel leaned across the table and kissed him quite forcibly on the lips. They had both nearly cried but they were neither of them exhibitionists and they bit back their tears. It was love. Love for each other. They both knew, of course, that the AIDS thing hung over Peter like the Sword of Damocles but it did not affect their falling in love. Indeed, it only deepened the intensity of their feelings for each other.

Consumers in the Western world are not used to low interest rates. You have to go back to post war [1950's] to find comparative levels. Low interest rates have lulled nearly all consumers into a false sense of security over debts and mortgage payments. Debts appear easy to service and certainly as a proportion of disposable income today's debts are very manageable. In fact the *manageability* of debts has never been easier, yet, at the same time the **total** amount of personal debt is at an all time high. Low interest rates arrived at a time when the stock exchanges were collapsing. It was very easy to borrow money to buy houses. In fact with the de-regulation of the mortgage market and the increasing competition it has never been easier. Interest rates were lowered to try and stimulate a world global economy that was slowly sinking into the doldrums. The house price inflation that followed was an unintended consequence. It should have been foreseen but it wasn't. At some point it will correct itself. When will this happen? It will depend when confidence collaspes. House price inflation might even go on for a few more years. Everyone has been expecting it to slow down: but it doesn't. Many people have waited to buy their house in the expectation that house prices will go down but they have only gone up. Eventually, it will slow down quite naturally. As the market declines people will continue to wait. Thus lowering prices further. This process of collapsing house prices has nothing to do with affordability, mortgage interest rates or abundance/shortages of appropriate property. It is simply about confidence.

If someone had told you that the stock exchanges would collapse by fifty per cent over the last three years you would not have believed them. Interestingly enough it is a sentiment which is now shared by most mainstream economists. The most detailed analysis occurred in "The Economist" magazine May 31st 2003 in a fifteen page article devoted to the subject. The Economist predicts an average fall in house prices of twenty five per cent over the next four years. My own prediction is nearer to fifty percent over six or seven years. This event alone will have massive repercussions in the economy. Such a collapse in house prices will bring to an end the massive equity withdrawals which are currently running at £55 million a day. All this excess money is being pumped back into the economy to keep it afloat. But this money is not real. It has been artificially created by artificially low interest rates. One would think, logically perhaps, that low interest rates make it *very easy* for people to borrow money and one would be exactly right. However at the end of a highly explosive series of bubbles low interest rates actually indicate the end of the road. Debts will be constantly renegotiated downwards and that's why we will have deflation. The false money and false asset inflation in houses is one of the last symptoms before systemic collapse because houses eventually return to being places of refuge. Or in other words our homes.

Many people argue that a collapse of house prices cannot happen because interest rates are so low and mortgage debts are easily serviceable. The experience in Japan shows this to be a false assumption. House prices in Japan are now almost exactly half what they were before their stock exchange bubble burst in the early 1990's. Ominously the collapse in property prices occurred almost exactly three years after the collapse of the stock exchange.

Thirteen per cent of house purchases in London over the last three years has been as investment. Much of the money was taken out of the stock exchange and reinvested in private housing because it offered a much better rate of return but this particular inflationary bubble has already come to an end. At the end of the day what bursts the bubble is simply confidence and sentiment. When stock exchanges start to sink investors start to ask. Should we bail out now? When enough of them bail out then stock prices collapse. The same is equally true of the housing market. Like all markets when the bubble eventually bursts there is an over correction.

The Economist magazine, the mouthpiece of assertive optimistic capitalism, is already predicting a twenty five per cent collapse. The Economist is quite aware that its **influence is so profound** that it enters into the realm of self-fulfilling prophecy. Although it is probably too late the mainstream economists are beginning to realise that this bubble like all bubbles before it, has occurred because it has gone on for far too long. House prices will decline, with luck fairly slowly, because people will still be prepared to buy some houses as homes but house prices will never again reach these extraordinarily stupid and unrealistic valuations. Just like oil; house assets are moving into an era of depletion.

The Economist goes on to state that "a bout of deflation, [as some economists fear] would make prices plunge even more steeply".

This is clearly frightening for many people. I am often asked what one should do? The answer I give is however not based on conventional economic thinking. From the point of view of your personal financial welfare the best thing to do when house prices are collapsing is to sell your house as quickly as possible. But this is to assume that your house is merely a financial asset and not a home. If everyone tries to bail out then the problem deepens and **all of us** are more profoundly affected. So maybe it is time to think about how we are all connected to this economy. Maybe it is time to wake up to the fact that we need to work together to create fair and equitable conditions for all. In this respect, Capitalism has surely also failed us but since an impractical idealism called communism failed it has been the **only** alternative.

The effect of a house price collapse will be profound and it will come just at the wrong time for the economy. Most people who own their own house will not, at least initially, be happy when the value of their house collaspes. Everything is relative. What with the oil shock waves and deflation; stagnating industrial growth; increasing taxes to pay for increasing government deficits, well...the **positive side** of all this gets harder and harder to see but **there is** a positive side.

My prediction is that debt will become so immovable that interest rates will sink towards zero. Debts will be constantly **re-negotiated** as there is little chance of recovering the debt through foreclosure since this will only deepen the problem further.

It is all part of the process, the very necessary process, of slowing down.

Many people have been aware of the strange imbalances in the economy over the last few years but now all these different stresses are being taken to their limits. The reason is simple but it is not yet generally understood. Capitalism is fighting for its

Barclays issued over \$3.5 billion of credit bonds between 1999 and 2001.

At the time they were issued 2.9 billion of them were rated AAA by Fitch, a credit rating agency. Today, in March 2003, only \$128 million worth of the bonds survive as AAA. [i.e less than 0.3%].

In the meantime the underlying debtors have defaulted on at least \$120 million and the value of bonds rated below investment grade has ballooned from \$196 million to over \$1 billion. Last week Fitch put these issues on negative credit watch because of further concerns about deterioration.

Volume Five - 2003
Miranda

She was late. She had only fourteen minutes to complete the household chores. Suddenly her thin arms started to flash. Cups and saucers were swept haphazardly into the dishwasher. Miranda moved without grace or calmness of spirit. Each action was forced from her reluctantly. The floor was swept briskly and lumps of congealed salad cream were caught up in the black stiff hairs of the broom. Now and again she would swat a fly with the tea towel. Jars were thrown back or squeezed into cupboards already brimming with condiments, their contents dripping profusely from around their lids. The smell of her husband's curries was permanent. Large patches of the white, plastic formica were stained orange from the yellow turmeric which seemed to taste of nothing but dyed everything with which it came into contact. Rubbish and refuse, dead milk cartons and children's discarded crisp packets were shovelled into a large, black plastic bin bag until, finally, with one particularly violent movement, she thrust a large Perrier bottle into the bag. The bin bag split at the side and remnants of rice and pickle trickled stickily onto the plastic floor.

life. It is unsustainable and it knows it, but dismantling the system in an intelligent and organised manner does not, indeed cannot, occur because its intelligence 'centre' is detached from reality. Too many rich and powerful people and rich and powerful corporations have 'too much to lose.' But although the system is past its sell-by date, it will not be discarded. It will take a series of 'shocks' to finally destabilise its foundations. The short-term effect, i.e. over the next three to four years, will probably create a deflationary environment. The general economy will not get sufficient stimulation from consumer purchasing to push it out of the doldrums and into growth. There is some hope amongst bankers, economists and the Chancellor of the Exchequer that this expected shortfall may be made up by corporations beginning to invest. However this may be a false hope as the investment from corporations is also based on confidence and this has been severely dented over the last few years by the precipitous fall in the stock exchange.

When businesses see the consumer faltering it is unlikely to boost their confidence. It may in fact do the opposite. Tax receipts will fall, government finances will deteriorate. The government will probably borrow money, just like the private sector, to finance its increasing deficits. All this does is just push the problem further into the future. Many economists will argue this is how economics work. We borrow now on expectation that increased future income will enable us to repay future debts. In the past this financial manoeuvring has worked quite well. Quite often a significant dose of inflation managed to eliminate debt without our doing very much about it. Unfortunately it now seems almost certain that financial inflation is not coming to rescue us from the present debt mountain. Inflation nearly always accompanies **growth** because when economies grow and demand is high prices can be raised. Why didn't this happen recently when US growth [1997 to 2000] stormed off into the stratosphere? Because the growth was illusory. It was a bubble. It was exuberant all right but it was entirely irrational. In fact, eventually when the oil shock waves really start impacting, we will have, simutaneous financial deflation and product/consumables **inflation**. Anything made with oil, or anything including our basic food, will become dramatically more expensive but all financial assets, shares, bonds and treasuries will deflate. This is not a paradox, it merely indicates the system is about to sing out the last notes of its swansong.

The other solution to debt is growth; an increase in real net income. In other words, the creation of wealth. That also seems unlikely in the present economic scenario. We are likely to be left for some years with growth in either negative territory or virtually non-existent. Interest rates could fall a little further but they do not have much further to go. And what happens if they get to zero as they are already in Japan? For years economists have been saying that it can't happen to Western industrial economies. But it is. When interest rates hit zero there is no more ammunition left in the financial war chest. What happens to debt? It becomes a solid, inert, immovable lump.

In Japan non-performing loans represent more than thirty per cent, possibly as much as forty per cent of the banking system. In other words, the banks are actually bankrupt. Why don't they go out of business? Quite simply because companies can afford to 'service' their loans – for the simple reason that interest rates are so low and banks don't put pressure on them because they know they will be forced into bankruptcy. Low interest rates make debts serviceable but immovable.

The total outstanding non-performing loans in Japan is over $300 billion. The banking system in Japan is essentially bankrupt. Stagnation and deflation follow. For the last few years Japan has been trying to think of ways of getting rid of the mountain of bad debt but, unfortunately, the only way to get rid of bad debt is to let the companies default or go bankrupt. This could bring on an even more severe recession and you end up in a downward spiral with the possibility of systemic financial collapse. Of course the Western economies and the US will never getting to this position. Or will they?

Demographics

Demographics is the study of births and deaths. More generally the study of population ratios. In other words how many old people there are as a proportion to young people. Specifically, today, this is about how many young people are in work and paying taxes which can then pay for old people's pensions. It is an issue which will assume a great deal more prominence in the next twenty or so years because the proportion of old people to young working people is about to go through the most profound change ever experienced by any industrialised society.

In about twenty years or so young Japanese people will have to support twice as many people as young people do today. In theory they will have to pay twice the amount of tax to achieve this. In fact of course it will not be possible.

In order for pensions to keep up with present day retired lifestyles the world's stock exchanges will simultaneously need to be racking up double digit annual growth. This will also not be possible. The changes will be immense. Most Europeans are in a similar position. Italy will be the most affected.

In terms of recognising a crisis before it actually becomes a crisis, demography is in a little universe of its own because we know precisely how many people will be sixty in 2033 because they are now in 2003, *precisely* thirty years old.

Demographic ratios is the time bomb *that will go off*. Short of killing off vast numbers of old people these demographic changes are inevitable and they come with an added financial burden that simply doesn't add up. Here are two simple tables. The first table shows old people in the US as a percentage of the working population.

OLD PEOPLE IN THE U.S.
ELDERLY POPULATION (65+) AS A PERCENTAGE OF WORKING AGE POPULATION (24-64)

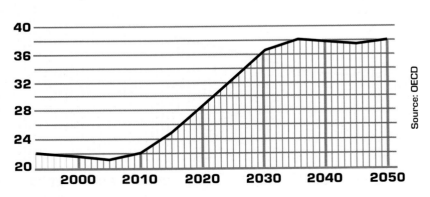

Source: OECD

"Bugger, damn and shit!" cried Miranda out loud, desperately trying to hold back the floods of tears which she knew were just ready to pour out and wash away what might remain of a useful, creative day. Of course, there were no more bin bags to be had. The tears were about to become screams. Miranda resisted it with an impressive display of self-will. She remembered her mantra, Soham Hi Decca, and started to repeat it to herself but the harder she tried to hang on to the mantra, the more elusive it became. She needed to be quiet to start her mantra, not frantic.

The bottom of the bag now collapsed and the entire contents sprayed themselves over the freshly waxed, solid pine floor. It was the last straw. She sat down in the hall next to the broken bin bag and let the sobs flow. An ocean of self-pity and misery cascaded from her. The salt burnt her delicate skin. Her anger bubbled, then subsided. She wailed gently to herself. She looked inside for that place she knew existed within the waterfall of tears. That centre from which everything was being relentlessly drained. That spot where sadness and stillness became one, where the overwhelming sorrow of life gathers itself up and taunts you. Beats you up with your own ultimate uselessness.

She was already late for work, her voluntary work down at the immigration help centre.

Slowly, life began to fill her up, not with joy but with resignation; a much worse feeling than sadness. She started to blame herself for being weak and selfish. If she wanted to write, to write about other people, she would have to become those other people, live out their ups and downs, get inside their heads, rummage about inside their hearts and float around their emotions. Somewhere, someone, she desperately reminded herself, was having an absolutely most fantastic moment.

Somewhere, Miranda reminded herself, right at this very instant, someone amongst the planet's six thousand million inhabitants, someone was in touch with paradise. Somewhere patient lovers were finally consummating their relationship now, at this very instant, wrapped round each other in perfection.

Somewhere a baby had just been born to loving parents. Somewhere, a scientist was making a breakthrough after a lifetime's work.

Somewhere, a prophet was touching his vision; a child was learning to ride a bicycle; rain was falling after drought.

The second table shows the amount the Federal government [in other words the American administration] will need to find, in billions of dollars over the next fifty or so years.

What the table says simply and graphically is that old people [over 65] as a proportion of American society are about to double in size. The table shows that in 2005 the over sixty-fives represent just eighteen per cent of the population.

By 2035 this proportion will have leapt to thirty-eight per cent. At the same time the number of people working in order to support this thirty eight per cent of the American population will simultaneously have declined from eighty-two per cent to sixty-two per cent!

More simply: from a ratio of **four to one** [workers to retired people] it will become a ratio of less than **two to one**.

In reality of course this will not happen. Old people are probably going to have to continue to work almost indefinitely by the year 2035. Hopefully, by then we will have designed a much more gentle and benign society for them to work in.

Whether we do or not remains to be seen. Personally I hold out a great deal of hope that a new world is about to be born. Birth nonetheless is never easy. Indeed I know many first time mothers who wonder if it could possibly be worth all that gross physical effort and discomfort. A sentiment, fortunately, that changes with amazing rapidity when they finally hold their new born baby in their arms.

Whilst the population ratios are switching round in most European, Australian, Asian and North American countries there will be many refugees on the move. I hope and imagine that as all our old people will need looking after we will welcome them with open arms rather than barbed wire. We might need them.

Which brings me to an American nation with such burdensome debts I can scarcely bring myself to tell you about them. [Let's forget the moral debts for the moment and simply focus on their financial management of the World economy].

Just look at table two.

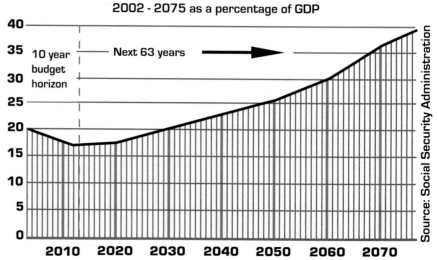

FEDERAL OUTLAYS
2002 - 2075 as a percentage of GDP

Source: Social Security Administration

Federal outlays are projected to increase from **twenty** per cent of Gross Domestic Product to forty per cent in the next seventy-five years. This fiscal imbalance, according to highly placed research scientists in America, [see note] will lead to an overall deficit of **forty five thousand billion dollars.** [US Dollars].

It looks equally impressive in numbers.

$ 45,000,000,000,000.

Let us put it another way. This amount would represent taking the wealth away, entirely, from forty five million millionaires.

Actually **there aren't** that number of millionaires in America even in today's heady times. With thirty years deflation this would mean that America would owe twice what it's worth to the rest of the world. The American nation is already in debt to the rest of the world. When the dollar collapses, as it is already doing, then this amount of debt will grow.

These same American scientists calculate that in order to finance this Fiscal debt payrolls would need to have **16 per cent** more removed from them or income tax would have to rise by **66 per cent**. Or , preferably, perhaps, from many peoples point of view, the government would simply have to **stop spending** or borrowing any more money. Financial mathematics on this scale can be truly frightening.

But doing **demographic** mathematics can also be quite stimulating. There are considerable similarities between demographics and oil depletion. They are both **chartable** and **knowable in advance**. It is no coincidence that at the point we have used half the world's oil we should all start to wonder what we should do with the remaining half. Just as in much the same way those who are currently half way through their working life might be wondering what the final half of their life is going to look like. I'm in that situation myself.

I'm certain quite a few people could feel quite frightened by the momentous changes being forced upon us and certainly crisis can be painful.

It will surely be worth remembering that crisis can be **transformative** and, once one has emerged at the other end, even **miraculous.**

Rolling Over The World Debt

The growth in the secondary debt market for ordinary poor people has had its parallel in the world of global finance which, as we all know, is primarily run for the benefit of the   extra-ordinary rich people.

From June 2001 until December 2002 protection credit insurance payments in the Western world quadrupled to two trillion dollars. That is 2,000,000,000,000 dollars. It is estimated that in 2003 this figure will double in less than a year to four trillion dollars.

Volume Five - 2003
Nicole

Nicole sat on one side of the bed and dipped her fingertips into a small, silver bowl. The sharp, tangy aroma of pure essential lime and tangerine oil pervaded the room. Scarcely touching Jim's skin, Nicole caressed the oil on to his body. He wriggled deliciously beneath her touch. Nicole could feel Jim's craving crawling up through her fingertips. It was tangible. Her fingers seemed not to make actual contact with his body but just hovered fractions of a millimetre above the skin where the soft, blonde hairs on his back were hardly noticeable. It was electrifying. He felt himself stiffen and tried to lift himself up to ease the pressure but, instantly, Nicole removed her fingers. She always made him lie completely still. It was as excruciating as it was pleasurable.

Nicole's feet climbed up Jim's calves, her toes digging into his muscles, then she was up, bent like a panther, her hands upon his shoulders, the oil slipping and slurping over his buttocks and then climbing salaciously all the way down to the arches of his feet. As she crouched down further, Nicole's nipples touched Jim's back, submerging him in a luxurious current of ecstasy. As she rode up and down upon his body, her thumbs and fingers and toes and feet caressed all the strain out of his muscles. She moved like a boat rowing up and down upon the crest of a wave, somersaulting and then tumbling down again. The wooden fan whirred above them and Nicole purred silently with delight. On and on went the ebb and flow. The balls of her feet pressed into the small of his back. He felt the vertebrae of his spine separate. He felt himself growing hard and then subsiding again, sinking into a rich seam of sensuality that was beyond the hot desire to come. As if sensing this change, Nicole paused, rolled off and sat on the bed.

"It's time to roll over!"

In July 2001 six Barclays investment bankers dined at Petrus, a posh restaurant in London. They were celebrating their ability to make money out of credit derivatives. The six of them managed to spend $66,000 on dinner.

"Protection payments or credit insurance is a financial Armageddon steadily building into imminent catastrophe. "

But you do not need to take my words alone on the subject. Warren Buffet, the world's second richest individual, describes them as "weapons of financial mass destruction." But what exactly are they?

In essence, protection payments allow lenders to pass on the risk that the borrower may default. It is a kind of insurance. It works like this. A bank lends $10 billion to Enron. The bank knows Enron is a bit risky so they get insurance companies to insure their exposure. If Enron goes bust (well it's gone bust) the insurance companies, rather than the bank, have to pay up. This spreads the risk. It operates rather like reinsurance operated in the Lloyd's market which went spectacularly bankrupt some years ago.

Here is a simple way to understand it. Say a country has one hundred banks. Each of these banks is independent. Each of the banks lends to a variety of companies. Suddenly a few companies go bust. If any one particular bank is over-exposed that also may go bust. This is bad news but there are still ninety-seven or ninety-eight relatively healthy banks left. The weaker ones, the unlucky ones, or the ones that made bad investment decisions are the ones to get weeded out. This has been the system in banking and finance up until the last few years. But recently, because banks are worried about their debt exposure, they have dumped much of their debt onto insurance companies.

The increase in these companies is breathtaking and has absolutely no parallel in the history of finance or capitalism. We are talking, quite literally, about a market that has jumped from $0.5 trillion to two trillion dollars in just twelve months from 2002 to 2003 and is going to double again over the next twelve months! Like everyone else I am bemused when I am instructed to think about trillions of dollars. I am very aware that many people are millionaires and I am very aware that a few people have over one thousand million dollars and that this makes them billionaires. But I find it hard to think that a trillion dollars equals a thousand billionaires. It is almost too big a leap to make but that is exactly the kind of leap global financial capital and our pension fund money is doing.

The reason is that banks are getting very unhappy about the levels of risk they are taking. They have recognised that if they chuck all their debt obligations into one big bundle with all the other banks and lending houses then they can all share the losses when corporations go under. In other words, all the banks are responsible, ultimately, for each other's debt. Temporary risk seems less because it is being shared out but, in fact, it just <u>concentrates</u> the risk.

The reason, amongst others, why Lloyds re-insurance went bankrupt is because everyone had eventually re-insured everything with everyone else, thus actually defeating the objective of re-insuring.

When a big company like Enron or World Com, or even a country like Argentina, goes bankrupt the hit is taken by the Insurance companies. These insurance companies work on the principle that only a **relatively small number** of companies will go bankrupt at any one time. It's no different in principle to car insurance. There will only be a certain number of car accidents so it is easy to work out the premiums. But how do you work out the premium on most of the world's increasingly shaky debt? You think its not shaky! Come on! This market has **_doubled_** in size **_twice_** in two years. Of course debt is shaky! That's why all the banks and financial institutions want to share it all out. If it weren't shaky why would you pay all that money for additional re-insurance? When bankers and economists really get to grips with the reality of these financial instruments they will realise that they have signed their own death warrant.

This type of global debt insurance and re-insurance ad infinitum is the last refuge of the world's tremulous capital and so far this insurance and re-insurance system has held up rather well. The effects of Enron and World Com and Marconi etc going bust were shared by a vast number of different but interlinked financial corporations. The tremors in the system remained just tremors. There was, most importantly, no earthquake.

Because there was no financial earthquake this Capitalistic juggling is increasingly **_justified_** by the central bankers who control our financial destinies. Indeed not only is this type of re-insurance now being justified it is being positively, euphemistically and optimistically encouraged. It seems that the only two people really worried about it are Warren Buffet, the world's second richest man and me, one of the poorest.

This type of financial manoeuvring will send this particular brand of financial instrument into the strastophere. It will be the last final balloon of capitalism. Inflated to such extremities it will destroy itself. It will be the final financial bubble to burst.

The effects of multi-billion-dollar bankruptcies like Enron and WorldCom did not cause great tremors in the financial system. So far so good.

Economists and central bankers have come to the conclusion that spreading the risk lessens the individual risk. But unfortunately it is not quite that simple. Or at least it is that simple until we get a situation where there are multiple bankruptcies. If that happens then the entire world financial edifice comes tumbling down. Could it happen? A series of oil shock waves over the next twenty years will **_certainly_** insure that it does. An oil shock wave will decimate certain industries. Some of these industries are obvious. They're the ones that are most dependent on fuel and oil: Automobile manufacturing, airplane manufacturing, shipbuilding, import/export companies; copper, steel, aluminium mining. World trade in general. However to isolate these companies as the only ones that will suffer does not take into account the incredible inter-relatedness of the whole economy.

At present these debt insurance companies work on a four per cent capital adequacy ratio. Now what on earth does that mean? It means, quite simply, that if they are called upon to pay out on their insurance claims they can afford only to pay out on four per cent of their outstanding insurance obligations. After that they are bankrupt.

Just four per cent.

It wouldn't take much of a worldwide global recession to put four per cent of worldwide corporations into bankruptcy. In fact,

A Reader's Comments

"I thought that Stephen Hamilton - Bergin's description of 2070 rather charming. Almost quaint. Definitely utopian.

My children however, after reading it simply said that is where they would like to live. One of them, a 12 year-old, asked me where this place was. I told him it's the place that you are supposed to design.

With luck, I thought it could become the world in which my twelve year old might be able to retire. The more I thought about it the more I wanted to live in this world and then the more I thought about that the more I realised I would have to spend the rest of my life, along with every one else of my generation, sorting out the mess we'd all made."

Volume Five - 2003
Norma and Fred Littie

Fred could tell his story of the tin can journey for forty minutes and not get bored. "Right! Well then, bauxite, the ore is mined in Australia, trucked to a chemical mill for reduction by about fifty per cent to aluminium oxide. Thence onto a giant, absolutely enormous, sorry," he said, "a giant container and off to Norway or Sweden, where there's loads of cheap hydro-electricity, which turns a ton of alloy oxide into half a ton of aluminium metal, in ingots ten metres long. Then it's shipped to rolling mills in Sweden or Germany, where the ingots are heated to nine hundred degrees Fahrenheit and rolled down to a thickness of just one-eighth of an inch. These sheets are wrapped in long coils and then off to another cold rolling mill, often in yet another country, where they are rolled into one-eightieth of an inch ready for fabrication. Then the aluminium is sent here, say, to England, where the sheets are punched, formed into cans, washed down, painted onto a base coast, painted with product information, lacquered, flanged, sprayed protectively inside, then shipped to the bottler." Fred stopped impressively.

"You know," continued

according to many conventional economists, more than four per cent of American companies are already bankrupt but they keep trading (through chapter 11) and they keep raising money through issues of bonds. Ford Motor company for instance was recently issuing junk bonds secured against its customers promises to pay for their vehicles over six years at zero rates of interest.

Companies presently issue bonds (or, in other words, financial institutions will still buy these bonds) because the stock market (i.e. shares) is presently a dangerous and unattractive place to put all one's investment. It is a perfect recipe for complete disaster. Essentially what debt insurance does on this scale is to expose the entire global financial system to the possibility of financial Armageddon. It may not be one or two banks or insurance companies going under. You could find the whole damned lot going down at once. Fortunately it won't happen because, according to all the world's leading economists, the world economy will soon resume its historical growth patterns. Unfortunately the world's leading economists have not factored in the series of oil shock waves which will be coming our way over the next twenty years.

The world financial architecture is now dangerously inter-connected. One piece of the jigsaw is intimately connected to the next piece. The system is set up like a row of dominoes. It is very likely that at some point in the not-so-distant future the row of dominoes will start to fall over. Then there **could** be what is commonly referred to in the trade as a systemic collapse. No one in the conventional world of economics presently believes this could happen. ***The same people, however, have not investigated or analysed with proper scientific detachment the reality of the coming oil shock waves. They also happen to be the same hundred economists who predicted every single year that the stock exchange would go up when every single year the stock exchange went down.**** The importance of oil shock waves simply cannot be overestimated. The theory of oil shock waves is being ignored. Some regard it as a dangerous fallacy.

But if it is a **fallacy**; in other words <u>if</u> there is no substance to this science, then how on earth could it be **dangerous?**

The answer is of course that the truth can be very disquieting. What I am portraying, [the final death throes of Capitalism?] may be dangerous for the simple reason that these theories may help to cause a collapse in confidence. And yet, God help me, I am trying to **restore** confidence in a process that exists beyond and behind and yet also strangely **within** the system we presently have.

If you can persevere with these theories I would very much like to think that far from **removing** confidence from the system I am actually **putting** confidence back into the system.

I hope this particular aspect will become clearer as we progress. The main thing to grasp is that there is a system beyond Capitalism but we haven't quite yet discovered how to use it. The theories which I expound in this essay are not mine alone; there are many intelligent, thinking people who have come to the same conclusions but we will, quite naturally, have a particular, individual way of analysing these issues and predicting how the crisis will unfold. In fact many of the world's leading economists and many of the world's leading governments, like America's, are perfectly aware that the oil shock waves are coming. Why else is America in Iraq? The world financial system is not actually that stupid but presently the conventional political powers are gambling that technology will charge along like a rescuing knight in financial armour and save the Western world from impending Armageddon. What they don't realise, however, is that Armageddon, as long as it is a mild dose and not a terminal one, is going to be good for us. It will be a necessary, if somewhat severe, cleansing of the system that is now, to all extents and purposes, essentially bankrupt, both financially, morally and ecologically.

Unfortunately, however, the longer we leave preparing the foundations for our future 'alternative' sustainable models, the harder it will be.

As I finished this essay the leaders of the world's eight largest economies are meeting in Evian in Switzerland.

In the final press conference the leaders were quite effusive. This was their concluding statement.

"The Iraqi unpleasantness [stated M. Chirac] *was over; oil prices were down, interest rates were low and likely to get lower. The world's leading democracies were agreed that the future was bright. They were ready to work together once more to ensure economic stability. Everyone should have the confidence to go out and spend."*

This little statement probably represents the nearest we will ever get to a Capitalist mantra. There is nothing to worry about as long as everyone keeps consuming at an *ever increasing rate*.

For the last three years the stock exchange has gone down fifty per cent and house prices have gone up by seventy five per cent. The stock exchange is now probably on its way back up, at least for a while, just as house prices are about to decline. *The system is seriously unbalanced* but the world's economic leaders cannot see it because *they do not want to see it*. They see their job as pumping confidence back into a deflating system. The Iraqi *unpleasantness* is over! What an unimaginably crass and insensitive word to use about the devastation imposed by the West upon the poor Iraqi people. As if war could *ever* be described as simply *unpleasant*.

The reason there will be a crisis, eventually, is quite simply because the people who rule the world can't see it coming and they won't even recognise that an impending crisis exists until it washes them away and yet beyond this crisis:

A Wonderful Technological Future Beckons

Furthermore, it will be built out of the *ashes of the fossil fuel* era.

Literally.

One of my most fervent hopes is that my essays will reach as large a cross-section of the population as possible. I have spoken to many bankers and financiers privately. Many of the more thoughtful ones are quite worried. They have reason to be. They should be. It is in all our interests to take on board a little new

Fred proudly, "the tin can actually cost more to produce than all the rest of the raw ingredients put together."

"Derivatives are 'financial weapons of mass destruction", opined Warren Buffet (second richest man on the planet), Chairman of Berkshire Hathaway in his annual letter to shareholders last week.

"Central banks and governments have found no effective way to control or even monitor the risks posed by these contracts," Mr Buffet concluded.

"They are," he continued, *"time-bombs" waiting to go off."*

philosophy.

If one were to take a little snapshot of technology since 1900 it would be very interesting. If I had to quickly think of six things that have most radically altered our lives in the last hundred years I would say, without hesitation:

Cars Planes Computers
Telephones Television
Nuclear Energy

The Wright brothers' first powered flight occurred just at the turn of the century. The first tractor arrived in 1904. Cars have mobilised us all immeasurably [and immobilised a few others through automobile accidents]. Planes have shrunk the great planet to a wee, wee world over which we can scarper and putter about at will. Computers have connected our brains together in ways unimaginable just fifty years ago. If we glance back over the last ten years however there has been one "invention" that has done more than anything to change the technological shape of the planet's processes. I refer of course to the internet. It is, remarkably, only about **ten years old**. It is, I believe, technology's **gift** to the end of the millennium. We now have the opportunity of connecting individual brains into a single globally conscious, locally responsible, being. The closed conventional mindsets of those who presently rule the world should not be despised. They should be pitied. The world is going to move on without them. For the moment they are in charge and they are still convinced that the continued development and growth of the world financial systems are under their control. In this respect all politicians and all world leaders are mistaken. We are but servants to the Earth's greater purposes and when we finally begin to realise this truth we will be much happier for it.

The world is about to experience some extraordinary events. The economy is about to go through the most momentous changes in a very short time span. Present mindsets will not welcome these changes. In fact, initially, very few people will welcome these changes. I don't relish them myself but I do at least realise that they are absolutely necessary if we are to be saved from our own arrogance and greed. These momentous changes are already happening but they will increase in intensity very shortly. It is clearly impossible to be precise about the timing. In the very, very short term [I'm just talking about two or three years] we may experience some temporary relief. A little boom, a last gasp at growing before we go bust. The system is literally gasping for energy. The Americans and the British have temporarily brought a little energy relief by appropriating Iraqi oil. As M. Chirac said at the end of the G 8 world conference; The oil price has come down. But for how long? The French, Russian, and Chinese governments mostly opposed the war because they were going to be deprived of valuable oil contracts that they had negotiated with Saddam Hussein. [I am talking here of governments not people.] Now that the little 'unpleasantness' of the war is over it is back to things as usual. It is time however that we realized that the main enemy we all have to face is not the psychotic terrorists or the Muslim world or the inevitability of a shrinking Global Economy. Our main enemy exists in the mindsets of those who cannot see or accept the need for change. Some people may think that I want to see the system brought to its knees. They would be right. A little humility would not go amiss. We pray on our knees.

HOW OUR OPINIONS ARE MANIPULATED

War, Terrorism, Politics, Media and the Middle East

This essay was written in the few weeks prior to the Iraqi war. I have kept most of it as I wrote it but I have partially updated it on June 2nd 2003.

In the last two essays I dealt with oil and the economy. My intention was to specifically focus on how prepared the world economy is to deal with oil shock waves. Of course attempting to predict the exact timing of the oil shock waves, and trying to determine how the world economy will respond is not an exact science. Perhaps, more importantly, the oil issue and the readiness of Capitalism to deal with oil shock waves is not the only issue confronting the modern world. It just happens to be, in my view, the most critical because it will eventually have the most profound long term consequences for our future.

The forthcoming war in Iraq seems to me to be inevitable. In a few weeks the so called "coalition" will invade Iraq on their "supposed" liberation. It now appears that no one is really certain what the motives for this war are.

When I started writing about an American invasion of Iraq five years ago it was simply based on my impression that oil was going to become an increasingly important political and economic issue. I also foresaw the increased threat from terrorism but I never envisaged or imagined it on the scale of 9/11. As a famous politician once remarked, "you can make all kinds of plans and predictions but the best of them can always be overtaken by events."

What will eventually happen? It is too easy to say "no one knows." The sun comes up every day with such perfect regularity we cease to marvel at it. Other events like the fact we are gobbling finite fossil fuel resources are also predictable. The only uncertainty is at what rate we are going to gobble them up. The depletion of the Earth's oil tanks is an event which will have serious and important repercussions for the continued development of civilisation.

So is this Iraqi war about oil? The answer is surely yes but it is not quite that simple. It is not **only** about oil. It is probably more to do with fear, paranoia and hatred but you won't find much written about that in the Western printing presses. I read recently that if one were to put all the words that have been written about this present war in Iraq in a row they would stretch to the moon and back.

I haven't tried to verify this particular statistic.

Some people wonder why I anticipated a war in Iraq over oil back in 1998. Well *actually* it wasn't that difficult because America

> The reason for the War is probably quite simple; the Western world wants to stay wealthy.

A Reader's Comments

> "Danger! This book could give you sleepless nights and wakeful days."

Volume Five - 2003
Olga Roscovitch

"Miss!" came the cry once more.

Olga stared ominously at the very large fifteen-year old boy in the front row. His name was Bog, or Dog, or something similar, she couldn't be exactly sure. "Yes?" she said eventually.

"What's the Russian word for rubber johnnies?" said the boy. He was grinning horribly and beaming at his school chums. Olga had no idea what the boy, Dog, was talking about. She was almost certain it was rude and possibly obscene. She had already been caught out once or twice before like this.

"You must explain yourself a little better first," said Olga, throwing the gauntlet back at him.

"Ask her if she wants you to give her one."

"I can do better than that!" said Dog. He fished inside his greasy, denim, non-regulation jacket and pulled out a very scruffy condom packet and held it up in the air like a prize. Most of the boys were slightly hysterical. Olga knew what Dog was holding up but she pretended not to.

"Let me see it" she said innocently. Dog threw the condom packet at

set the agenda itself for this war in 1998. In that year Donald Rumsfeld, the present U.S. war secretary, wrote that "stability in the Middle East oil fields should be a central platform of US foreign policy and that it might require American military assistance."

My prediction for the Iraqi war is that the coalition liberation will not be seen as a **liberation** by most of the Arab world. Indeed it will not be seen as a **liberation** by many people in Western democracies. In the Arab Muslim world, and with what I now know about the world's imminent oil depletion, I think a great many people will come round to the conclusion that this war was a lot more about oil than any politician **presently cares to admit**. There are one or two remarkable exceptions to this generalization.

An American democratic congressman, Dennis Kucinich, who is running for the American presidency in 2004, stated in an article in Resurgence magazine of June 2003", Why is the Administration targeting Iraq?" His answer was simple: "Oil."

The justifications for this war change daily and the arguments put forward by the American administration and our own Prime Minister are getting tenuous to say the least. That said, the motivations that have drawn America and Britain to pursue this war are not based **solely** on oil. I do not believe that Donald Rumsfeld and George Bush agreed that oil was the reason for the war. There is however a very strong **smell of oil** in the air since it would hardly have been possible to discuss with any seriousness the invasion of Iraq without also discussing the possibility of having to run the worlds second largest reserves of oil.

Whether or not the issue of owning and running Iraqi oilfields would have been considered useful at a moment when world oil supplies were becoming critical is something we can leave to your personal conjecture to determine. I imagine that the subject of Iraqi oil was discussed in political circles but I have no way of verifying this assumption. My reasoning is based on my analysis of human psychology and the observation that unconscious hidden motives can be the most powerful ones. I believe the American government believes that their war of liberation in Iraq is just that. They have to believe that because that is the only motive that could be **saleable** to the American public. The issue of oil would have come under the agenda "oil and energy security". Saddam is a monster the U.S. helped create, now he is a monster who is no longer under their control. Securing the situation is therefore a moral obligation. To Bush and Blair, oil is just a side-issue. They can only view the situation from their narrow point of view. That is why they are so dangerous.

In order to 'sell' the war to the American and British people the American Administration and Tony Blair first had to sell it to themselves.

Within the process of power, corruption always rests like a patient cancer. If the process of power develops too far in any one direction, self-regulating natural mechanisms ensure that the cancer of corruption eventually eats away at the foundations of power, thus bringing about its eventual collapse. Civilizations collapse from the centre of power. The Roman Empire may have physically collapsed because the Northern Barbarian hordes eventually overwhelmed the Roman army but the corruption of power had already destroyed the Empire from the inside out.

This ill considered invasion of Iraq will eventually bring about the demise of the present political status quo. Tony Blair's position will become untenable. Power requires massive energy to sustain it, both psychological energy and physical energy. When these facts are more publicly established there will be an outcry. Once the public becomes more fully aware that oil depletion is imminent pertinent questions will have to be asked and the media will be forced to ask them. There is an overwhelming consensus that real change is needed but change does not suit our political masters.

The Americans are desperate for more oil. No one disputes this particular fact. How far will they go to get their hands on oil? This is a question it is difficult to answer. Without it the American lifestyle, their economy and their pride will be seriously impoverished. Iraq is but the first step. Will they continue their "liberation " of the Middle East and take over other oil countries? I think they will unless a fundamental change in public perception starts to take root. But just blaming our politicians is too easy. We are all responsible for the creation of the political system that put them in power. Maybe I'm not very observant but I have yet to see any human society operate without flaws of some sort. As any old politician will tell you it isn't easy. One cannot please all of the people all of the time. However when we reach the state, as we have today, when nearly everyone is heartily sick of world politics and posturing politicians we may have reached the threshold when fundamental changes can start to take place. The momentum for political and economic change is unstoppable but not because **we all want it**. Change will be enforced on us. **By necessity**. Without the imminent oil shock waves and their effect on the world economy, political change would not occur. The changes that will occur are beyond political control. **Indeed they are beyond human control altogether**. We will not create a **new** political system. We will simply be forced to understand, respect and live by the principles embedded in the basic laws of nature.

Powerful men may seem overwhelmingly self-confident but they are driven by fear because fear is essentially a sense of **insecurity** . A kind of inner whirling wheel of worry that **one isn't** in control of the situation. Fear breeds the need to control one's environment. Clever, cunning men tend to be the most effective at controlling their environment and **that** is the reason we have the politicians that we have. It is actually quite a natural state of affairs. Fear makes one **want to change things**. Unfortunately one can be very clever and very cunning without being intelligent or wise.

Fear in America has grown into epidemic proportions since the 9/11 bombers stole American civil passenger planes and flew them into the Twin Towers. The overwhelming fear that this event created has had many diverse reactions. A major wave of fear grew from the sense that America was vulnerable. Its supremacy as the most powerful nation on earth was threatened. Its supreme, overwhelming, military might, its global intelligence systems and its vast wealth had been unable to prevent 9/11 from happening and the resultant wave of fear has induced a kind of blind psychosis.

Olga's table. She looked at it carefully.

"Should I open it?" she said innocently and the whole classroom collapsed into giggles.

"Whatever you like Miss!" said Dog with mock humility.

Olga ripped open the packet and extracted the condom. She pretended to look confused for a moment, holding it up by its rubber teat and looking at it carefully from arm's length. After a few moments she rolled the condom out, put it to her lips and started blowing into it. Half of the children were hysterical, the other half were giggling. When it was the size of a large football, Olga casually picked up a paper clip from her desk and made it explode.

"Just like boys and sex" she said solemnly. "It all gets big very quickly, then explodes into nothing."

Olga saw other cars go by, headlights streaming in the mist. Well-lit shops beamed down from above the sidewalks and the streets were full of people. What kind of world is this? She cried to herself in a mixture of strange joy and fear. It's strangerous, she said to herself, so strangerous. Was this an English word? She tried to think in Russian. It sounded rather odd. Almost

militaristic. Too practical. She wanted the passion of noise to over-whelm her again. Instead she found Timothy lean-ing down, leaning over her. "God you're gore just", he seemed to be saying. But what did he mean? What was that? Was she looking strange in some way? Yes, that was it; the colours of the lights were no longer the colours with which she was familiar. And the smell. What smell? So many smells. The armpits of the men and the warm, greasy perfumes of the women mingled inside the damp black cab. Then there was the reeling again, like being on a wheel turning inside out. Her head was in her stomach, rattling in her nervous shell of a body. It was deep, warm, it felt like death. Yet shouldn't it be cold? Timothy's tongue, wet and probing, was now in her ear.

Olga sat at the side of the great dancing hall and watched the dream go by. She had no idea of time any longer. It was no longer day or night. No longer the relativity of right or wrong. No longer defined by the mechanics of the tiny watch on her small wrist. It was about forty minutes before the Ecstasy tablet really started to take effect; the first thing she felt was her feet starting to lift off the floor. With astonishment she could

Why was 9/11 such a surprise?

Were the Americans so blind to the opinions, feelings, thoughts and cultures of the rest of the world that they did not realise how they were becoming a central focus for all the hatred and disillusionment bubbling up in the oil field countries of the Middle East? I have no way of knowing, but maybe 9/11 wasn't such a surprise. Maybe it was just the excuse the American Adminstration needed so they could invade the Middle East.

It is very difficult to see how the conflict in Iraq is going to resolve itself quickly. There are so many unknowns and so many new uncertainties. Years of repressed emotions are exploding to the surface. The coalition forces may declare their intentions of not bombing civilians but children in Iraq will have to try and sleep with the rattle of bombs in their ears. Even when the bombing has stopped, the brains and minds of these children will sleep with the rattle, the memory rattle of bombs diving down to the very deepest, most fearful centre of their being. They will have been traumatized for life. It will be a life sentence imposed by the West's brutality. It is almost certain to lead to anarchy and unhappiness. Change that is imposed from without is rarely welcome. Change imposed by violence never leads to gentleness. This lesson is so entirely obvious and has been demonstrated so tirelessly throughout the course of mankind's bloody history that one would think the human race might, by now, have learnt its lesson. No such luck!

Politicians and generals rarely experience the physical horror of war. The generals of olden days remained on the hills above their warriors. The same principles apply today but now it is all done by remote control. Bush and Blair will only see the bombs drop out of the Iraqi sky on T.V.

Today's politicians have their hands firmly on the joystick of war and they have waggled it to suit their present political purposes. It would also be naïve to imagine that this war is not connected to the economy. One only has to look at the reaction of the stock exchanges in Britain and the US to see that there is a direct correlation between the war and the economy. Indeed, there was almost a direct relationship between American military success and confidence in the stock market.

When the American military managed to overwhelm the Iraqi Republican Guard and enter Baghdad it was worth several hundred points on the Dow Jones even though wars, of course, cost a lot of money.

The war in Iraq is estimated to have cost, so far, about $100 billion. The equivalent, in monetary terms, of building ten thousand hospitals in Africa, feeding the entire world quite well for many years, or creating fresh water and sanitation for the thirty poorest countries on the planet. As a lesson in resource use at a time when resources are getting harder to find, the use of B52 bombers at 0.01 something gallons to the mile or Sherman tanks at two gallons to the mile takes some beating.

In the present Capitalistic model war can be quite good for the economy, especially if it is behaving rather sluggishly just before re-election time. It is also an excellent time to share out huge infrastructure projects to one's campaign contributors. Once the dust has settled the Americans will no doubt pat themselves on the back, feel proud that they have brought peace and security to the Middle East, start shopping again, and get the economy on a roll. The war in Iraq is all too *distant* to Americans who have been brought up on a diet of war films and fast furious action in which no Americans get killed but vast numbers of the enemy are wiped out. American media is not just sanitized it is perverted and corrupted. Many of the words that come out of the mouths of politicians are completely disconnected to *any sense* of integrity. Words have become mere political playthings to be spun like shiny glass baubles in front of a gullible public. Even our own Prime Minister has beguiled us.

Power and Fear are the two most primitive and potent motivations in the human psychological repertoire. Being motivated purely by either one or the other, or a heady mixture of both, is always a recipe for disaster eventually, and disaster is where American foreign policy is presently headed. The negligence is without precedent. To be so entirely oblivious to the effect one is having on the rest of the world is an arrogance which can exist only because power ultimately blinds the powerful. Whilst the raw energy for maintaining power, the nice oily combustible hydrocarbons, is still abundantly available, America will continue to dominate the global economy and a vast proportion of its financial wealth, but when oil starts to get scarce the American nation will be put in a temporary state of 'Shock and Awe'. Two words used, I believe, by President Bush to describe what he was going to do to the Iraqi people. At what point this actually happens cannot be determined. If it takes longer than I imagine we will at least have that much more time to prepare the ground for the new political foundations which will need to be built.

Now this might be a good point to try and separate the American people from the American Administration. In a perfect world the people and its government would be a perfect complement to one another but somehow this American administration is getting further and further removed from its founding principles: Liberty and Justice for all. It is true that all around the world, and not just in Muslim countries there is a great deal of hatred for America and all it stands for. Such an unbalanced attitude lacks compassion and understanding. To scoop a little phraseology from the great Bard: "we are all but actors upon a stage playing our various parts." Blame will not help. Much of the story of our planet and our little civilizations is being written by forces way beyond human control. This is probably, ultimately, no bad thing.

In fact at the last US Presidential election only fifty per cent of the population voted. Of these almost exactly half voted for Bush and the other half voted for Al Gore. So Bush is in the White House with only twenty five per cent of the American electorate behind him. Then you have to remember that big business and the media finance the President. Of course The Media is manipulated on a daily basis by the Government but in times of "war" when the "patriotism" card is used this becomes no longer just manipulation but actual lies and propaganda. During war the government and the media call a truce. Our own papers did the same. Once all our troops were in Iraq we all felt obliged to support them. There are rumors circulating that many elements of the military were distinctly unhappy with this war and how it has been pushed relentlessly forward by the politicians. They are most specifically very unhappy that a second UN resolution was not forthcoming. Military commanders however, as servants of

see that nearly everyone was dancing. The lights were going on and off, on and off, very suddenly, very, very quickly. No one was dancing with anyone else and yet it also appeared that everyone was dancing with everyone else. It was as if order was being carefully orchestrated by chaos and anarchy. Olga slipped away onto the dance floor. She recognised no one but yet everyone seemed completely familiar. It was not strange. That was the most weird thing of all. It was not at all strange. It was super-naturally normal. It was as if life was, at long, long last, exactly how it was always meant to be and how it was supposed to feel. It was simply ecstasy. The music came in long drawn-out continuous waves of supersonic throbbing energy. Eyes closed or eyes open. It no longer seemed to make much difference to the overall effect. It was all as one. Inside or outside. Everyone was intimately and infinitely connected.

Olga was completely unaware of how many hours she danced. Then suddenly her head went bang quite badly and quite nastily. It was a terrible surprise, her head returning so noisily and brashly. When she looked around, the dance floor was still heaving but long, slow, winding away music was playing.

She heard Russian Cossacks singing on the Siberian plains and then Tibetan monks and bells chanting in the Himalayas.

Then she heard the theme song to Postman Pat.

Or did she?

Volume Five - 2003
Professor Greenwell

In October 2000 the Sussex floods started in Uckfield, just up the road from the Professor's house. After the third day of storms and almost constant rain, his house was under two feet of water. The Professor had attempted to raise his books off the ground (there was no upstairs) by balancing them on every piece of furniture he could, but then the furniture itself had started to float. The matter was not helped by his twenty-five stone physical bulk, nor by his stamina.

When the floodwaters oozed even higher and got rather brown, smelly and insidious, an altogether superhuman and unnatural shot of adrenalin provided him with sufficient impetus to

the Government and the Crown are not free to express their personal views.

The American people cannot be blamed for having being manipulated into corruption. Ordinary American people are amongst the finest in the world just like the ordinary people in Iraq or indeed in **any** country in the world. The quantum leap that we are patiently awaiting in the evolution of the human psyche will arise when we start to celebrate **human cultural bio-diversity.** The person we should feel the most compassion for is George Bush himself. He is simply a puppet being pulled about by various members of the American administration all of whom are linked by one mechanical worldview which sees America as superior in virtually every single area of life. George Junior has probably never written a single political speech in his entire life. He has probably never had an original political thought. He is manifestly incapable of providing any new vision. In fact he is the perfect person for the job. He is living proof that the job description is about to change. Propaganda and dissembling, turning the truth upside down is a commonplace practice in war time but now, with instant world-wide communications, its effects are that much more devastating. *So it's possible to admire and indeed love* the American *people* whilst at the same time feeling both sad and sorry that their Prime Political Institution is riddled with Blind Ignorance, Imperialistic Brutalism and an almost complete disregard for the destabilizing effect it is having on the rest of the world.

Terrorism

Terrorism was the third theme in The no 19 Bus. Like everyone else I could not foretell precisely the events of 9/11 but I could have told you America, or rather the American Administration, was getting very unpopular in many places around the world. The US is, as we all know, today's super military power. It is presently spending over $350 billion each year on its military. *It has more weapons of mass destruction* than every other country in the world added together. Presently the American administration has convinced itself that it is on a mission to Americanise the rest of the world. To Americans, Americanisation is the same as civilisation. There is no other model in their psychological repertoire. For Americanisation – why not simply read: A mechanisation, or mechanistic philosophy. It is crude, brutal and righteous.

In creation opposites will eventually manifest as extremes. Both extremes, one could say all extremes, are undesirable but the fact is they feed off one another. One extreme cannot exist without its exact equal and opposite. The forces opposing American imperialism are fundamental. I suppose one could call them primitive. The two extremes, these two sides, are completely incapable of sympathizing with their opponents' positions. The only thing that matters to these two protagonists is the other's destruction.

Fortunately when two extremes manifest so profoundly there is a third reaction, or rather a 'middle reaction.' This is the desire for all things to return to some kind of equilibrium or 'middle way'. Most people today want to take the middle way but don't know where to find it. It doesn't exist within the framework of conventional democratic political systems. Politics is about the pursuit of power and the adherence to the short-term goals necessary to attain that power. In the UK we have, for year after year been bamboozled from one election to the next. Our choice narrowed down to one party divided into three. In America it's just one party, the party of big business, divided into two. Minorities are hardly represented. At the same time there is an enormous undercurrent of disaffection but with no political means of expression much of this disaffected minority simply falls into apathy. We don't vote we just complain. We are power-less. What is the point of protest? Perhaps most importantly what are the alternatives? There don't seem to be any. We no longer vote for policies since all the three major parties have the same policies. At least when Labour represented the struggling working classes and the Conservatives represented the old established landowning classes we had some *real division*. One of the great checks and balances in our present political system has been the fact that the strongest government often arises when there is a strong opposition. Simply because one has to fight that much harder for what one believes in. Now President Blair is, properly speaking, a conservative. He had great difficulty persuading his own party to go to war but the Conservative Party was behind him to the last man. Tony Blair has recognized that to attain power and then more importantly to retain power one has to be in the same incestuous bed with big business and the media. It may make for a slightly uncomfortable three-in-a-bed at times but it is essential if one is to *retain* political power.

The issue hanging over the aftermath of the Iraqi war is weapons of mass destruction. Some little while ago I was certain that they would find some because I knew that the U.S. administration and the British Government had sold lots of biological and chemical weaponery to Saddam in the 1980's. I also felt, rather cynically, that if America didn't find any weapons of mass destruction then they would plant some. Now I am changing my mind for the simple reason that the issue of Weapons of Mass Destruction is *not* the political hot potato in the US as it is here in Britain. In fact, the Democratic Party are discussing whether or not it would be politically advantageous to take an anti-war stance: Many Americans feel very gung ho about their "wonderful war leader" and apparently many of them now want America to invade [liberate] Iran. But over here the British press is driving very hard at this same issue. When it becomes apparent that the subject of serious oil depletion has been studiously suppressed by the Government we may find, at last, that this issue will start to really get some mainstream media coverage. When it does we may find Tony Blair fighting a rearguard action to preserve his political future. There is a very strong movement to determine if Tony Blair's actions in taking us to war actually constitutes a criminal act for which he should be indicted as a war criminal.

Today we can only vote for personalities not policies. We have now, finally and properly, reached a point where most politicians do not represent the central cortex of ordinary human thought and ordinary human feeling. It is time for a change. It is worth remembering that change is the one guaranteed element of life.

There is a terrorist in my novel, The no 19 bus. He is called Zafir Mohammed Allah. He is living somewhere in Brighton. No one knows where. No one knows where he came from. Our terrorist has almost infinite patience. His enemy, America, and other capitalistic allies, on the other hand, are very, very impatient. They want to settle the squabble now.

Indeed, although it has been less than eighteen months since

drag his bedroom wardrobe underneath the hatch to the attic. He clambered up, somehow, and collapsed. In order to give some stability to the wardrobe, he had filled it with the nearest available books, including an exceptional first edition of Gladstone's autobiography. Henry had no clear idea how he managed to heave his twenty-five stone on to the top of the wardrobe and into the attic. Like his books balanced in piles on the floor, the act defied the law of physics.

Outside, the thunder rolled and rolled. The gods were not just angry, they were seriously unhappy. This was a cosmic hangover of virulent nastiness. In a moment of madness, Professor Greenwell promised that if he got out of this alive he would change his habits. The rain lashed outside: an insane, irregular smash-ing of water, windborne waves of sheer nastiness. Then, just for a while, it would let up. Henry prayed that it might have stopped. He pleaded with it to stop and it did so for an hour or two. Then it started again, even more ferociously, and thunder boomed away across the valley and he knew that he was almost certainly going to die.

Volume Six - 2003
Robin

Amongst his friends Gavin was known as 'The Chemist' because he seemed to know which pill should follow which pill and in what quantity. Gavin was not a dealer. He was a user – a serious user.

Most people would not believe the quantity or variety of drugs that he could take in the average week. It was a veritable cocktail. He was always the first to try out something new and underground chemists were inventing new drugs faster than institut ionalised chemists could analyse, test and then ban them. One of Gavin's favourite cocktails included Viagra, Prozac, Vodka and half an 'E'. Understanding the branded drug schedule usually requires a degree in molecular physics or inorganic chemistry but Gavin went purely on intuition. He only had two parameters: How good a life you could have, and were you capable of getting up the following morning? Gavin's life did not run on the average Monday to Friday cycle. His indulgences only ended when he overdosed on something so badly he had to take more than one or two days off work.

During these periods he vomited profusely over everything and Robin cleared up.

9/11, most Americans actually believe that destroying the Afghans and the Iraqis has probably ended the terrorist threat. This delusion is based on their own primary psychological framework. Fast food, fast sex, fast films and fast-forward to the next invention, gadget or toy. Generally speaking [though I hate to generalise as it only ever expresses a small part of the picture] the American psychological framework cannot comprehend the quiet, meditative states of patience that direct the Muslim fanatics' mindset. Indeed, patiently waiting is the terrorist's most powerful psychological weaponry. If the American government sincerely believes that it can defeat terrorism by applying, with even more brutal vigour, its past and present foreign policies it is clearly quite desperately and sadly deluded.

American policies and UK policies for that matter have created a geo-political situation that is just perfect for the ***fast breeding*** of dissent and terrorism. What these administrations do not realise is that discontent is not uniform. ***Many*** people in the world are unhappy with government policies, ***some*** are very unhappy but most would never dream of allowing this discontent to boil over into the pure, unadulterated, fundamentalist hatred which is necessary in order to find the commitment to self annihilation. It is a spectrum of discontent from those who are just disappointed in politics all the way to suicide warriors. It is worth remembering perhaps that is only because we have a spectrum of light that we actually see anything at all. Calling these suicide fanatics cowards totally underestimates their commitment. To blow oneself up along with one's fellow human beings requires an act of perfect desperation and near ***total faith***. It is this faith that the West completely underestimates and utterly fails to understand and Oh Lord are we in need of understanding! Western international politicians need to stand back and try to understand the hatred that is being so violently bred. But do they? No, they do not. They seek only retribution which they then blindly and stupidly call justice. Enemies never simply appear from nowhere. ***Enemies are always made in the enemy camp.***

In order to bring the world back from the brink of disaster it will be essential to look to ourselves, to local communities, friends and families. As and when the crisis deepens, a sense of community could become critical to our eventual successful survival. We may not be able to make Tony Blair retreat. He is set upon his course and he will sail his course until the sun has set but, as a community, we can retreat to ask ourselves some of the most important questions about life. Indeed we can do more than that. We can defeat terrorism, and we can defeat the brutish imperialism of the American war machine. How? Just realise that they will **all** shortly become ***irrelevant***. We do not have to do anything. In fact the less we do the better. At the moment the geo political horrors are unstoppable. In order to defuse the situation we need to retreat. Jumping in and stirring up an already boiling pot of poison entirely defeats the object. We should return to looking after and caring for those in our immediate vicinity. We should not be afraid nor guilty but quite shortly we are going to have to worry a lot more about what is ***going on around our local community*** than what is ***going on in the big bad world*** out there. It will be terribly hard for the human mind to accept but we will learn much more by standing back than jumping in.

There is already a huge movement developing to regenerate local farmers, local markets, local food and local resources. This is just the beginning of a revolution. Global economics is not going to collapse **over night** and we should be very grateful that is the case. Collapse nearly always leads to anarchy. Those who are so entirely critical of the present world economy need to realise that no system will ever be perfect. The definition of a system, any system, is that it is always going in and out of balance. Otherwise there would be no movement, no dynamics. But a retreat from factionalism, partisanship, yes even patriotism, will be necessary if we are to heal the explosive and **extreme** divisions in the psyche of the human race. We should embrace our differences whilst simultaneously healing our divisions. For the moment it probably means that we will have to live **parallel** lives partaking, as most of us do, every day, in the globally traded economy whilst simultaneously planning for the time when we will have to depend on our local economy and resources. There is only one Earth. We all live on it. The Earth and its resources are finite. We cannot make more resources. We can only ever learn to use them wisely.

The word 'terrorist' is the label applied to those who cause complete, unconventional, physically destructive mayhem. Their actions are totally inexcusable, their methods grossly psychotic but our moral judgments on these matters should **not hinder our understanding**. The terrorist's destructive tendencies **have to** focus on 'soft' human civilian targets because they lack any sophisticated mechanical technological armory with which to fight the American Imperial war machine. The inequalities in technological prowess are profound. We are in the midst of the third world war but the protagonists have very different ways of conducting the war because they have very different arsenals. Indeed the contrast could not be more extreme. The immense brutal armored plating of a caterpillar tracked tank and the soft flesh and blood and bones of a suicide bomber.

I believe George Bush famously said a few days after the twin towers came down that *"You are either with us or against us."* We should all resist being taken in by such rhetoric as it clearly originates from a blind sense of revenge. **Indeed this whole idea of being merely for or against is at the root** of the psychological battle that is being waged. Most of us are sick of these two extremes. Most of us would like to find a middle way.

As always in nature at a moment of real crisis, the cell divides into two. These continued divisions and re-divisions eventually send the protagonists to the very extremes in creation where they then mutually destroy each other. It would of course be very simple for Americans and terrorists to defuse the situation. All they would have to do is realise that they have, in fact, become one another. Deeper, even, than brothers in blood. Fortunately however, as these two extremes are accelerated out to breaking point at the edges of creation, the middle ground **IS** being developed, even though this particular aspect is not immediately obvious. When politics moves so far away from the peoples inner heart, it eventually self-destructs. We may, at last, be at that point in time.

Recognising that there is **no solution** to this present war on any political, social or cultural level is important. It can allow us to relax. Our destiny is in safe hands. Out there, in the world at large, the damage has already been done. The monster Saddam Hussein has been violently poked out of his lair. If he is clever and cunning, as I imagine he is, and he had any biological weapons left then I can only imagine he has taken them away with him. Most of the toxic chemical weapons were sold to Saddam in the

The main purposes for which oil is used are food and transport.

Agriculture is entirely dependent on oil for cultivation and for pumping water, and on gas for its fertilizers and pesticides.

For every calorie of energy used by agriculture, five more are used in processing, storage and distribution.

Volume Six - 2003
So Yung

So Yung drifted with the morning sounds of birds outside and the rustle of the eiderdown she shared with her three younger sisters. The morning sounds were her thoughts. When the morning cacophony died away a few simple desires filled the spaces left in her little heart. Her sleep was always untroubled for So Yung rarely drifted into the realm of dreams. She moved with the emotion of the winds and leaves steaming in the morning mists. She lived in her little house with her three sisters, her three brothers, her mother, father and several other assorted relatives.

Then she remembered. She was not going to the rice paddies his morning; instead she was going to meet her Uncle from Shanghai. He was coming to tell her about a job in a factory in Shanghai which made shoes for Americans.

Wung Shuei had been as good as his word. He embraced So Yung fervently and they stole one of their few passionate kisses before embarking on an old, broken down boat. There seemed to be at least fifty of them. They were all hurriedly crammed down into the hold and then a heavy steel trap door

1980's by the American and British governments. Indeed it is probably because we originally supplied him with these weapons [to fight the war against Iran] that Tony Blair still seems certain we are, eventually, going to find these weapons. I imagine Saddam is on a boat somewhere. I imagine further that he might now consider selling these weapons to the highest bidder. I leave it to the reader's imagination as to who the highest bidders would be.

Truly, the Iraqi people may have been liberated from a monster but what, I wonder, is the monster planning now?

I doubt he is thinking of inviting Donald, George, Colin and Tony over for a barbecue and a family reunion!

The Media

The media, meanwhile, has to watch all this happening and then try to report on it according to the spirit of journalism. The word journalism comes from the root 'journal' or a notebook in which one keeps a note of the basic details of one's journey. The original purpose of writing a 'journal' was to stick to the salient relevant facts, without undue embellishment or analysis. It was supposed to remain impartial. But being impartial is nearly impossible. Even the simplest description of facts can be given a particular slant. Every day newspaper editors and journalists sit down to discuss what "angle" they are going to choose to portray a specific piece of news. There are numerous "spin-doctors" who variously manipulate the media to insure that their own private desires are being satisfied. The owners of newspapers are not supposed to interfere in editorial processes but we know for a fact that they all do and **spin-doctors are not confined to political circles.** "Spinning" is the operative word:- taking something and turning it around until you are presenting the image **you** want to portray.

Being a serious, objective journalist these days is very difficult and consequently, therefore, quite rare. In fact it is probably impossible. It is impossible because one cannot actually use words in a neutral objective manner. Words are designed to wield influence. That is why they are so powerful. Fortunately even today, when trillions upon trillions of words zoom out of every media orifice in the world there is still room for words that **really mean** something. It is often not the words themselves. It is the **meaning, intent and motivation** behind words that matters. President Bush has repeated parrot-fashion many fine sentiments but these statements are virtually meaningless. They are not his words. They do not come from his heart or his soul. Eventually more and more people will come to recognise that the very purpose of words themselves and human communication is being debased. In the end everyone gets found out. If real words, words with passion, power and integrity find resonance in enough minds at the same time, **then** they can be turned into a movement that can **alter the course of history.**

The words being spun out variously by the media and politicians in today's poisoned climate rarely have the satisfaction of being related to any sense of real integrity. In fact words, or at least the words upon the public stage have never been so sorely used and abused. Even as I write, questions are being asked in the British Parliament about the "spin" that was attached to the subject of Iraqi weapons of mass destruction. One can only hope that the media **has** sufficient integrity and enough tenacity to pursue this particular issue to a satisfactory conclusion.

All of us are soon going to experience first hand the first truly global synchronized crisis. It is all boiling up into something quite breathtakingly huge.

Politicians and the media are now [like the transatlantic twins and Osama bin Laden] blood brothers in a guilty drama of revenge and hatred. Of course politicians and the media may profess to hate one another sometimes but, in fact, they are also indispensable to one another. Recently our Prime Minister has had to use up all his vast reserves of self-belief to steer the country's opinion towards his way of thinking. That he has been mostly successful speaks volumes for the effectiveness of power when it is wielded so cleverly. Self-belief is deep in the heart of every soul which is driven by ambition. For the very simple same reason, poets and philosophers rarely seem to reach giddy political office. Perhaps they are always far too busy trying to come to a conclusion that is always eluding them. Not so, however, with a grand ego, buckets and buckets of integrity, self determination and the will to see it through to a conclusion, whatever the consequences might be.

In the giddiness of power the price the soul might have to pay resides in a purely abstract future and is safely ignored.

The Middle East

The Middle East is currently in considerable turmoil. The vast oil wealth of the barren desert has not so far served the majority of its ordinary people very well. Saudi Arabia is run by about 30,000 people, fifteen thousand of whom are Princes whilst the rest are serfs. The average income of the 30,000 royals is over a million dollars a year. The average income of the ordinary person in Saudi Arabia is less than $4,600 a year. If you then go further and include, as I do, all the other ordinary people in Saudi Arabia, such as all the imported slaves from the Third World, then the average income sinks to less than $2000 a year. In fact most of the population in Saudi Arabia are simply *slaves* to the royal families and their friends. I believe they are called domestics.

Unfortunately for Saudi Arabia, the country where the 9/11 bombers originated, and for Iraq, the two countries between them have nearly *forty per cent of the world's oil* and this percentage is increasing because they are not using up their oil at the same rate as other countries.

It is an astonishing fact, [which I have verified] but **fifty per cent** of Americans sincerely believe that Saddam Hussein and Iraq were responsible for the 9/11 tragedy. This is such a vast lie that it is almost impossible to believe half the American nation could attach itself to it. It illustrates however, perhaps better than any analysis of human psychology, that governments and the

clanged shut on them. In the damp, rank smelling hold rats ran freely around the pipes which dripped with stale, rancid condensation. For nearly three weeks, Wung Shuei, his two cousins and So Yung lived in the steel hold. They were allowed up on deck, five at a time, for just five or ten minutes a day.

Otherwise they had to stay cramped and crammed together in the corner of the hold. They were constantly damp and many of the passengers caught colds and flu or worse. The toilet was an old wooden bucket stuck in the corner behind a makeshift, ramshackle bamboo door. There were a few kerosene stoves on which to cook their food, which they had had to bring with them; a small sack of rice, jars of pickled radishes and dried bean curd. When they arrived in the Yemen neither of them had any idea where they were in the world. They both felt very, very ill. They had lived amidst the sickening smell of diarrhoea and vomit until their noses had become almost de-sensitised. It was a putrid stink that was to remain in So Yung's nostrils for the rest of her life, and returned violently whenever she was to smell somebody being sick.

The journey from the Yemen to Holland was a little better. They were now on a huge container ship loaded with videos, cameras, watches and TVs which had all been manufactured in Singapore and were en route to America.

Apparently, according to Wung Shuei, who was becoming an expert in the matter, America still didn't have enough of these items to satisfy the demands of the American people. According to Wung Shuei, everyone in America had a car, a washing machine, a fridge that was so big you could get inside it (except you couldn't because it was so full of food), videos TVs (at least one for each child over four years old!), computers and a large number of miscellaneous gadgetry, of which he was only vaguely familiar.

The journey was less unpleasant; there was a little more space and the weather was less humid and calmer.

In Holland they were picked up by a small boat in groups of ten and ferried to the shore at dead of night when they were herded into a small van. Eventually they were pushed & crammed into the back of a container truck that was full from top-to-bottom with boxes of tomatoes.

media, when they work together, can make the people believe virtually anything they like.

If one thinks of America, Europe and Eurasia as profligate in its use of oil it is equally unpleasant to look back and see how the oil wealth of the Middle East has only benefited a very few people. The princes of Arabia ban alcohol in their own countries and then drink and whore their way through these most westernised pleasures at their leisure in the western world's finest hotels, many of which they happen to own. Saudi Arabia also happens to be the biggest customer for American military hardware.

Saudi Arabia, well at least the royal family of Saudi Arabia, also owns vast amounts of real estate and business in America. They are amongst the largest 'foreign shareholders' of American companies. These two facts have kept the Americans and the Saudi royal family on the best possible terms. The American administration is not choosy whom they have as friends as long as they are politically convenient, and it is this attitude that so many people are beginning to find offensive.

In dealing with the Middle East it is impossible to pass by without *mentioning* the subject of Palestine. But it is one on which it is *difficult to comment briefly*. If one were to take a history lesson it would involve Jews, Christians and Muslims. The conflict over the Jewish Palestinian homelands is quite biblical, whether or not you believe in the Bible. There is a central poisoned core here. Perhaps remnants of the original apple left in the Garden of Eden? The Middle East is definitely in the 'middle' of it all and also in the middle of all the oil so it was inevitable that history would return to this area to eventually find its way back to Mother Nature. The Jewish Palestinian story has some way yet to run. Final destruction or reconciliation?

The dreadful problems in the world do not have a *viable current political solution* but over the next generation the anticipated series of oil shock waves will divert attention away from frightening global issues to quite frightening local ones instead. In this sense it is mostly good news. Politics, media and business will have enough at home on their plates to worry about. This inevitable return to localization will of course be the means by which our saviour, the Priestess Gaia, will manifest. Indeed she is already amongst us.

At some time, hopefully in the not too distant future, we may be able to see that most of what has taken place during the process of human evolution has been both inevitable and necessary to get us this far. It is indeed a tale of violent drama but it is also a story of hope and love. It is ironic that *all we need to do to bring* about the downfall of all the world's dictators is nothing very much. They are completing the job quite successfully for themselves. The invasion of Iraq by America and Britain is probably the most successful recruitment campaign for terrorism ever devised. Thousands upon thousands of disaffected and disillusioned fundamentalist Islamic warriors are lining up to extract their revenge. It may seem very strange to suggest but the best thing, probably, is to let them all get on with it.

It is very likely that terrorism will deal a final death blow to world tourism and the airline industry. It will not be long before a few airliners are brought down using one of the vast numbers of rocket launchers that America has so thoughtfully manufactured for the process.

Those who lust for power and revenge breed hatred. In the end their hatred will poison them. At this point in the great drama of civilization bashing itself apart at the seams it is perhaps best to remember how much the people closest to us really mean to us. This is the centre of the place to start the real revolution. Conflict takes energy and we will need to be really, really careful with the use of the Earth's raw, brutal fossil fuel energy. If we are to reduce the conflicts in our environment we will firstly need to reduce the conflicts in ourselves: localization and re-establishment of community would be a good place to start. Politics only gets dangerous, very dangerous, when it wants to rule the world. Local politicians, local politics can be, probably will be, silly, cantankerous, annoying and indecisive; indeed irritating to the extreme, but it is unlikely to be life threatening.

Here is a chart showing U.S. Fiscal Expenditure 2002: in billions of dollars. Note: How the Military Budget is 350 billion dollars. PLUS 87 billion dollars for Iraq.

Expenditure on energy is virtually zero. For humanity to have any chance of a decent technological, civilised future, these two expenditures will have to reverse themselves. The U.S. will need to spend at least 500 billion dollars a year to create a viable alternative energy infrastructure. This reversal will need to take place very rapidly (within the next ten years?). The American nation will need to acquire new political leaders with vision, insight, compassion and intelligence.

A Reader's Comments

"Few books are entertaining and great literature. This is one of them."

"If we do not act, we shall surely be dragged down the long, dark and shameful corridors of time reserved for those who possess power without compassion, might without morality and strength without sight."

Martin Luther King

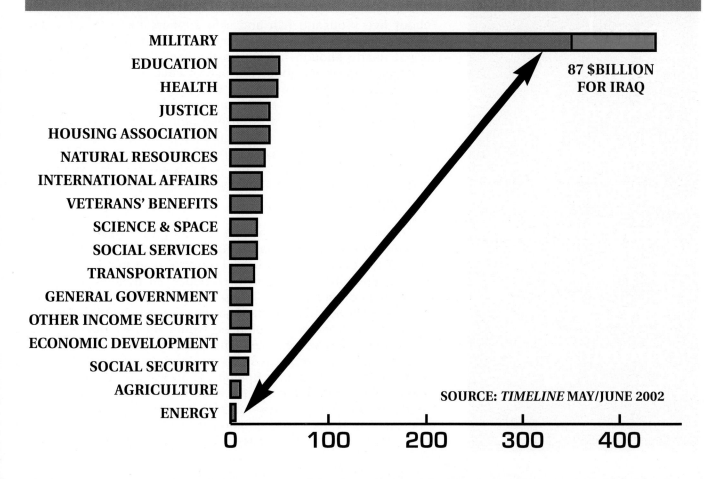

FISCAL YEAR 2002 USA DISCRETIONARY BUDGET (U.S. DOLLARS IN BILLIONS)

MILITARY

87 $BILLION FOR IRAQ

EDUCATION
HEALTH
JUSTICE
HOUSING ASSOCIATION
NATURAL RESOURCES
INTERNATIONAL AFFAIRS
VETERANS' BENEFITS
SCIENCE & SPACE
SOCIAL SERVICES
TRANSPORTATION
GENERAL GOVERNMENT
OTHER INCOME SECURITY
ECONOMIC DEVELOPMENT
SOCIAL SECURITY
AGRICULTURE
ENERGY

0   100   200   300   400

SOURCE: *TIMELINE* MAY/JUNE 2002

Alternative Energy

Whenever the subject of oil energy depletion occurs many people respond with a challenge. And so they should! I have made my best effort to understand the information available to me. I do not have, I hope, an exclusive contract in human knowledge. However, the first thing that needs to be understood is that my analysis will **inevitably meet with denial**. People simply do not believe that the oil resources remaining in the earth are so limited and they do not want to follow through, logically, the consequences but if they take **some time** to look at the scientific geo-chemical, geological analysis they will probably come to similar conclusions to those presented in the first of the essays in this book, at least from a technical point of view.

The science of oil depletion/peak production is not perfect. It is such a vast subject and there is such a vast range of possibilities. In fact the major oil companies do not differ that much in their oil depletion projections from the petroleum geologists. The difference comes in emphasis and, more importantly, **interpretation**. The difficulty then arises of how we put all the various elements together. Once oil depletion is established as a fact and once the scientific arguments begin to convince even the most sceptical that oil is going to start slowly running out, you will find that the arguments will take an entirely new direction. Right then! So there's going to be a bit less oil each year! So what! Alternative energies will, they assure us, come in time to avert any crisis.

At various times I have been told that we can run our transportation system on waste fish and chip oil. Though it is certainly true that fish and chip oil can be utilised in a combustion engine, it might be worth pointing out that, in order to run just the cars in the United Kingdom (excluding aeroplanes, heating oil, shipping oil or road freight oil), we would each need to eat about five thousand fish and chip suppers three times a day. Apart from the digestion problems such a diet might cause there is not nearly enough fish left in the sea. I have heard similar fantasies expressed about the use of coconut oil, or oil made from biomass, like linseed rape. But, at least here we are getting on to more stable scientific ground. It is indeed perfectly possible to grow an acre of linseed rape and produce anything between one thousand to two thousand litres of combustible fuel. However, the energy required to actually grow and harvest the crop and then convert it into oil takes anything between forty and eighty per cent of that energy (depending on whose figures you choose).

To keep fifteen million cars on the road using only the products from biomass fuels would take most of the agricultural land of the country out of use. I recently read that experiments have been done in Holland to produce an aviation fuel from biomass (biomass is actually agricultural organic produce, such as rape, willow, sugar beet, sugar cane, even chicken shit). It is estimated that one acre of biomass would enable a Boeing 747 to travel about sixty-seven miles. Thus it would take in the region of three hundred and fifty acres of agricultural land to make one trip to Australia and back in a Boeing 747. To keep all the passenger and freight planes in the sky, the ships on the sea and cars on the roads would require several planets the size of the earth dedicated only to growing biomass. I have investigated even more bizarre theories. These include building nuclear power stations on the moon and beaming back the energy to the Earth, to a self-propelled rocket working on the principle of extracting hydrogen from the atmosphere as it travels at about three thousand m.p.h. through the lower stratosphere. Most bizarre of all is the theory expounded by a highly respected Russian scientist, Professor Razinov. In fact Boeing, the world's largest aircraft manufacturer, has financed him to do further research. His plan? To do away with 'gravity'!

It is not surprising that these bizarre and totally unscientific theories start to gain some credence at the moment when we are approaching an energy crisis. The simple fact is that there are many alternative energy sources. The main ones, and certainly the benign ones, would include electricity produced from wind or wave and tidal movements, or from the heat of the sun, as in solar panels, or from a kind of organic technical photosynthesis through capturing light in 'photovoltaic panels'. I will discuss shortly, in more detail, the technicalities of some of these alternatives, their benefits and their limitations. There is, however, one aspect of this discussion that is rarely considered amongst the scientific community, and even more rarely considered amongst the global economic capitalists who wish to maintain the global trading status quo. The fact is that energy depletion will inevitably f**orce us to consider major changes** to our lifestyle and energy consumption patterns. The reason changes to our lifestyle are not considered is quite simple to understand. The present structure of our economy will not work if we all use less, consume less and generally do less. **Therefore it does not exist as an economic alternative**. Therefore we **do not** think about it. There is no point in thinking about it. Economists, politicians and big business are simply determined to secure an alternative source of energy which can maintain the continual growth patterns of the past. It is here we also meet one of the greatest stumbling blocks to change. As individuals we may well be able to entertain the idea of drastic change but within corporations drastic change cannot be considered. Let me give you an example. When the reality of oil depletion becomes apparent to the powers that presently control our economic destiny it would be very sensible for the human species to simply stop making motor cars and aeroplanes. Even on the absolutely best prognosis of oil depletion patterns we are only going to be able to use oil for a generation or two at the most. **For this period of time we <u>already</u> have enough cars and planes upon the planet to last us**. We might have to look after them but that would be no bad thing. Additionally we would save ourselves billions of tonnes in damaging carbon emissions. This won't happen of course. My *individual* common sense tells me so. Car and aeroplane manufacturers will fight to the bitter end. They have no desire to arrange and then attend their own funerals. But a shrinking oil supply will most disrupt our mechanical combustion transportation systems, such as passenger planes, freight planes, ships, boats, lorries, cars, trucks and vans, etc., since these are *entirely* dependent on conventional oil.

Now many people will be familiar, at least partially, with the idea of a hydrogen economy. Let me say firstly that the no 19 bus - the novel, which starts in 2070, has, as its primary source of transportation energy, a sophisticated hydrogen system. I would go further:

The design, creation and implementation of a hydrogen energy system will be critical to our technological and civilised survival.

Of course, it all comes as such a surprise!

It takes time to make alternatives work:

Don't rush in.

Stand back:

Think:

Study:

Analyse.

One should read like a HAWK. Keep a wary eye on proceedings and keep your own counsel.

> The interior imagination of the human consciousness is fortunately always greater than it's exterior manifestations.

> It is useful to remember that technology is invented by the imagination. If we alter our imaginations (our image creation) we alter technology.

> It will be our choice: benign technologies - or more war.

Having said that, there are many limitations. Hydrogen is not freely available. It has to be made through a scientific and technical process that, in itself, requires a great deal of energy to be 'put in' before any 'excess' energy, i.e. hydrogen, is produced. Before, however, I get down to some of the nitty-gritty details regarding the specific technicalities, limitations and benefits of alternative energy, I would like to take a step back for a moment and deal with the basic *philosophy* of energy. I will then briefly return to these alternative technologies from a practical point of view.

For myself, whenever I begin to think about an important subject, I always start with the Oxford English Dictionary. In this situation we have to look at the definition of two words: Energy and Alternative. According to the O.E.D. then:-

- ◆ **Energy is work.**

- ◆ **Energy is force.**

- ◆ **Energy is power.**

- ◆ **Energy is vigour.**

- ◆ **Energy is in fact, actually, chemically, well, absolutely everything!**

In fact, the very first and most basic law of physics is called the Law of Thermodynamics.

Everything is energy.

Energy is never created or destroyed; it is merely transformed.

This is a very essential scientific fact to understand when we begin to consider the energy needed to fuel mankind's industrial endeavours. What is obvious with oil and its derivatives: petrol, diesel and kerosene (kerosene is airplane fuel), is that it is very *readily available* and it is very easily *transformable* into a combustible form to create power for mechanical modes of transportation. Other forms of energy are of course available since everything is energy but these forms are:-

NOT SO READILY AVAILABLE!

Alternative forms of energy have to be harnessed, either from the sun, the Wind, the Water or the Earth. In fact, we do not lose energy overall in the Earth's systems, for the very simple reason that we have the sun. The sun is actually where the Earth gets all its additional energy from. Every day the sun gives us energy and we lose it by using it up. This system itself will break down one day. At some point in the very far distant future the sun will no longer burn, but this moment is too far off to currently concern us. The physics that we need to understand presently is the nature of our own industrial and technological energy requirements. We need to understand what is viable, what might be viable and **what is not viable**. We also seriously need to understand **the timescales involved**. Someday we are **inevitably** going to create a wonderful hydrogen economy but it's not going to happen tomorrow and it's definitely not going to happen in time to save us from the impact of severe energy shortages.

The sun gives us sunlight or heat. It was the energy from the sun that created fossil fuels. In reality, fossil fuels are just stored sunlight that has taken on a variety of chemical disguises. The sun, in conjunction with water and other elements on the Earth, created various 'reservoirs' of condensed hydrocarbon energy: wood, peat, coal, oil and gas. When they are used up energy will have to come from the sun directly, i.e. through solar panels or wind or water or biomass. We will have used up what is in the storehouse and we will have to now start to "Earn our Energy."

Let us now turn to the word Alternative. Back once more to the Oxford English Dictionary. Its most basic definition means 'stating' or 'offering' two things or more. It involves, in other words, creating choice. Alternative means looking a little differently at the same things and thereby transforming them. In the process we can transform ourselves. Most of life is just sharing labour and time. It is actually that simple. When you put the two words together you come up with 'Alternative Energy'. Alternative is not merely about alternative fuels for our cars, it is about alternative **energy** systems and alternative **political** systems and alternative **philosophical** systems being created in our minds. Since the whole of the total universe is energy, the only cause for disputation or debate is how we actually use the available energy, and what effects the usage of our energy may have upon our well-being, our society's well-being and, most importantly of all in today's world, the effects that it will have on the planet as a whole.

Today I think the words 'Alternative Energy' are beginning to define themselves mostly in terms of renewable sources for sustainable natural energy systems that man can utilise to further propagate his lifestyle. Did I say propagate? Of course I meant profligate! Let's put it this way. It isn't just alternative energy or oil that we should be worrying about, but alternative energy systems inside our whole way of thinking, behaving and being. In other words, the environment we want to create amongst ourselves. Alternative Energy is about the alternative community we want to create. At this particular energy crossroads, we have the opportunity to decide whether we want to create an Alternative Energy system, and thereby maintain as much as possible of the status quo of the modern industrial and technological systems, or whether this might be a grand opportunity to look at the creation of a society which is based on much simpler lifestyles. But before you think. Oh Lord! It sounds like a return to feudalism - just think for a moment! Most international travel today is identical. Cities are becoming clones.

Activities for a low hydrocarbon community:

music

dancing

storytelling

growing things in the garden

chatting

walking

sports

gliding

sailing

running

yoga

meditation

...

It may seem cruel that all these crisis are drawing together from all directions at once. This is quite simply because everything is connected to everything else in a planetary web of being.

Americanisation is everywhere. In this world which apparently offers us almost infinite choice, there is, in reality, **less and less real choice**. There used to be over three thousand common strains of rice. Now over ninety per cent of our rice comes from just three. Do you want a new little car. Can you tell the difference between them? The Western world, through marketing and advertising is trying to sell us all the image of quality and choice but, in reality, all we are getting is increasing volumes of the same old stuff. Most mass produced items are intentionally designed to have very short life spans because in that way we will soon need to buy some more of them and this is what keeps the old economy rollicking along. This does not mean we have to throw our best or most inventive technology away; that would be nonsense but much of what we are driven to possess only fills our pleasure centres for a few moments and inevitably leaves us feeling spiritually unsatisfied.

We have been the servants to our technological genius; never its masters.

Our amazing corporate empires are actually dehumanising us. Our creativity is stifled. We are no longer in touch with the land or the growing of food. We don't **make** music we **listen** to it. We don't **make** entertainment we **are** entertained.

The changes that will occur as a result of massive disruptions to our present energy systems are going to create the most volatile and productive debate in the history of *any* civilisation that has ever existed. There will not be one solution that fits all of us. The intensity of this discussion will be directly related to the intensity of the oil shock waves soon to be coming our way. The discussion will deal with every aspect of life. It will be an integrative progress. If we are intelligent and imaginative and compassionate with one another it could even be a vibrant and joyful process.

Now let us deal, albeit briefly, with a few of the technical bits. What kind of alternative energies are there? How will we use them? Who will develop them? How much will they cost? Perhaps most importantly of all, which of them will help us develop transportation systems for people and goods?

Windmills

I love the word windmills. No need to define it I hope. It's "wind" and "mills" as in a "miller" or a man who makes flour. In other words, it's wind equals bread. The word derived from the fact that the earliest windmills were use to grind wheat or corn for flour.

There is some confusion and dispute as to whether windmills are very pleasant to look at and there is some issue about whether they are dangerous to our bird life. As a lover of bird life this issue is of some importance to me. I do not have a simple answer to the problem. I can imagine however that in time birds will learn about the dangers of windmills. It illustrates the fact that mans relationship to nature is never without some kind of difficult compromise.

Windmills can make electricity out of the power of the wind. Electricity is what powers most electrical stuff: computers, ovens, fridges, lights, etc. Windmills don't make oil. Pity really! Windmills make electricity. In fact this is where modern windmills differ from those pretty, old-fashioned windmills. Old windmills made mechanical energy – usually to grind corn and turn machinery of some sort. Windmill technology has come a long way in the last twenty years or so. Nearly everyone will have seen windmill farms either in pictures or in reality. Recently the Germans built a wind turbine [that's the modern jargon for windmills these days] that has a propellor span of over 120 metres! This one wind turbine will provide enough electricity for nearly three thousand homes. It is a miracle of engineering. In Denmark, the country with the most advanced wind turbine system, just over twenty per cent of all generated power on the national grid is provided by wind energy. Unfortunately this is about the maximum amount of wind that can be fed into a national grid. The reason, without getting too technical, is that the wind is intermittent. Sometimes it blows and sometimes it doesn't. This creates unbalanced power surges. In a national electricity grid like Denmark's these power surges are dealt with by traditional power stations running on fossil fuels. A few years ago, when the wind didn't quite blow as forecast, there was such a huge surge that vast amounts of electricity had to be sent down a cable to Sweden. The power surge sent down the cable was twice the amount that the cable had been designed for. There was a distinct possibility that parts of the Danish National Grid could have actually blown up. Fortunately that didn't happen but it illustrates the limits of wind power in a national grid.

In fact this limiting principle applies to most alternative energies. Wave power is intermittent, the sun doesn't always shine with the same intensity every day and the wind doesn't blow to order. Because the power produced by these sources is intermittent it will be necessary to design storage systems. Batteries which get charged when there is an excess of electrical power have been designed but the conversion/efficiency ratio is very poor. Most wind technology and most wind installations are on a very large scale: huge turbines and huge wind farms. There is probably a wonderful wind world to develop on a very small localised basis but this area does not presently attract any investment.

The most important point for the purposes of this present thesis is that windmills only make electricity. They don't make oil. There is another dimension to the development of wind turbine technology which is given no consideration. Presently the manufacture of windmills is done on a very large scale in huge factories. These factories are run on fossil fuels. The steel to make the windmills is made using power from fossil fuels. The equipment to transport and then erect these windmills comes from fossil fuel sources. Presently fossil fuel energy is very cheap but this would clearly change if there were to be fossil fuel shortages. When there is no more cheap fossil fuel windmills will **first have to make the energy to make more of themselves.** No one can presently predict exactly how long a windmill will work before it reaches the end of its useful practical life. Once our best scientists and engineers really start to get to grips with the technical elements of wind turbine technology we will probably discover how much harder it is to "earn" our energy. It will be more expensive, it will be less constantly reliable and we will probably have to be judicious and thoughtful in its usage. Windmill energy will not replace oil energy.

In today's terms the average American energy diet is equivalent to having nearly sixty human energy slaves working twenty-four hours a day. If one were to purchase this energy at the going market rate for a barrel of oil it would cost over two thousand dollars. But this is now about to come, quite abruptly, to an end. Ironically, the hydrocarbon slave trade may force Americans to become more physical and to do more things for themselves. This may reduce obesity which is now at epidemic proportions and costs the US billions of dollars a year in associated health care costs. There will be many more benefits to a reduced energy lifestyle. Not all of them will be initially popular.

Photovoltaics and solar

Solar panels, with which most people are probably familiar, are simply energy collectors which concentrate the heat of the sun. Photovoltaics are panels which **generate** electricity through a process which is quite similar to photosynthesis [that's the process by which plants turn light into energy/food]. Photovoltaic uses *light* rather than heat.

Both solar and photovoltaic are simply wonderful sources of electrical power. I have absolutely no idea why these technologies haven't been designed as a matter of course into most modern architecture for the past ten years. I have even less idea why they are not being planned in every house under construction today. This technology is perfectly adaptable to local use. Roofs made from solar panels could provide **most** of the electricity an ordinary household needs for appliances etc. **Unfortunately this technology does not make oil and the power produced from it will not run passenger planes, ships or cars**. Well that's not exactly true. Some of this energy could be used to power battery/electrical cars for limited local use and with small payloads. The same problem applies to this technology as to wind. It is intermittent and produces only electricity. It is presently very expensive but that will no doubt change quite dramatically when it is manufactured on a much larger scale.

Water Wave and Tidal

This would include hydroelectric schemes and energy produced from the movement of waves in the sea or tidal movements in the oceans. Hydroelectric has been around for a long time. There are some **natural** hydro schemes in mountainous areas like Sweden and Norway which use falling water to "turn" turbines and create electricity. I use the word **natural** because in this context the water is not being collected in a dam. Most hydroelectric schemes around the world work by *stopping* the flow of a river, collecting all the water in a dam and then releasing the water as necessary to generate electricity. Eventually the river behind the dam silts up. In the next twenty to fifty years most of the hydroelectric schemes presently in place will seize up because of silting. Presently, hydroelectric power provides about three per cent of the world's electricity. Brazil gets most of its electricity from hydro schemes. Unfortunately in 2002 it didn't rain very much in Brazil and they had desperate energy shortages as a result. Of course Brazil is a country in which it should rain a very great deal since the country is four-fifths rain forest. I leave the reader to ponder the significance of this natural phenomenon.

Wave and tidal power is a very new and, as yet, mostly untested technology, but it looks very promising. Around Britain and particularly Scotland, wind and tidal power could provide a significant amount of our electrical needs. Notwithstanding the fact that there is a very distinct upper limit to how much power can be generated in this manner and then pushed through the national grid.

Unfortunately this source of energy also **only produces electricity** and not oil so the same limitations apply as to wind turbines and solar/photovoltaic.

Biomass

Biomass is organic matter. It might be straw, chicken shit, linseed rape, sunflower seeds, willow, hemp, sugar cane, sugar beet or indeed one of thousands of natural agricultural residues. In some instances it is dried and then burnt in generators to make electricity. But some crops are suitable for refining into vegetable organic oils which can be used to combust engines. We've already mentioned in passing that we would need several planets in order to grow sufficient crops to make sufficient oil to service our car/plane/ship fleets. Like the other technologies it will no doubt provide us with some of what we need...as long as we don't need so much. It would make perfect sense, for instance, for a farmer to grow sufficient fuel crops to run his tractors and heavy agricultural machinery. [Unless of course you all want to go back to cutting wheat with a sickle]. It may well make sense for the farmer to grow **some** fuel crops to service the **local** buses. In every case the emphasis is on **small** needs and **local** needs. I can promise you that Farmer Jones, who farms a few acres on top of the Sussex Downs, will *not* be doing any kind of a deal with British Airways to provide fuel for multiple trips to Benidorm. Let me stress that these alternative energies are benign, natural, dependable, and the base source: wind, sun, water and crops will not run out. In fact they will never ever run out if we are wise because these energies can operate within a natural cycle. If you haven't got the picture yet I hope it is about to dawn on you. Oil from fossil fuels is a one-off. It helped us to get here. Now we have to get **off** the oil treadmill and **jump** up into the air into high-tech windmills, **splash** about in the Ocean waves and *look skyward* to the essential and original source of all being.

The Sun

Perhaps one brief word is in order about the possibility of running our transportation structures with electrical vehicles. There are two main issues. The main one is the power to weight ratio. Put simply, what this means is that the more power you require the heavier the batteries become. At a certain point the equation goes negative. In other words you are producing all your power simply to carry your batteries around. I think everyone is familiar with the weight of a car battery which only provides minor electrical, not propulsive power to a standard car. A golf caddy kart which can carry around a couple of people for a few hours at very low speeds has quite huge batteries. Now just try to imagine how many batteries you would need to power a 747 Aeroplane. Exactly. It is not physically possible. Nor will batteries operate huge road freight vehicles or ships for the same reason. This actually illustrates the limited thinking that is being done upon this vital subject, because nearly everyone who starts to think about oil depletion immediately thinks of petrol and then their own car. Cars are important people carriers, and fortunately there are enough alternatives to keep some of us on the move **now and again,** but the real limitation of most alternative power sources is that they will not keep the *global* trade in goods and tourists going at its present breakneck speeds of dispatch. In the not so distant future, [thirty years?] goods will probably have to be sailed somewhere in sailing ships. As it happens, electrical cars would be ideal for low impact, low energy, local transportation needs. There is another issue. Batteries are very toxic to produce and very toxic to dispose of. The electricity created in a battery is made from chemical reactions. However batteries could play an important part in storing the excess energy produced from wind turbines or other sustainable sources.

In the US in 2002 the Rand Corporation gave a briefing to the Pentagon. They described Saudi Arabia as the "kernel of evil". They proposed that Washington should have a showdown with its former ally, if necessary "seizing its oil fields which have been crucial to America's energy."

A Reader's Comments: -

"The story of 2007 is enthralling, mesmerising. Could this be our future? It is certainly one very possible future. If the writer's predictions of the future are as accurate as his portrayal of the present, we all have a great deal to think about."

A Reader's Comments: -

"Spirituality amidst the debris, the shattered chaos of the world. A cauldron ready to explode. A vision of harmony returning. God I hope so!"

We now use over 200 million tons of inorganic nitrogen fertilizers manufactured from petrochemicals.

In the year 2002 less than one per cent of US electricity generation comes from renewable sources. Under the enlightened Bush energy plan it is estimated that this total will rise by the year 2020 to 2.8 per cent. Fortunately many companies and countries around the world ignored the Bush energy plan and windmills are being produced in high-tech situations with a growth rate unmatched in any other industry.

Interestingly enough, doing less does not mean that we have to do nothing. On the contrary, it may mean that we will have to get even busier than we are, whilst at the same time using vastly less energy. In essence, this means that *we will have to return to using our physical bodies.*

Can you hear the groans!!

We will be forced to find the energy inside ourselves as we will not have a large lump of fossil fuel energy to do the work for us. Fossil fuel gives every American the equivalent in energy of sixty human slaves. It will be harder in the short term but much better for the planet and for our physical health in the long term. Goodbye couch potatoes!

This brings me finally to consider the Holy Grail of alternative energy systems: -

Hydrogen and the Fuel Cell

Firstly a few hydrogen facts: -

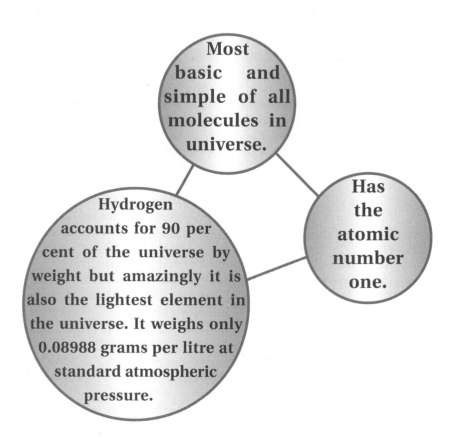

Hydrogen is very excitable and therefore difficult to control and contain. Hydrogen **attacks** any container or pipeline it is put in. Hydrogen will **eventually** escape from any container. The molecules are so small they can leak through metal. Liquid Hydrogen for space rockets is stored in tanks made from fifty layers of double Aluminised Kapton separated by Dacron net. The rate of loss [technically it is called boil off] of Hydrogen from a tank depends on its insulation properties. From space tanks as described above net loss is only 0.2 per cent per day. In standard tanks net loss reaches over 1.5 per cent per day. For this reason, amongst many others, most research establishments studying hydrogen have rejected it as a liquid fuel.

The storage temperature for liquid Hydrogen is –253 degrees centigrade.

Clearly there are many technical problems and limitations with a liquid hydrogen system. There are however many incredible benefits, not least of which is the fact that it produces no carbon dioxide. Interestingly enough, all the problems of production and storage seem to have most of their solutions when hydrogen is manufactured locally and used immediately at source. For instance, public buses could park overnight at windmill stations which produce electricity to make hydrogen. They would then use up the Hydrogen next day. Thus getting round the problem of pipeline infrastructure, distribution systems and boil off.

With electricity from windmills, Photovoltaics or Hydroelectric [indeed any source of electricity] you can make hydrogen. But this takes us to another interesting basic physics lesson because it brings us back to one of our most basic molecules, water, or H_2O.

To cool fire you need water

When you consider that Hydrogen is both the lightest and the most prolific element in the universe it is hardly surprising that it gets itself involved in most of the chemical reactions on the planet.

In the very earliest stages of physical evolution the planet was very hot. Boiling with volcanic lava. In order for the earth to be cooled it needed to create water. Water as we all know, cools fire. Yet amazingly water is made from Hydrogen, which is fantastically combustible and mightily inflammable when it exists in a free state. As it happens Hydrogen, although the most abundant element on this planet, **does not exist in a free state**. It has to be made. The earliest cosmic chemistry may be quite simple but it is also utterly profound. In this essential early chemistry lies the secret of understanding what ultimate evolutionary use we can make of Hydrogen as an element. The energy that bound Hydrogen and Oxygen together to make water was enormous. In like manner the energy required to split Hydrogen from Oxygen is also enormous. Think of it like this:-

Water is two parts Hydrogen and one part Oxygen.

Hydrogen is one of the most flammable chemical elements in existence. But what happens if you try to set light to water? Exactly. Now try setting light to a nice barrel of petrol. It's much easier. But just getting Hydrogen out of water is only the first part of the energy equation in creating a Hydrogen economy.

Having helium cool into hydrogen and combining with oxygen to make water is one of the most primitive and important chemical reactions upon this planet. It is what 'cooled' our planet down and created the possibilities for biological life. As we all know, water makes up about two-thirds of the surface mass of the planet. If all the hydrogen on the planet were converted to a pure liquid form it would be able to fuel any transportation systems for many trillions of years. Unfortunately hydrogen does not occur in a liquid form but needs to be made into a liquid so that it can be used as a fuel. The basic process to turn hydrogen into, or rather to recover hydrogen from, water is a slow energy intensive process called electrolysis. It is necessary to run electrical power through water to separate the hydrogen molecules (two of) from the oxygen molecule (one of), i.e. H_2O. When you run an electric current through water you are creating hydrogen gas. You now need to collect the hydrogen. When you

There is much discussion about creating a world in which everything is recycled. Some of these ideas include burning all our rubbish so that we can get heat from it. When we have got this heat we will then be able to sell it to industrial processes which can create more packaging and waste product which can then be sold back to the companies that will then heat it again and produce more electricity and so forth and so on. It is not difficult to understand that this is a self defeating process because every time the process takes place some energy will be lost in the equation. Although it may seem extraordinary it is possible to think of and therefore design a system in which virtually no waste is created. This is in fact how nature works. However since virtually every system that mankind creates is fundamentally flawed it is clear that we will never achieve the Utopia of zero waste. As in all things it will become a balance.

have collected it you need to freeze it [through compression] until it takes up 800 times less space. Then you need to keep it in a pressurised tank. If it ever gets out of the pressurised tank it will completely evaporate and disappear very quickly. In fact liquid hydrogen will disappear from inside any container because the hydrogen molecules are actually capable of dispersing or leaching out through solid metal at a rate of up to 1.7% per day. The rate depends on the insulation properties of the tank.

Once you have created the compressed hydrogen you then need to get it into the tank of your car, which needs to be converted to run on hydrogen. Unfortunately, modern fossil-fuel cars are not suitable for conversion to run on hydrogen and, unfortunately, the volume hydrogen takes up as a liquid is seven times the volume of petrol. So, in order to use the hydrogen, you'll have to have one of these funky new fuel-cell cars that runs off pure hydrogen. Hey presto, it would seem all our energy problems are completely over. If only it wasn't for those unfortunate chemical energy-intensive bits in the process it would have all the answers to our energy requirements. One might add, at this juncture, that hydrogen, even if it could be created in sufficient volumes, will not be suitable to power the existing planes and super-tankers whizzing around the skies and the seas at the present moment.

Hydrogen, as I have previously mentioned, **may** become the energy basis for transportation vehicles in the future, **but it will not appear directly or immediately as an alternative to the petrol combustion engine for the simple reason that it will take trillions upon trillions of dollars of research and investment** and presently, the only country with that kind of wealth is spending it on bombs to bomb Baghdad so that it can get its hands on another big blob of the black evil stuff: the oil.

Yes, it may well be that when history gets the publication rights on the story of oil, it will be likened to the slithering, evil serpent of the Bible. One has to ask: If a hydrogen economy is economically and technically viable and could easily replace an oil economy why hasn't it been developed? Why indeed? Because the simple physics of hydrogen manufacture, storage and distribution means that it is going to be vastly more expensive than cheap oil. In fact it may be so expensive it simply won't be viable for holiday flights to the Costa Del Sol. This is why the most important thing we can do is reduce our primary energy needs.

I hope that many other people are beginning to feel that maybe a change of lifestyle might not be such a bad thing. A reduction of primary energy needs, such as cars and fridges, could soon reduce the necessity for these things to such a point that they actually become an anti-social phenomenon. This point, of course, is some little way off. We can at least guarantee, due to the excessive short-term ignorance of those presently in charge of the planet's wealth, that this subject will not be dealt with on any broad, intelligent, political or business basis until it becomes an acute crisis. When it does, the subject of Alternative Energy will probably be the biggest subject humanity has ever dealt with.

Where will our energy come from when the oil has gone? How much energy will we need and how much will it cost? Let us go back to the hydrogen energy system. Hydrogen will need to work in conjunction with what is called the fuel-cell engine.

Contrary to many people's belief, a fuel-cell engine is not actually fuel. It is merely an engine. It works on a very different principle from the combustion engine and uses a platinum catalyst to create heat that is converted to electricity. The electricity is then converted, very effectively and efficiently and very quietly and (best of all) in a non-polluting manner, into energy for a car to run. Fuel-cell engines are already in production, particularly as small generators, and there are a few experimental processes going on.

Within the major energy corporations there is an increasing awareness that fossil fuels are actually finite. However, the major energy corporations have an overwhelming faith in man's technological ingenuity. The world's leading energy companies are already designing, at least theoretically, an alternative energy system based on hydrogen. They anticipate a few problems designing and then building the world hydrogen system but, as far as they are concerned, the problems are simply financial and political. Technically, companies like 'Shell Hydrogen' or the 'American Hydrogen Association' are propagating the idea that a total hydrogen system is not only viable, it is also inevitable and that it will replace, quite seamlessly, the present fossil fuel energy systems. Are their theories correct? Or rather, will their theories prove to be correct? Until the practical consequences of a world hydrogen system manifest as a day-to-day reality of life, we will not know. My understanding is that the attempt to miraculously develop a total world hydrogen system that will maintain the global trading/energy status quo is simply a profound form of wish fulfilment. My reasoning is based on an understanding of the most basic physics.

The chief executive of Shell Hydrogen recently made a report to the House Committee on Science of the US Government (March 2003). He painted a very rosy picture. His message was simple: Please give us lots and lots of money and we will provide a hydrogen system. It is my intuition that 'unlocking hydrogen energy' will not be as simple as they imagine. I believe they will discover that it is not simply a matter of money and politics. It will be a matter of physics. Hydrogen might be the simplest and busiest little molecule in creation but I have the feeling that it may remain our master rather than our servant. Whether I am correct or not in my analysis will only be known some time in the distant future.

The manufacture of hydrogen from water does have a simple mathematical formula: -

$$2H_2O + e = 2H_2(g) + O_2(g)$$

This states simply that to turn H20 Water into Hydrogen gas and Oxygen gas requires Energy (that's the little "e" in the equation). The letter "g" is simply the symbol for Gas.

In written form it would read as:- Take water add energy/heat and you get Hydrogen gas and Oxygen gas.

What it ends up meaning [when you've worked out the value of "e" is:- if you put 1.3 kilowatts of energy into the equation you will get just 1 kilowatt of energy out (in the form of hydrogen gas). More simply: Hydrogen requires more energy to make it than there is in it. Put another way: It is inefficient. However, many industrialised processes are inefficient. Any transformative

Climate change is not linear.

A 10 per cent increase in a storm's windspeed can double the damage.

A further 10 per cent increase would quadruple the damage.

What most wind power enthusiasts have not realized is that presently windmills are being made in factories using fossil fuel power.

When fossil fuel power is used up windmills will have to make windmills. This changes the energy factor considerably as you might imagine. It means that much of the windmill's energy needs to be directed towards creating windmill "Children".

If we build windmills from our cheap fossil fuel power and then we simply use all of the windmill's electricity for our appliances etc we may find that we do not have enough power left to generate the next generation of windmills.

This principle applies equally to all of the energy equations concerning renewables as all these equations are created from the same source of being.

reaction is inefficient. The principle is this: Will it be worth producing 1.3 kilowatts of electrical energy to produce just 1 kilowatt of hydrogen energy? If you then add in all the other energy factors, such as:

- **Energy required to build hydrogen collection devices**

- **Energy required to freeze hydrogen gas to a liquid**

- **Energy required to store liquid hydrogen**

- **Energy required to transport hydrogen**

- **Energy required to build vehicles able to use hydrogen**

You can see that this equation changes to:

$$2H_2O + (e) + (eb) + (ec) + (ed) + (ef) + (eh)$$
$$= 2H_2(1) + O_2(g)$$

e	=	initial electrical energy for electrolysis energy
eb	=	collection energy
ec	=	freezing energy
ed	=	storage energy
ef	=	transport energy
eh	=	vehicle production energy

No one that I have found so far seems to have produced a satisfactory working model of this equation. (I have been through several hundred web sites in search of it). *I would like to take this opportunity, in fact, of inviting hydrogen engineers to produce theoretical values for e-b-c-d-f and h.*

My estimate is that we will need in the region of 10 to 20 kilowatts of energy to produce 1 kilowatt of **pure** hydrogen energy (as an end use). If I am correct in my analysis, this will not represent a good energy trade off. In other words it will be too expensive. It would not be expensive of course if we had lots and lots of spare kilowatts coming from somewhere. So there's a big question. Where will all the kilowatts come from?

You have to remember that this visionary hydrogen economy is planned to be built at a time when oil and other fossil fuels are running out. It simply doesn't add up. Why don't hydrogen scientists realise this? Realistic hydrogen engineers, who have some real sense of what alternative, renewable, sustainable energy systems mean, are telling us very clearly that hydrogen systems may be wonderfully suited to localised production. In other words, when there is free wind and no electricity is required, the 'free' capacity can make hydrogen. This hydrogen can then be used directly on site in a fuel cell engine to provide electricity when the wind isn't blowing, or liquid hydrogen for use as a local transportation fuel. The emphasis is on the word LOCAL.

These small, localised systems would be benign. Most importantly of all, they would allow local communities to manage their own energy needs. This would make them less dependent on the National Grid, which is controlled, of course, by national and international politicians and big business.

It is not in Shell Hydrogen's interest to develop small, low-tech, local, sustainable solutions as they would no longer have a business; at least not a major international business that provides the world's industry with fuel for global trading purposes. For Shell Hydrogen to consider making their business windmills/ photovoltaics for local hydrogen systems, they would have to adopt a 'local' mindset rather than a 'global' one. Their mindset will not adopt the localisation principles at present because they can't. To do so would mean that the whole world financial architecture would have to be almost instantly redesigned. It is therefore impossible for them to see any other solution than the creation of a hydrogen energy system that simply replaces fossil fuels.

Understanding how a possible global transportation system based on hydrogen might work technically and logistically is not easy. There are numerous Hydrogen enthusiasts who will describe with utopian fervour a vision of a hydrogen economy that will provide all our existing transportation needs. Some enthusiasts even state that the price will be so cheap it might not even be worth charging for it! I seem to remember that the same enthusiasm was generated by early pioneers and advocates of nuclear energy. Here is one example amongst many that you will find in the Hydrogen literature.

"You slide your credit card over to pay your $7.50 to pay your fuel bill, you gloat a little knowing that you'll refill the tank of your fuel-celled sports utility vehicle for another 500 miles."

This extract was taken from Ty Cashman and Bret from "Yes" the coming hydrogen economy.

Much of this utopian vision is based on wishful thinking and a blatant disregard for the physical facts. When you study the science in more detail the technological problems indicate a very different scenario. Scientific research bodies like Mannheim in Germany and even Shell Hydrogen estimate that to get a working hydrogen system up and running in the US alone will cost over a thousand billion dollars and take thirty to fifty years to fully implement. The problem with hydrogen as a transportational fuel is not insuperable *technically speaking*. The problem is one of timescale and cost in building the infrastructure and distribution systems.

Many hydrogen enthusiasts describe, as I have done earlier, that the use of hydrogen is a natural progression up the hydrocarbon tree. Wood-coal-oil-gas and then hydrogen but they fail to mention the most significant fact. Hydrogen needs to be manufactured. We don't require energy to manufacture oil. It already exists in underground and underwater reservoirs in a free state.

Some of you may have seen an advert where a man is filling up his car with a hosepipe. I wish! To get a common sense view of this just try dropping a match into a glass of water. And then dropping a match into a glass of liquid hydrogen. The reaction is totally opposite. One match will explode, the other will go out.

A detailed study of the switch to renewable energy was published by the LTA Research Group in Mannheim in 1998. It found that if the development of renewable energy systems were supported by a decisive, well coordinated action by governments in a sustained programme lasting for fifty years, renewable sources might provide thirty-five per cent of the energy used at present.

In 2000 a huge dust storm from northern China reached the United States. It was the biggest the world has ever seen. In April 2003 an even bigger one is forming.

A dust bowl is formed when arid conditions literally tear the topsoil from the earth and spins it up into the atmosphere.

In fact you can't physically drop a match into a glass of liquid hydrogen because it will instantly disappear from any open container that has access to the air.

In fact many major companies are engaged on the development of cars and buses which run on hydrogen but, in the words of the Daimler Benz hydrogen engineers,

"Hydrogen for at least the next twenty years will have to be made from conventional hydrocarbons."

What does this mean exactly? It means that hydrogen can presently **only** be **manufactured** economically by using **fossil fuels** such as oil or gas as the base resource. But clearly using oil or gas doesn't help the hydrocarbon depletion issue! So why bother? The answer comes in two parts. Many hydrogen enthusiasts are only vaguely aware of the oil depletion scenario that is about to unfold quite soon. The reason they enthuse about hydrogen is based on the fact that hydrogen is less polluting as a fuel and will therefore help mitigate global warming caused by CO_2 emissions. California has recently passed a state law which requires twelve per cent of vehicles to be emission free and this is the area car manufacturers are aiming at. In fact using oil or gas to make hydrogen just makes the energy more expensive and expensive is not good for the world economy which is based on very cheap oil energy. The scale of the problem is mind boggling. Unfortunately hydrogen enthusiasts, particularly the utopian sort, do a great disservice to humanity because they attempt to delude us into thinking that everything is going to be OK and that a hydrogen economy will come charging along and allow us to carry on with the same high energy lifestyles. These enthusiasts are fixed in the mindset that man's technological ingenuity will solve all our energy needs. In this mindset man is the centre of intelligence and nature has once more been defeated. This battle, between man's ingenuity and nature's recalcitrance to comply with our wishful thinking will be at the crux of man's **spiritual** battle with his environment.

When we belatedly realise that hydrogen will not come along like a knight in shining armour we will have some serious thinking to do and we will need to make some rapid and momentous changes to our lifestyles. Presently these changes are not being factored into the world economy for the very simple reason that the world economy is utterly dependent on global growth to keep the debt mountain from falling on top of us.

It is perhaps worth repeating that a Hydrogen economy is not only desirable it will be essential to our continued technological development. Once all the fossil fuels have gone it will be the **best possible** available source of liquid fuel but we need to understand the physical limitations and the resultant cost implications. Everything in creation comes with a **price** but it is not simply a **financially measurable** price. Shortly the world is about to experience profound energy shortages. This has never happened before. Even the oil shocks in the seventies didn't lead to any more than minor disruptions to supply. True there were lines at the gas pumps in America but these were short-lived and were mostly based on panic buying because the price was going up daily.

When we begin to experience actual shortages the price will rocket and the world economy will lurch into the deepest recession it has ever experienced. Whilst experiencing these actual energy shortages and the massive shrinking of available financial capital the utopian hydrogen enthusiasts make-believe that billions upon billions of dollars will suddenly become available to put in place a pure hydrogen transportation economy. My prediction is that the utopians will find themselves rudely awakened to their illusory realities. My intuition tells me that the cheap hydrocarbon age is rapidly coming to an end. Petroleum science tells us that cheap hydrocarbons are coming to an end. My long term vision tells me that a hydrogen economy will **eventually** be established but only after we have learnt to have some real respect for nature and learn to live **within** nature's limitations. Our first reaction to this crisis will force us to look to our local economies and this will be no bad thing.

Fossil fuels presently put New Zealand lamb, Kenyan green beans and Egyptian new potatoes on our plates for Sunday lunch. A leg of lamb costs twelve pounds. The fossil fuel cost per pound was not a significant part of the economic equation which led to the commercial decision to ship this food across the world. This economic equation will change when the price of oil eventually sky rockets. A medium-sized container ship burns about four tonnes of oil per hour. They travel for twenty four hours a day. They therefore burn about 100 tonnes a day. That is equivalent to about 120,000 litres per day. Presently container ships collect fuel from major ports which are situated next to crude oil refineries. It is not taxed at all. It only costs a few pennies a litre. Hydrogen will not cost a few pennies. It will cost many dollars per litre and therefore shipping food across the world may not be quite the same economic equation as before. World trade will have to dramatically decline.

WHEN WORLD TRADE DECLINES THE WORLD ECONOMY DECLINES.

This **must not** be allowed to happen but **it will**. Eventually. Sure enough it won't happen tomorrow or next month or next year or maybe for five or even ten years but it will eventually happen and no sort of alternative economy is being designed to replace it. The idea that the US *will build three hundred nuclear power stations* to make electricity to hydrolyse water to make pure Hydrogen to fuel container ships is simply absurd.

Sometimes I feel like the little boy who is crying wolf! And the wolf never arrives!! Lots of people think this is doomsday merchant philosophy. Well let them think what they like. **Let's establish the facts** first and then see **where we really are** with respect to the world's future energy availability.

Now I realise that quite a few people will have become aware recently that various automobile manufacturers are demon-strating hydrogen fuelled vehicles. In particular Ford, General Motors, Daimler Benz and Toyota are all producing prototypes for fuel cell hydrogen powered vehicles. A brief word of technical explanation may be in order. Firstly: **A fuel cell is not a fuel source**. It is really a kind of sophisticated battery. When a fuel cell is provided with a fuel source, such as hydrogen, it creates heat/electricity which can be utilised to create mechanical movement. In other words a working moving vehicle.

The world's leading manufacturer of fuel cells is called Ballard. The technology of fuel cells has been rapidly developed by Ballard over the last few years. Only a decade ago many people,

The human mind is designed in such a manner that it likes to separate creation into many different aspects. Separating creation into facts and theories occupies a great deal of human time and ingenuity. When this process goes so far and threatens to become destructive, processes occur naturally in the divine web to regulate the system. Presently we are at a point in our evolution when we need to take some conscious active involvement in the regulation of this system. Our first point of approach should be analysis but our first point of departure should be re-integration and renewal. The balances and checks that exist in the world's natural system are the same "balance sheets" and checks that exist in man's unnatural money systems.

Some people have the impression that we are *reducing* our emissions of Carbon Dioxide in the UK. In fact we haven't reduced them we have mostly just *shipped* them out to other countries.

The simple fact is that manufacturing in the UK has been steadily collapsing for decades.

We now buy most of our steel from Eastern Europe. Steel making is the most intense industrial activity and creates vast amounts of carbon dioxide. In fact, The International Energy Agencies 'World Energy Outlook 2000' *clearly stated that carbon dioxide emissions in Europe will increase by 15 per cent by 2010* and by 23 per cent by 2020. This scenario *includes* abiding to the terms of the Kyoto protocol. The more recent Johannesburg Earth Summit in 2002 made similar promises. We all know how easy promises are to make. We can also absolutely guarantee that these promises will not be kept. Unless it happens by default and western industrial activity is significantly curtailed by some other non-political factors. Oil Shock Waves perhaps?

even within the fuel cell industry, were skeptical that fuel cells could become powerful and efficient enough to power automobiles but Ballard's technology has recently changed that view. The technology is quite brilliant and promises, in time, a wonderful new future for transportation/propulsion systems. Ballard has now joined up with General Motors and Daimler Benz to create the first generation of fuel-celled, commercially viable vehicles. Indeed Daimler Benz, the most advanced and enlightened amongst the motor manufacturing companies, recently announced plans to produce 100,000 fuel cell engines. These fuel cell engines will run on hydrogen. HOWEVER they will not be running on **pure liquid hydrogen** made from renewable sources. The present fuel cell engines will run on METHANOL which will be converted on board the fuel cell vehicle into hydrogen.

METHANOL IS MADE FROM FOSSIL FUELS!

Why Methanol? Because it has been discovered through painstaking research and development that Methanol is the only economic way of getting a fuel cell vehicle into production.

Using "pure hydrogen" as a fuel source for fuel cell cars has been categorically dismissed by all the major automobile manufacturers.

Since these new fuel cell cars will run therefore on **FOSSIL FUELS** they will not effect the oil depletion scenario which is estimated to arrive in the next few years. These auto manufacturers have rejected the use of pure liquid hydrogen for many technical and economic reasons. They hope however that developing interim fuel cell cars running on Methanol will **provide a bridge** to an eventual fuel cell vehicle powered by pure hydrogen. Daimler Benz has stated quite unequivocally that fossil fuels will be needed to run fuel cell cars for at least the next twenty years or so. Geoffrey Ballard, the founder of Ballard fuel cells, believes that, "Nuclear power, possibly in the form of "fusion" will be needed to create sufficient electrical energy to manufacture pure Hydrogen".

Fusion is the science of trying to replicate the reactions which take place inside the SUN, where temperatures are measured in **millions** of degrees centigrade. Most scientists do not believe fusion will ever become a commercial reality. Billions of dollars has already been invested in the technology but it is still at the theoretical stage.

Hydrogen utopians are working on the assumption that we can somehow find or make enough power to keep the global trading status quo travelling at its present level of activity. They are well intentioned but deluded. We are about to approach an era of general energy depletion. There simply won't be **billions** of spare kilowatts to make the holy grail of pure hydrogen available for massive international use.

Hydrogen and the Fuel Cell

The Ballard fuel cell is called a P.E.M which stands for proton exchange membrane. It has been designed to work with hydrogen from fossil fuel resources. An alternative fuel cell, similar to ones used in the space programme, which works on an alkaline principle, but only runs on pure hydrogen has been **universally abandoned**. It remains the technology of the future. In fact many hydrogen enthusiasts state quite openly that the main reason for developing fuel cells is that the technology is much cleaner and less polluting than standard gasoline combustion engines. The fact that we will soon have fuel cell cars running on hydrogen is therefore something of a red herring when it comes to helping with oil depletion but yet virtually everywhere you look, particularly in the mainstream media, you will find it being touted as the next "energy" revolution. In fact the ignorance is quite astounding. Just to give you one small example; on the back cover of a book called "Powering the future: The Ballard fuel cell and the race to change the world" there is a quote from the highly acclaimed, world famous biologist, Dr David Suzuki. The quote is as follows:

"The Ballard fuel cell holds great promise as an energy source for the ecological millennium. It's a fascinating and inspiring story".

The only problem is: A FUEL CELL IS **NOT** A FUEL **SOURCE**.

In another book entitled "The Hydrogen Economy" by Jeremy Rifkin we come across another enlightening statement: -

"Critics argue that if the automobile industry commits to fuel cell cars with an on-board fuel processor – a portable thermochemical plant – to convert methanol into hydrogen it will be locking itself into an expensive and unnecessary long-term strategy that could cost more than $ 1 trillion dollars for the next car fleet."

Lastly another important book: "Tomorrow's Energy; Hydrogen, fuel cells and the prospect for a cleaner planet" by Peter Hoffman tells us: -

"During the 1970's and the 1980's much, if not most, of the hydrogen production research was aimed at splitting large volumes of water molecules. This was perceived as the crucial prerequisite to using hydrogen as a fuel. In the 1990's the emphasis shifted to making hydrogen energy - not necessarily ultra pure hydrogen- an industrial and commercial reality. Thus much more attention has been paid to improving the steam reforming of natural gas"

In other words, t**he production of pure hydrogen was abandoned**.

I'm very sorry to be such a bore repeating myself but this point may be one of the most **critical elements** in human technological survival because trying to create a huge fuel cell/automobile infrastructure designed to maintain our present transportation needs which is still based on **FOSSIL FUELS may lead to disaster**. It is unimaginative and dangerous because it *does not take into account the general depletion of energy resources.*

What is PURE Hyrogen?

It is simply the hydrogen hidden in water.

*Volume Six - 2003
Thomas Field*

Thomas did not think of farming as work; he didn't analyse it. Work was life. For most of this 'life' he had remained an optimist in the face of great adversity. Until now. He had never before complained about the back-breaking labour, being up at two or three a.m., helping a poor pregnant cow through a breech birth, or the battle against the endless vagaries of the English weather. Until now. He had survived having most of his fields flooded through October of 2000 and he had survived the last few years' collapse in grain prices. He had survived, but only just, the BSE crisis. He had never turned his cows into cannibals but had always fed them pure grains and grass. When his beef herd was slaughtered in 1999 he decided not to replace it but to concentrate on sheep and his few remaining dairy cows. Now they were all going to be slaughtered because they might be going to get foot-and-mouth.

Thomas followed the two slaughterers out to their van whilst they changed into white, heavy plastic overalls, white wellington boots and white plastic caps. They looked like germ warfare specialists out of a sci-fi horror movie. The two men took their bolt guns out

In the above paragraph we mentioned that most hydrogen production is planned to come from reforming gas. Where one might wonder is the gas going to come from? The US Department of Energy projects that natural gas consumption will increase from it's 1999 production output of 20.4 trillion cubic feet to between 32.2 trillion cubic feet by the year 2020 but **new** models of North American gas production point to **actual depletion** starting to occur by 2007! In fact this year, in 2003, gas prices in the US have **trebled** and in **one day they actually went up by forty per cent**. This is just another example of how one part of the global financial brain doesn't talk to the other parts. Richard Duncan an engineer who recently addressed the geological society of America's summit in 2000, predicted rolling blackouts in the US beginning around 2012 due to a shortage of natural gas. **Yet, at the same time, plans are afoot for millions of fuel cell vehicles running on hydrogen made from natural gas**. Something, somewhere, is seriously out of balance.

The main point is that the development of a hydrogen system is probably critical to our continued technical advancement but it is possible to take these developmental ideas in very different directions. Hydrogen may be the simplest element in the universe but it didn't get where it is today by making hasty partnerships. We will need to woo hydrogen like a lover and I'm sorry that sounds a bit weird. It just so happens to be wonderfully true.

It's worth asking the question: - In a world where fossil fuel is depleting, do we want to spend ten valuable kilowatts to make one kilowatt of hydrogen energy so that we can fly green beans from Kenya to the supermarket in Burgess Hill? In a word, when fossil fuels are beginning to run out quite quickly and there may be energy shortages, do we want to spend ten valuable kilowatts of electrical energy to produce one kilowatt of liquid hydrogen energy to drive to the school or the local supermarket? It's a matter of prioritisation. It's a matter of polarisation. It is probably a matter of localisation of physical resources in parallel with a globalisation of ideas and communication: Physical stuff, the lumps of matter and lumps of physical flesh (i.e. people) probably need to remain much more localised for much of the time. Or, **when we travel,** as I sincerely hope we will, it will be by **low energy** methods. Sailing, walking, cycling, gliding etc. Ideas, on the other hand, most specifically ideas about how to create alternative energy systems, need to be global. **Travel need not come to an end. It can simply become real travel again instead of cheap tourism.**

Many years ago I was taught that travel, more than anything else, broadened the mind and gave one the best education. Today many people think they are "well travelled" BUT THIS IS NOT THE CASE. Today's so-called travellers are merely energetic tourists locked in familiar mindsets, staying in identical hotels, eating identical international food and consuming identical international branded goods.

One might ask, then, if energy for our future society is not going to come from oil or gas, and the holy grail of hydrogen is not **simply** going to replace oil then where will our energy come from? The answer is very simple. The energy will come from the sun. Have we been here before? You may well ask. The sun is a master of coming round and round on a regular basis. All energy comes from the Sun now and it always has and always will.

What changes is the chemical equation.

We started using wood as energy. Primitive flames from logs that had fallen off trees, maybe.

Wood - Contains some hydrogen but also lots of carbon

Coal - Contains more hydrogen than wood - but still lots of carbon

Oil - Contains more hydrogen than wood or coal but still contains some carbon

Gas - Contains more hydrogen than wood or coal or oil - but still contains carbon

Hydrogen produced from fossil source - Contains hydrogen but STILL has carbon

Hydrogen produced from natural, renewable energy sources - Contains only pure Hyrdogen.

BUT

Pure Hydrogen as a liquid does not exist in nature.

Ninety-five per cent of hydrogen produced today is presently manufactured from fossil fuels, such as petrol, methanol or natural gas.

Over the mid-term to long-term, various research bodies have concluded that hydrogen could **just possibly** be made using nuclear energy to produce electricity to produce the energy to split water molecules into hydrogen gas and oxygen gas. The reason nuclear power is being suggested is that scientists still believe nuclear power is viable. The nuclear lobby **tries to pretend** that nuclear power is environmentally friendly because the generation of nuclear power that uses uranium or plutonium as its core energy doesn't produce carbon dioxide, one of the main sources of the global warming phenomenon. As we know all too well, however, nuclear power produces poisonous toxic waste that lasts for thousands upon thousands of years.

There is no solution to the long-term storage of nuclear

of their cases and headed determinedly towards the barn full of sheep. Thomas followed them.

Thomas estimated that about half his flock was left. They had now run into a terrified huddle at the far end of the field.

The men were still charging around shooting and murdering indiscriminately and the whole green field was now littered with lumps of woollen, bloodied death. The police came (the men had called them) and they took Thomas's gun away and led him back inside. It took another two hours for the men to finish their murderous work and then the JCB arrived.

Within a few minutes it was shunting the animals into great heaps and then piling them into the back of a large converted gravel lorry. One by one the dead animals were dumped. Just lumps of meaningless, lifeless matter. Once or twice it was discovered that just as the bulldozer's large claws were about to close on another animal, it was not quite dead.

"It'll be dead quite soon", said the man from the 'Department of Humane Slaughter.' "It's not usually this messy," said one of the men. "It was on account of the barn door opening and the animals escaping", and he gave another vicious look at Thomas.

Thomas was numb but he started to walk round the perimeter of the field to see that none of his animals had escaped or were wounded. Right in the far corner, behind some old brambles stuck in an old greenhouse frame, he saw the remains of Goliath.

He had smashed his way through the sheep netting and barbed wire and buried himself deep in the bushes. Thomas scrambled his way in. He was not quite dead. He had been shot clearly in the forehead and the blood was spilling and already congealing over his eyes, but they were still open and he was breathing quite heavily.

The rifle shot had smashed open his head and severed the base of his horns, but they were so strong and powerful that the bullet had not penetrated to the brain.

Thomas crawled up to him and rested his huge head in his lap. If he had had his gun he would have put him out of his misery but he had nothing. He could only wait for the inevitable to happen. He sat cradling Goliath's huge head until the sun went down and the hot, burning tears of rage and impotence washed away the blood on Goliath's smashed and broken head.

radio-active waste. Only morons or fools would bury toxic radioactive, lethal, poisonous waste in their own back gardens. Sending it off the planet into outer space has been suggested by the American government as an alternative means of disposal, even dumping it on the moon.

Fortunately or unfortunately, depending on how you want to look at it, the amount of energy required to send nuclear waste to the moon would use up more energy than the nuclear reaction originally produced.

In order to have enough nuclear power stations to produce electricity to make hydrogen gas and then freeze it would require vast amounts of uranium. According to the Federal German Ministry of the Economy, there is presently an 'estimated' seventy years of uranium left* – if used at the present rate. If the world transportation economy were to switch over to liquid hydrogen made from nuclear power making electricity, etc., then uranium would be used up in about three to fifteen years. I give the lowest and the highest estimates. In other words, if we totally poisoned most of the Earth with radioactive residues we could buy ourselves, maybe, ten years. The question should surely arise. Would it be worth poisoning the planet just to delay the inevitable? The political debate over the next few years will be increasingly taken up with this issue even though it doesn't appear to warrant much discussion at all.

The political powers that be may well favour using and developing vast nuclear energy resources when oil seriously starts to deplete because it will, for a while at least, enable them to control for a little longer the Western economic power-game model. Nuclear power needs massive research, development and construction. There will be massive up-front financing costs and these could only be achieved by a very strong central government imposing its political will upon the people of the pretty little planet Earth. Whether or not politics will succeed will, of course, be up to the will of the people. Or will it? One has to ask where the 'will' of the people is being led?

When the Earth made its 'will' and left, as a divine, natural legacy, the energy resources behind for evolution's later use, it managed to write-in various intelligent provisions. These provisions state that Mother Earth, the planet, will provide what is necessary in order for us to learn. Unfortunately, the Earth was unable to write out of its 'will' various codicils. These codicils state that the Earth must provide, in its legacy, sufficient poisonous energies to destroy ourselves. Thus illustrating the greatest law of all: That the True Law Maker must abide perfectly and utterly by its own laws. The creation of these natural laws probably took a long time to define. But that of course wasn't a problem, for the True Original Law Maker *also made time.*

Interestingly, nearly all benign alternative renewable sources of energy are most suited to **local** manufacture and use. This does not suit world politicians bent on maintaining their power structures, as central political control would be eroded. An enlightened political structure would be prioritising local energy infrastructures instead of going to war for a little more oil to keep the nearly defunct, dangerously poisonous, capitalistic trading system intact. At the very least a political structure with a

*Further research on ultimate Uranium deposits indicates there may be more Uranium available. Good news or bad?

modicum of intelligence would be asking some important questions. Alas this is more than we can expect from today's political elite.

Needless to add really, **but the driving force behind the technical and scientific research into using nuclear power to generate hydrogen liquid fuels is an American government** subsidiary-cum-scientific establishment called Argonne which is one of the US government's oldest and largest science/ engineering departments.

It is clear to many of us who have thought about the question of energy alternatives that a pure hydrogen economy (if hydrogen were readily available) would be the ideal sustainable and environmentally benign fuel source, so it should come as no surprise that the American government and its scientific institutes have also been studying this particular technology. It is clear, even to the American government, that if the American economy were able to exist on hydrogen resources that it manufactured internally, then the problem of depending on Middle East oil would disappear. As it happens, the American scientific establishments, such as Argonne, **have** investigated the processes of hydrogen manufacture. The results of their research indicate some very painful conclusions.

Argonne's research proves, quite conclusively, that producing pure hydrogen from natural, renewable resources, such as wind, solar, etc, **is not viable**. Quite simply, the amount of energy **required** to be put in does not justify the amount of energy **produced**. In other words, it is not cost-effective. It is for this reason that Argonne believes the only way a hydrogen economy can be created is through the mass building of nuclear power. It is perhaps worth taking a few moments to consider Argonne's position. It states:

"The US consumed 7.9 million barrels of gasoline per day in January 2003. On that basis, 210 million kilograms of hydrogen would be required to serve the US petrol fleet."

Actually 210 million kilogrammes doesn't sound like very much does it? Perhaps we should remember that Hydrogen however is the lightest element in the universe. It's the element nearest to God. It's atomic number is one.

Argonne states further:

"A small amount of high purity hydrogen is made by electrolysis of water. This process is about 60 to 70 per cent efficient in converting electrical energy into hydrogen energy. However since the efficiency of making electricity from the primary fuel is between 30 to 40 per cent the overall efficiency of making hydrogen by electrolysis is between 20 and 30 per cent."

Let us be clear about this. Argonne is the world's leading research establishment into hydrogen power possibilities. It is run by the US government. (Please verify the statements for yourself by visiting the Argonne website –

www.hydrogen.anl.gov/fuelcells

In fact 95 per cent of hydrogen is made from fossil fuels. The **reason** for making hydrogen is not to make fuel for combustion in transportation vehicles but for the manufacture of ammonia or

HYSOLAR was an organization set up by the German Government to investigate the possibilities of creating a pure hydrogen system made by renewables for use in remote or inaccessible areas. However in Autumn 1995 the German government decided to quit funding HYSOLAR.

The official statement declared that the energy was too long term [about fifty years] and far too expensive a proposition. The government came to the conclusion that it was the energy for the day after the day after tomorrow.

Every organization which has studied the production of pure Hydrogen from renewable energy sources such as wind or photovoltaics has rejected it as too costly. It will only work when there is an excess of free kilowatts. Where will the free kilowatts be coming from?

other chemicals.

Water you see, unfortunately for the capitalist energy enthusiasts, is very stable. It does not break down into significant quantities of usable hydrogen until a temperature of between 2,500 and 3,000 degrees centigrade is reached. That is, for the sake of comparison, about ten times hotter than heat in your average domestic oven. No degrees in physics or chemistry are required to recognise that producing these kinds of temperatures requires vast amounts of initial energy to get the reaction going.

Argonne plans that these vast amounts of energy will arrive in the US through massive new nuclear power stations. Now, at last, here is some good news. By the time the serious need for a pure hydrogen economy is recognised, starting to build nuclear power stations will be ineffective as it will already be too late.

At this moment in time we need to invite our very best scientific and technical brains to take a whole new look at the 'energy' equation. These brains will not only need to be scientific, academic and well-engineered, they will also need to be philosophical. For, in order to develop a 'new energy economy', new mindsets will need to be prepared. The solutions to the dilemmas presented to the scientists will not be purely scientific because they will involve redesign of consumer-driven, globally traded lifestyles. We can, if we want, produce lots and lots of 'new energy' from new technological and technical breakthroughs but we will have to decide what we are prepared to pay. Some people may want to continue with an unbalanced, profligate consumer lifestyle but they will have to work harder and harder for it. How much harder do people want to work? The answer to this may be quite simple. Probably not much. *Most people are already working far too hard.*

So the major element to the solution of our energy needs is reduction in energy requirements. It will be a trade-off, an equation which, by its very nature, will not ever be perfectly balanced. At least, not until the end of time itself.

For a few it will be 'back to the woods and cooking on horse dung.' For others it will be vast nuclear power station complexes making cheap hydrogen to try and maintain the global trading financial status quo and, of course, wealth! Somewhere in the middle we may meet. We can only hope Mother Nature is planning to arrive, with some timely help, at her own pre-planned destiny.

In any event, one day we may reach the point when we are actually grateful for the pile of shit we have to sort out. Life without challenge is no life at all. Our present challenge, to start redesigning our future together, would seem like a good place to start.

The blending of science with theological thought has already been anticipated by the physicists and by the theologians. So far, this relationship has been fairly abstract but in the next stage of evolution it will be practical, physical and philosophical. Indeed, it will have to be all three at once. Interestingly, finding theology in sub-atomic processes was facilitated by the splitting of the atom, the development of the atomic bomb and the advent of nuclear physics. Atomic energy, i.e. energy from the atom, is explosive. Quite bizarre when you really come to think about it.

We make our biggest bombs and our biggest bangs with what comes from the very, very smallest sub-atomic particles. In this simple fact lies nature's fundamental principle. The macro-cosmos is created by the micro-cosmos. Hydrogen. Our simplest element has created the foundation for most of life's complexities. It's not about to change its nature just yet. At least not to satisfy the rapacious lusts of Western consumers intent of stocking up with knick knacks from the third world. I would like to say. "Thank-you Mr Hydrogen"

Atomic energy has proved conclusively to humanity that everything is energy but now there is some pretty funky, rather paradoxical, new physics to measure and ponder over. The explosion of atomic energy had a parallel explosion in human consciousness but it wasn't noticed in quite the same way because it wasn't one big explosion; it was a series of sub-atomic shock waves in the conscious layers that make up our total human perception. This process is called individualisation. Being an individual means, quite literally, 'in divided duality'. Or 'one divided duality' or 'one divided into two'.

Our desire, our overwhelming spiritual desire, is to return to a feeling of oneness, but returning to the One cannot take place on one's own. It is going to be a shared process. Over the centuries, indeed over the past millennia, man has become increasingly specialist. This trend may well continue but alongside, in parallel with, indeed within, this process, humanity's best brains will be required to blend many different philosophies, geologies, theologies and sciences. In doing so we may realise, a little belatedly, that people are in fact much more important than things. We are all simply part of a process we cannot help sharing.

The Internet, the Worldwide Web, is one of the physical manifestations of this consciousness blending process that is taking place. The connections over the web maybe physically 'electronic' but communal ideas when connected together actually become a very poweful force for change.

The history of man's evolution has been the history of chasing ever upwards the hydrocarbon tree of life. Wood-coal-oil-gas-pure hydrogen. In fact, of course, all these hydrocarbons got their original energy from the sun. It is easiest to think of wood, coal, oil, gas, even nuclear, as a simple method for storing the intensive solidified energy of the Sun. Here's another small aside as a matter of interest. As I write, there has been no wind whatsoever for nearly seven or eight days. Everything is still and a purple shroud of pollution covers the top of the Sussex Downs. Windmills would not have been much use this week. They don't work too well without wind. In fact, come to think of it, they don't work at all. This might be annoying if you wanted to put the washing machine on. Now here's a strange, wonderful, disturbing 'Alternative Energy Idea': Maybe we will have to wait for a nice windy day to use all our electrical appliances! A windy day would then become a super busy day. When the wind blew and the windmills churned the electricity would flow and you would:-

- **Load the dishwasher**
- **Do several loads of laundry**
- **Get the lawn mower out**
- **Bake most of the week's meals and cakes and goodies**

> Making friends with Hydrogen, [Pure Hydrogen, not Hydrogen from fossils] will be quite a delightful and wonderfully gentle process.
>
> Hydrogen is pure and simple and essential.

We will not just survive this energy crisis, we will build the world of our dreams!

The same issues might actually apply to various small local industrial enterprises. If you were a miller, you would wait for a windy day. The wind would blow. The power would come. The milling wheels would grind, you'd heat the oven and bake the bread. You'd be a real, old-fashioned wind miller again. Only this time you'd have a high-tech windmill whizzing super efficiently around with titanium precision-engineered bearings and producing not just mechanical power but electrical power. When viewed from this perspective, we will have simultaneously moved backwards as well as forwards. One could go on but I don't want to make an issue out of it.

In these scenarios you would have to do all the chores fairly rapidly because you wouldn't be certain for how long the wind would be blowing. When you had finished your chores, you'd be left with so much time you would have to go shopping or talk to your friends. At the same time, of course (because you'd have a great deal more time on your hands) you would be fiddling and playing and generally fooling around. Children would spend their afternoons having concerts in the park by the Spanish Steps in Haywards Heath high street, which had, for some considerable number of years, been free of smelly, nasty traffic. There would be lots of cricket played in the spare time available. Who'd be in the factories making things? I don't ask such big questions for the moment! Maybe there are less factories and less things. Maybe there's more 'TIME' as a result.

Windmills are wonderful for making life move with the rhythms of the wind, i.e. the air. The air is a beautiful, generally gentle and benign original element. [It only gets angry if people keep chucking tonnes of carbon dioxide up into it]. Unfortunately, windmills won't make the equivalent of twenty-five million million million million litres of petrol every day. Nor will several thousand more nuclear power stations. There isn't enough uranium. Uranium, thank God is rare! All the other alternative energies, like solar, photovoltaic, biomass, wave water/tidal power, have one common denominator. They are all **secondary** energy systems. In other words, they need technology first to convert their primary energy force, i.e. Water - Wind/Air, Sun/Earth.

In 1976 the World Energy Forum predicted that the end of the oil age would begin about the turn of the century. Nobody listened. Well, nobody much. Since then we have done **virtually zero** on the alternative energy front. You have to remember that, simultaneous to oil energy shortages, **the world financial economy will be trying to save itself from Armageddon.** The wealthy like nothing less than to see their money running away from them. The vast amounts of money that the rich people have lent to the poor people will not be trundling back into their coffers with large chunks of interest added. This scenario will be unfolding and unravelling with a million consequences we cannot even begin to vaguely consider here in these short essays. I have left the consequences of all these particular issues and the effect they would have on individual people's lives to the main thrust of the plot in the ten volumes of the no 19 bus.

The future is difficult. Perhaps it is simply my personal regard for some of the simple elemental laws of life that make me feel so absolutely positive that we will not only find a way to go beyond our present dilemmas, but that we will turn our dilemmas into challenges that will eventually heal the unhappy spirits which are presently flowing across the earth.

The essence of the matter is simple. Present day capitalism is looking for a simple, straight alternative to oil. In other words, hydrogen instead of oil. Anything, indeed, to keep sports utility vehicles, space rockets, armoured Sherman tanks, B52 bombers, aeroplanes, ships, boats, cars, lorries, scooters and motorbikes whizzing about on their various, totally essential duties like bringing mangoes from India, bombing all the people in Iraq, bringing carnations from Venezuela to London, Paris and Madrid, avocados from Israel and broken biscuits from southern Spain. It is, of course, in this scenario absolutely essential that we manage to maintain a corporate infrastructure so that Nike trainers can come from sweat shops in China and all kind of totally essential electronic knick-knacks from Japan get into our shops and out of our shops on a regular basis.

What economists and capitalists want is a smooth, i.e. a straight, alternative transition from one energy source to the next. If there isn't a smooth transition, then wealth may be affected. We have already dealt with the fact that the rich man hates more than anything to see his money disappear. We are all familiar, I think, with the act and art of money disappearing. No sooner do we seem to have some than it's gone and we need to have some more!

A true **alternative**, however, is very different from a straight Alternative. The economists' capitalist model would like us to have a choice of continuing with two very similar shades of grey. There's nothing really new in their social, cultural, spiritual model. But a **true alternative** is ending all association with the present way of the world and learning to commune with nature once more. To ask nature to open out and share some of her secrets. To let us find the knowledge and understanding of the flora and fauna. To see whether healing plants may be grown to detoxify the poisons in the waste ground that we have created. This will let us befriend nature again and perhaps it is in the nature of friends to be benevolent to each other. Perhaps the pall of purple smoke presently hanging above the Sussex Downs can be cleansed and purified, re-imbibed and be invited back to the soil from whence it originally came.

Millions upon trillions of tonnes of topsoil are presently spinning about in the atmosphere when they should almost certainly be on the ground providing the basis for the food that provides the basics of life for all living creatures. It is all, or rather I sincerely hope it is, a perfect cycle, within which human history plays out its evolutionary racial wars. It will do so until it simply runs out of energy to do so any longer. At this point, survival suddenly switches quite spontaneously and almost electrically. Suddenly our survival is not going to be ensured by a brutal competitiveness. It is going to be ensured by our gentle co-operation with the re-born spirit of the land and a re-energised excitement in our souls. This is the real Alternative Energy. Working with the principles and spirit of nature.

Just think, when tidal power is perfected as a source of electricity and energy, we will have the most power when there is a full moon, because it is the full moon that always pulls the tides. In times to come we may work to the rhythms of the full moon. When the full moon is high up in the sky it will be time to work and saw and scurry and hurry. A whole seaside community together, for a while at least, in working harmony. The very best news of all is that we don't have to do anything very much to make it all happen. This is not a political

Make music.

Make musical instruments.

Make fun.

Make love (be careful not to make too many people).

Make mischief.

Avoid extremes.

A sufi mystic saying

124

A Reader's Comments:

"The authenticity of the characters and their diversity is almost overwhelming."

philosophy; you don't have to sign up. This is simply a natural, returning, eternal, planetary, centrally planned cosmic principle.

Many people have been anxiously wondering how a 'healthy alternative society' might come about. The environmental battle, population, demography, the world financial system all seem to have been heading in the wrong direction. It is now time to realise that the real changes will not come about through tinkering with the existing system. Many of us have wanted to see an end to the most destructive aspects of our industrialised, money orientated world but it has been impossible to see the way forward. Now at last we are presented with an extraordinary opportunity to work together to design local sustainable benevolent energy systems which will allow us to work with Mother Nature rather than against her.

The Environment

July 3rd 2003

I had a sleepless night. I was thinking about this essay which has to be finished tomorrow [July 4th] ready for the proof-readers and designers. I awoke wondering how I might introduce the subject. I wanted something real and possibly a bit frightening. My lovely wife came upstairs with a cup of delicious cappuccino, two pieces of toast [with marmite] and the morning newspaper. The Independent. The headlines in the paper were: -

Reaping the Whirlwind: Extreme weather prompts Unprecedented Global Warming alert.

I have believed for some time in serendipity. I have experienced first hand special moments when events seem to draw themselves together as if guided by an intelligence way beyond our comprehension. This seems such a moment. Below I have reproduced the article from the Independent newspaper.

From the Independent newspaper 3rd July 2003: -

"In an astonishing announcement on Global warming and extreme weather, the World Meteorological Organisation signalled last night that the world's weather is going haywire.

In a startling report, the WMO, which normally produces detailed scientific reports and staid statistics at the year's end, highlighted record extremes in weather and climate occurring all over the world in recent weeks, from Switzerland's hottest ever June to a record month for tornadoes in the United States – and linked them to climate change.

The unprecedented warning takes its force and significance from the fact that it is not coming from Greenpeace or Friends of the Earth, but from an impeccably respected UN organisation that is not given to Hyperbole (though environmentalists will seize on it to claim that the direst warnings of climate change are being born out).

The Geneva based body to which the weather services of 185 countries contribute, takes the view that events this year in Europe, America and Asia are so remarkable that the world needs to be made aware of it immediately.

The extreme weather it documents, such as the record high and low temperatures, record rainfall and record storms in different parts of the world show that, as the atmosphere warms, the climate not only becomes much hotter but much more

In 1950 we were adding about 1 billion tons of carbon. By the year 2000 we were adding 6 billion tons.

The rate is still growing every year. It is not difficult to understand global warming.

An 11 year-old science student can understand the science. If we fill the atmosphere with gas we will trap heat in the atmosphere and the atmosphere will warm up.

Nothing could be simpler or more dangerous.

There has been according, to science and archaeology;

Five great extinctions of life on the planet. Each of these extinctions caused an evolutionary shock wave.

Any species or situation or circumstance that threatens the overall balance of the planet will be eliminated by the planet's natural rebalancing systems.

This includes the human virus.

unstable. *"Recent scientific assessments indicate that as the global temperatures continue to warm due to climate change, the number and intensity of extreme events might increase,"* the WMO said, giving a striking series of examples.*

In Southern France record temperatures were recorded in June, rising above 40 degrees in places. In Switzerland it was the hottest June in 250 years. In Geneva since 29th May daytime temperatures have not fallen below 25 degrees C making it the hottest June recorded. In the United States there were 562 tornadoes which caused 41 deaths. This set a record for any month. In India this years pre monsoon heatwave brought peak temperatures of 45 degrees C. At least 1,400 people died. In Sri Lanka heavy rainfall exacerbated wet conditions resulting in flooding killing at least three hundred people. Last month was the hottest in England and Wales since 1976 [which was the hottest on record].

*It is possible that 2003 will be the hottest year ever recorded. The ten hottest years in the 143 year old global temperature record have now **ALL** been since 1990 with **the three hottest being 1998, 2001 and 2002.***

The unstable world of climate change has long been a prediction. Now the World Meteorological Organisation says it is a reality."

[end of article]

Of course to those of us who have exercised our **common sense** the phenomenon of global warming and its increasingly cataclysmic effects on the environment come as no real surprise. Now that highly respected institutions like the World Meteorological Organisation are getting seriously worried **will** there be an immediate and rapid change of sentiment amongst politicians and industry? I doubt it. The rate of economic eco destruction is only going to get worse. This year a record 25,000 square kilometres of Brazilian rain forest was burnt down by farmers mostly to grow genetically modified soy beans which are then mostly exported to Europe to feed our beef cattle to put beef steaks on our plates. At this rate, in **just ten years** an area of rain forest the size of the whole of the United Kingdom will **disappear** from Brazil alone! One has to wonder. When will this mayhem and destruction come to an end? Much as we might **hope** I do not believe it will come to an end because there is a quantum conscious leap in the world's political leaders. It will come to an end only when the economics of such behaviour become **unsustainable**. We are going to have to wait for the world's energy resources to run down sufficiently to the point where such global trade becomes untenable. It is a matter of some importance. Will the economic crisis be sufficiently intense to save the planet from a climactic Armageddon?

The devastation and degradation of our environment is being increasingly well documented and the facts, as the above article indicates, are becoming indisputable. It is not a pretty picture. Our consumption in the West and increasingly in Asia is **entirely** to blame. According to our political masters however it is essential to our financial well being that **we continue to consume not** just at the **present** rate, but an increased rate. We must increase our consumption and our activity to keep the economy from sinking. If the economy sinks much more the inter-related pieces of the financial jigsaw we call Global Capitalism may start to fall apart. The world economy as it is presently structured requires continuous growth. Otherwise the debt mountain will fall on top of us. A pretty dilemma. For the life of me I **could not** have personally constructed **more ideal** circumstances to give humanity a severe jolt. Indeed a very potent bolt of electricity right through the petty arrogance and greed that so typifies the world's dictators and despots. I include most of the elected **democratic** dictatorships in the same category.

Over a long period of time the same words, even very important daily vital words, can begin to mean something different. One such word is environment. A dose of the English Oxford Dictionary shows us the root of the word: Environ. Literally environment means to 'encompass' or 'surround.' To be environed is to be 'surrounded.' In the Victorian age a man might most commonly use the word in reference to say his 'family environment' or his 'work environment.' A hundred years ago the word environment would have been something rather close, personal and important. Now just take the word ENVIRON and add the word MENTAL: - ENVIRONMENTAL

Today the word environment is likely to be preceded by the definite article: 'The' environment. It seems that at this particular stage in our evolution we are finally realising that there is only **one** environment and we are both part of it and part of the making of it. Perhaps, at last, a more spiritualised civilisation may be approaching, yet it will be a civilisation created not through internal spiritual pressures but through simple and possibly rather brutal **economic** pressures.

The powerful need **energy** to sustain themselves. The meek and the mild have no such need. It will not come as a surprise to many that the development model for a new gentle world order will come through processes of localisation not globalisation. It will be a slow process. We are not talking about revolution which is always rather violent but **accelerated** evolution. A **global** outlook is outside and beyond us. A **local** outlook is inside and within us. In these reflections we will discover much more about our common humanity which is, ultimately, the basis for spirituality. It is the spirit which unites us after all, and our physical flesh that divides us.

Around the world at the moment there are some awesome horrors and unimaginable retributions taking place. Many people I know will not be able to see through this horror to the other side. There appear to be no solutions to the conflicts. The divisions are only growing deeper and deeper. In fact the drama of civilisations is always played out like this. It just so happens that at this particular moment in creation these dramas are particularly intense and are travelling outwards to the furthest limits in creation. It is worth remembering one thing. At the beginning of Time when the Creator was faced with the agony of deciding what kind of creation to make the Creator had only two choices. The first choice was complete and utter perfection but unfortunately that would mean remaining in the state in which the Creator presently existed. In other words the only **perfect** creation is **no** creation. The only perfect balance is a place which has no space. A world where there is no contrast, no time, no passion......indeed just nothing. An unmanifest and unknowable creation.

Clearly not much of a choice.

Oh I forgot to mention. What was the Creator's second choice?

The word ecology comes from the Greek word oikos: Meaning house. If you look in the Oxford English Dictionary the word ecology is directly and immediately followed by the word economic. Some will argue this is just a linguistic game but it may not be coincidental that ecology has to exist before the economy.

Far too much of the Earth's topsoil is spinning about in the atmosphere. The reason for this is very simple. By overgrazing and over ranging we have turned soil into dust. In its most natural state soil is bound to the earth by its water content. When the water content dries out to the extent that the soil becomes just dust then the dust is free to return to the atmosphere.

Water tables are falling under large expanses of the three leading food producing countries in the world China, India and the United States.

The water table under the North China plain is falling by over 5 ft per year.

The Arral sea which just a few years ago yielded 130 million tonnes of fish has now entirely disappeared.

It is a moonscape. It is not the only sea to disappear. Many of the world's greatest rivers no longer reach the sea. The water is constantly being stolen before its cycle has been completed. Nature's systems are organized in such a manner that we will only be allowed to steal so much of it for so long before the planet will ask for it back. In the summer of 2003 the Rhine and the Danube in Germany, the Po in Italy, the Yellow River in China and the Darling River in Australia nearly disappeared.

All this, all this tempestuous stupendous terrifying life. Everything allowed to become what it **wi**ll become without limits of any sort. In this creation everything will have to manifest itself ultimately as extremes before the inevitable inner cycle is enabled to return. How and why does this inner cycle manifest? Quite simply because the pressure in the centre, the intelligence within the middle re-asserts itself and draws the extremes back towards themselves where finally they will recognise that they were but two sides of the same creation. The heads and the tails. The good and the bad. Faced then with these two choices, all or nothing? what would you choose. Exactly. It's going to be awfully exciting and I use the word awfully in its strictest and most proper sense. Full of Awe.

As I write it is the 26th March 2003. Today has been quite preternaturally warm and humid. Although a sunny day, it's impossible to see the Sussex Downs from Ditchling Common because of the thick, purple, sandy veil of pollution hanging over us. There isn't really much science involved, or necessary, in determining that we and our fellow human beings from somewhere else on the planet have deposited this thick veil of pollution that now shrouds the hot, unnaturally hot, spring sunshine.

When we talk about 'the environment' today we are mostly referring to the weather, global warming, pollution, loss of animal and plant diversity, etc. But **the** Environment is, of course, infinitely more than just physical. We live presently in a very dangerous **world** environment: People, not just things, form the environment. Indeed human biodiversity is probably the most prolific of all and human biodiversity is now being threatened by the enforcement of a brutal ideology from one militaristic superpower and the resultant backlash from fundamentalist warriors who are prepared to die in the bloodiest and most dreadful way possible. Could this be the moment when the two extremes are at the furthest zenith?

We are in the midst of a violent revolution in the Middle East: the imposition of power by one super-state over the future politics and resources of a foreign state. It may be personally remote to most of us. We are not all living in Baghdad but the 'political environment' surrounds all of us. We are also in the midst of violent and unprecedented retribution. The events of 9/11 were not the origination of this retribution; it was simply **one** of its most spectacular consequences. The environment is not merely the clouds in the sky or the gases that are causing the planet to warm up. **The environment is everywhere**, both inside us and outside us. There are poisons everywhere and many of them are the words falling from the mouths of men.

Today, ecology and environmentalism are generally considered from man's, mostly selfish, **limited** perspective. Of course mankind, uncivilised modern man, constituted as he is of arrogance and prejudice, will find it hard to accept that **Mother Nature** retains the upper hand when it comes to deciding how to protect her planet Earth. The weather has always been unpredictable but it is getting increasingly more so. Quite simply, our industrial activities are too intense. They are upsetting the balance. The present global economic system is becoming unsustainable. We created this system. We were given the physical means to create this system by the generosity of nature. This 'generosity', however, fortunately or unfortunately, depending on your point of view, has its limits. The real enemy we should be facing up to is ourselves, for we have created the world in the image of our desires but **our desires are not sustainable**.

If someone came down from another highly evolved and intelligent planet to have a look at how our little earth was getting on there is little doubt that they would be horrified by the way we all live. In one half of the world we consume vast quantities of unnecessary food and unnecessary products wrapped up in unnecessary packaging and then we bury these vast mountains of waste into toxic landfill dumps that pollute our water systems and almost certainly cause respiratory problems and all kinds of serious health problems. In the other half of the world people starve. Three hundred million people in the world are technically obese. Three hundred million other people are starving to death. At the same time, bombs are raining on Baghdad and filling the 'environment' with fear and loathing and hatred. This is also the environment in which I must live and you must live. This is my political environment as it is yours. In fact;

'The Environment' is:

◆   *Everything that is going on inside you.*

◆   *Everything that is going on outside of you.*

◆   *Everything that is going on inside us.*

◆   *Everything that is going on outside of us.*

It is clear from any **simple** analysis of the physics and chemistry of our planet that all systems are inter-related and connected to one another. Every day the earth spins around 360 degrees. Every year the Earth orbits the Sun once. Each and every twenty-four hours humanity adds about sixteen million tonnes of carbon dioxide into the atmosphere. [over six billion tonnes per year] This is an *additional* sixteen million tonnes. This is a fact. Of course it is **quite hard to imagine** sixteen million tonnes so here is another way of looking at the same statistic.

The average human being produces one litre of carbon dioxide waste gas every minute.

The average American produces one litre of carbon dioxide waste gas every eight seconds.

480 million of the world's 6 billion people are fed with grain produced by over pumping the world's natural aquifers.

Babies in Los Angeles get enough toxins in their bodies in two weeks which the World Health Authority thinks we should get in a whole lifetime.

The Earth's atmosphere is **not** limitless or infinite. Although there has been some discussion about reducing carbon dioxide levels, **this is not happening.** Most of the increase in the carbon dioxide levels comes from our industrial activity – but there is another problem. The continued **increase** also comes from the degradation of carbon dioxide-absorbing oxygen transmission devices, i.e. plants and fauna and, most particularly, trees. All our moist, abundant rain forest is most vital in this process.

If the rain forests dry up and rain does not fall, [It's already happening in Brazil] weather patterns will dramatically alter. All the water that previously fell on the rain forests may well begin to fall elsewhere, where it is not really wanted. The rain is already falling in torrents in drought stricken Africa, in Sri Lanka, Mozambique, and forty other countries where it is not **really wanted** presently. At least **not** in the quantities it is arriving. Heating the atmosphere increases the speed with which water evaporation takes place so more and more water is being recycled quicker and quicker. Precipitation [rain] needs particles in the atmosphere to form round. Pollution is increasing the volume of these particles. There will be more rain. There will be a more energetic weather system. There will be more storms. There will be more extremes.

If the rain forests dry out we will lose a huge carbon dioxide absorbing process. It **isn't** scare mongering or silly to simply state that such conditions of overheating cannot continue indefinitely without major repercussions. Presently all the different crises are co-inflicting their own crisis on each other. It is at this point that simple rebalancing takes place. Mother Earth, as all good mothers, can nourish but not command. Mother Nature cannot **tell us** to stop our anti-environmental behaviour but she can and will produce the circumstances whereby our fossil fuel-burning recklessness is dramatically curtailed. She has simply arranged for us to run out of oil. Hence the oil shock waves. **Of course mankind will probably wring out every last drop of oil he <u>can</u>** in an effort to keep the present system up and running but it won't ultimately make much difference. In using up all the oil we will probably also manage to bring the atmosphere to the boil and then we will have to learn how to stabilise the atmosphere by working out a balance in conjunction with the intelligence of Mother Nature. Stabilising the atmosphere will be a task of extraordinary magnitude. Perhaps of even greater magnitude than the civilisation building that has taken place over the last few thousand years.

We are, day-by-day, converting solids like coal, or liquids like oil, into gas and chucking them up into the atmosphere. The physics are very simple. We are going to get more and more gas into the atmosphere until we either:

* **Choke to death**
* **Get poisoned to death.**
* **Explode.**
* **Drown.**
* **Use less and less fuel and begin to reverse the equation.**

We need to convert less and less old fossils, the bones of our descendants, into toxic gases but we will not presently do so of our own free will. Soon however we will be using less and less fossil fuels for the **simple** reason we are using them up and a great rate of knots and they are not being replaced. It is good to reflect that fossil fuels are exactly that. Fossils. Fossil fuels are no more than the fossilised remains of our earliest organic ancestors.

Using up these energy sources is almost certainly a part of the divine plan because without this energy input from fossil fuels we probably wouldn't have been able to run up the evolutionary tree.

So **no one** in particular is to blame for this state of affairs. In fact we all have to take some culpability. Of course some human beings and some societies are more culpable than others in this respect, which brings us back to the Americans who, with five per cent of the world's population, produce over thirty per cent of the world's pollution. This statistic may well be transferable. In other words the American nation may well be responsible for thirty per cent of the worlds poisonous political pollution. In fact the Americans are now having to live, **increasingly**, in the **environment** of fear they have created and it is getting worse by the minute.

If you watch the other world satellite channels which are following reactions in the Arab/Moslem world to the American/British bombing of Baghdad, you will observe the suppression of the Iraqi people and the growing unrest. Thousands are being called to the jihad to fight the oppressor. Virtually every Muslim fanatic is dancing with impatience to have the chance for revenge. **Attacks against the so called coalition forces are increasing every day. Many of the internal Iraqi dissenters are being joined by Arab extremists. Oil pipelines are being attacked over three times a day, all over the world.**

Our sanitised USA and UK television media does not <u>choose</u> to show us much of this coverage.

Water that goes up must come down. There are exactly the same number of molecules of water around now as there were since the beginning of time or at least the beginning of the evolution of the physical elements of this planet. The problem however is twofold. Water may not come down exactly where we want it to. It may also not come down in the quantity or the regularity that we desire. Like all ecological problems the fact that the planet now sustains six times as many people than 80 years ago make these growing problems even more acute.

50,000 freshwater lakes in the US contain levels of mercury that make the fish in them unsafe for human consumption. The mercury has come from industrial activities.

It will not be up to mankind to decide if he wishes to live in an ecologically sustainable manner.

The planet has already decided this for man.

The word 'planet' and the words 'plan it' speak for themselves.

The political environment in the Arab/Muslim world is also becoming increasingly fearful and sentiment will, no doubt, divide along serious fault lines. I wonder how the Americans will feel over the next few years as they begin to sense the wave of hatred that is being generated across the globe and **poisoning our environment**. Just like the additional carbon dioxide thrown up into the atmosphere, this hatred is being thrown onto the fire that fuels retribution and hatred and we will all have to live in this 'new environment'.

If further terrorist attacks against Britain and the USA were probable, they are now absolutely unpreventable. Just like the physical environment involving our weather, we also have a global political environment that equally creates its own 'human weather' systems. The bombs are not just falling on Baghdad; they are falling on the whole of the human race. It is one last reminder from Mother Earth that time is fast beginning to run out. We only have a limited window in which to get the human evolutionary chemical experiment just right. At this moment the very worst thing civilisation could do is rush off with massive military hardware to the world's hottest geopolitical G-spots to grab a few more years of the black, choking oily stuff. What is civilisation doing by the way? [Perhaps it is still gestating in the womb].

Here is a curious but wonderful fact. If the world had fifty or sixty years of oil left (assuming we use it at the same or at an increased rate), rather than just thirty or forty years, then the human race would **almost certainly** march relentless towards its own extinction. **I personally do not believe it is a <u>coincidence</u> that peak production of oil is occurring at a moment when the planet's eco-systems and atmosphere are beginning to reach a critical level.**

We **are** at the **point** of **critical** balance. But perhaps that is ultimately how the divinity of Mother Nature manifests itself. The most obvious thing of all in life is that we share the same environment. We certainly share the same water.

Do you ever wonder, when you're standing under your shower, where on earth the water in the shower has been? It's actually quite possible that it has been to China and back, and then back to China and back, oh, maybe a million or more times. How could this be possible? Because water as a molecule is actually very resilient. There are still the same number of molecules about now on the planet as there were twenty or thirty or forty thousand years ago. Indeed the **age** of the molecule of water in your shower is **almost** timeless. Water is not new. It is one of the oldest molecules. It is, of course, one of the four basic principal elements or building blocks of life.

For those who need reminding of something entirely obvious, there are, in fact, four basic principal elements: [I use the word element in its strictest original sense and straight out of the Oxford English Dictionary].

In ancient philosophy the **four basic elements** also represent the **four basic principles** of life.

Modern chemistry on the other hand defines the word **element** as something which cannot be reduced:- in other words a **basic** chemical structure rather than a compound. There is something about **ancient philosophy** however that suits our present purposes.

When things have become too complex it helps to go back to the basics to understand the founding principles of creation: -

Earth Fire Air Water

Lets talk about the air for a moment. Chemically it's just Nitrogen [80 per cent] and Oxygen [about 20 per cent] Yes I know that makes **100** per cent. I can add up. In fact there are only **traces** of carbon dioxide. This **vitally important gas** is only measured in **parts per million**. However, **small** increases **dramatically** alter the **balance** of nature. **In fact** nature creates most carbon dioxide and man **actually** creates very little.

The average American creates about 19.53 tonnes of the stuff every year. Or about seven times the **average** planetary production of carbon per person.

A peasant farmer in Bangladesh working within his local environment and developing dependence on local organic produce probably **takes** carbon dioxide out of the atmosphere. **Mathematically** this suggests that Americans owe the Bangladeshi peasant farmers a **very large rebate** in carbon dioxide permit trading.

Imagine if you like for the moment the following picture. You are sitting on one end of a see saw. You [for **you** read mankind] are holding **twenty thousand billion tons** of carbon dioxide in your hands. On the other end of the see saw is Mother Nature. She is also holding **twenty thousand billion tons** of carbon dioxide. The result? Equilibrium. Now mankind adds a few million tonnes. The result. The see saw goes **down**. It is never the **amount** that matters it is the **balance** that is achieved. Personally I regard this balancing process as theological art. I have no real idea how it works but I am eternally grateful that it does.

Water is probably very important. Without it we seem to die very quickly. I can only imagine, as I am directed by common sense that it would be preferable to have clean pure natural water than poisoned toxic rebleached nasty chemical water. Most water today has about fifteen thousand different trace chemical compounds floating in it. As compared to say just 100 years ago when about ten or fifteen basic compounds were in the water flow. It is possible to turn water into wine and you **don't** need a **miracle** just some nice juicy grapevines and some water and some sunshine.

One of the main functions of the atmosphere surrounding the earth is to **clean** the pollution from the water that is sent to it. As one might imagine this job is becoming harder and harder. You and I are making it so.

Clearly the importance of the four basic elements is not in question. What is seriously in question, however, is whether we could so poison the planet that we could reach the point where we were unable to undo the chemistry experiments that we have begun. Because, in the not to distant future, we will need to distil the chemical-poisoned ponds we have built from the mounds of putrid garbage we are burying every day.

It seems almost too obvious to state but the only reason we have life at all on this planet is because of the sun. Of course just because it's a little old ball of bubbling, boiling helium burning ferociously away, we don't tend to think of it as an intelligent being in the sky. Just great balls of fire. Ancient pagan religions who were still in touch with the Earth's natural magic, attributed intelligence to the four basic elements, but as mankind has symbolised itself and become more technologically advanced, it has reduced these great 'supreme beings of nature' to unintelligent lumps of matter.

The earth and all its biodiversity is actually just a homage to the sun. Throughout the course of philosophical history there has been a great deal of discussion as to whether there is a fifth element.

The general consensus of the present Western scientific world, is that there is no fifth element.

This is because the scientists can't find it; so they can't measure it, weigh it, or sell it.

In fact the fifth element does exist. The **fifth** element is the **blending** of all the four **elements**. It is this blending of the four basic elements that forms the crucible in which the fire burns to make the foundations of our conscious existence. You could call this the elemental soul. To discuss the elemental soul would lead us however to a discussion of theology and I'm not prepared to go that route, at the moment. If anyone is interested there is a special edition of the no 19 Bus called 'Playoemook'. This discusses in detail the origins of the fifth element, describes how the fifth **element** is, in fact, actually a fifth **dimension**, and also describes the processes by which you may explore it.

For the moment, the most important thing to understand is that everything is perfectly and divinely and permanently connected to everything else. You are the centre of the universe and, simultaneously, we are all the same centre of the universe. There is ultimately only 'one' environment. We simply happen to experience this environment as individuals.

It is well to remember that that the vast complexity of today's society still originates from the combination of the four basic elements. From these elements we have created the chemistry of the modern world. Indeed today, each and every year, we create fifteen hundred new chemicals. These chemicals make up most of our fertilisers, pesticides, perfumes, bleaches, dyes and inks. In fact, most of these chemicals also come from oil. We are slowly turning the ossified remains of our ancestors' blood into the daily poisonous products of Western civilisation. Of course to call all the chemical produce poisonous would do a disservice to humanity. It is not **all** bad. In fact much of it is good. It's simply that we haven't generally considered, in enough detail, or with enough respect, the consequences of creating all these 'new' chemicals or what their long-term residual effects will be in the general environment. But let us leave the 'philosophy' of the environment for a moment and look a little more at some practical issues.

Fridges in the USA use **seven per cent** of all total generated electrical power-load across the country. Domestic fridges and freezers alone use all the power generated from **twenty-five large electricity-generating plants**. Budweiser's and yesterday's pizzas, various pickles and jars of mayonnaise will be cold but, meantime, about twenty or thirty million tonnes of carbon dioxide is spinning about in the sky just above the fridge's home. The planet's atmosphere will, as a result, get hotter. It's a trade-off. Some cold in the fridge for my beer equals **hot** for the atmosphere. The trade-off is now a seriously unbalanced equation. **Most** of us today will see fridges as being an essential part of our **lifestyle** but it is, in fact, our lifestyle that *makes* fridges so essential. We don't eat from the earth or the soil around us. We buy and store and thus we have to keep it chilled. It is a kind of silly merry-go-round. When the energy crisis takes hold, as it surely must in the next five to fifteen years, we will have to review our usage of energy from an entirely different perspective. If I were to venture an opinion at this juncture, I think that somewhere, in the divine natural chemical mixture of the planet, a perfect experiment is taking place. It is strangely wonderful that there is probably just enough oil on the planet to create a perfect crisis and just enough oil left to survive it. If there was but twenty per cent more oil on planet Earth (enough, perhaps, for another eight years of intense, profligate climate warming) it is very likely that the climate could be so severely disrupted that it would be technically and physically impossible to return the planet or its atmosphere to a state of natural health.

The coming energy crisis, therefore, at least from the point of view of the poor planet, is excellent news, **even though this will be very difficult to understand initially**. I think the coming crisis will threaten the very foundations on which we seem to base our existence. Then it will take those foundations away entirely and then, at last, we will be able to celebrate salvation from our own destructiveness. There is something rather extraordinary and wonderful that the last and final revolution in this particular cycle of evolution will be about healing and gentleness. War, terrorism and the rapacious lust of humanity for more and more

It was always going to end like this.

A Reader's Comments

"Jump aboard. The no 19 bus is leaving.

Don't miss it. There's room for more inside. Move along now.

ding ding.

Once you've started his journey you won't be able to get off."

God only writes a beginning and an end:

Life in all its infinite forms writes the story in between.

Must be time for a cold beer.

consumables torn out from the fossil fires of our ancestors are only a recipe for perfect disaster. We will need to learn to touch a little more lightly, tread a great deal more gently and communicate with each other a great deal more sympathetically and happily if we are to survive.

Today the people who call themselves 'environmentalists' rarely tend to see the spiritual side of these events. Progress, humanity, civilisation – call it what you will – has not been and never will be **universally** negative or **universally** positive. It has been, quite categorically, **a great deal of both**. We have poisoned much of the Earth because we have experimented so haphazardly and so carelessly. But then it isn't difficult to stand back for a moment and see that scientists and chemists are simply adolescents playing with an extraordinary cosmic chemistry set. For a moment or two in mankind's history the creation of atomic bombs made us pause, but we did not pause for long. Recognising that the global environment is something which we all have in common may well be the catalyst for us to heal our cultural and racial antagonisms. Indeed, before long, it will probably be essential that we all learn to co-operate with nature and treat her as a friend and ally. The world will still retain all its theological and religious, political, social and cultural differences for the foreseeable future. But when we have to fight the battle together to save ourselves we may find these differences dissolving in mutual necessity. Indeed, when one stands back for a moment from the majestic miracle of creation, it is not difficult to understand that it is **our differences** that make life worth living. Each and every dictator who has tried to impose his will upon the rest of the world, whether it be through military or religious means has **always ultimately failed**.

The nature of life is diversity, not simply the biodiversity in our oceans, our jungles and in all the myriad physical environments of the planet, but also the diversity that exists within the human heart and within the human mind. For many hundreds of years people have been calling for world peace and calling for major changes to the political infrastructure. But it has never happened and it will never happen whilst man is in charge, or, at least, 'thinks' he's in charge. This will not change in the near future. It will not change because of political pressures. The political party conferences are fiddling with issues which though they are not inconsequential, are simply miniscule in comparison to what is coming. Dictators will not be replaced by gentle, benevolent societies acting through political or ideological motives. Don't think I'm naïve; I'm not. I have as much cynicism about power and politics as you can possibly imagine.

The world will change simply because it is running out of the essential energy to maintain itself in its present form.

Global politics and global tensions *will be* dramatically reduced when the enormous injustices of global trade are dramatically reduced. This will be an *enforced* economic event caused by a very simple physical fact. It will not come through political changes in the present system. However, we may soon be able to recognise that there is an intelligent process designed into the essential fabric of creation. A process that will not allow us to persist with our own arrogance and self-conceit.

For the past twenty years the evidence for global climate change has been getting more and more obvious. During this same twenty years a considerable number of otherwise respectable scientists have managed to convince themselves that global warming is either not a reality or that it is merely a small change of emphasis which can be dealt with by practical and technological means. These scientists may believe that the answer to flooding is flood defences. They may even believe that the answer to pollution in our atmosphere is filters for this pollution. The same people may believe that waste product is a marvellous opportunity to burn the waste product up in great waste incinerators to create more energy and, with it, more poisons. Simultaneously, however, there has been a huge growing undercurrent of disaffection with the present state of the system. There is a growing volume of literature about environmental degradation, much of which is detailed, analytical and intelligent. Indeed, if you look, there is a **complete catalogue** of the various abuses that man has perpetrated upon his environment. These voices are, at last, beginning to be heard. Ecology has been operating very much on the fringes of Western society and human consciousness. Indeed, even today mainstream capitalist economics regards environmental problems as nothing more than a technical hiccup in the race to our all-consuming material utopia. For many people with a conventional global outlook there is only one road that technological man can walk, and that is the road he is on.

All mechanisms in nature are ultimately self-correcting but all mechanisms tend to self-correct, at least initially, by over-correcting. A pendulum goes from side to side before it finally finds the still point. The still point is the centre of creation. When we have found it we will want to make the pendulum swing again. We will **want** creation to begin again. The present eco-political pendulum is swinging crazily from one extreme to the other. We may just want to slow it all down. Slowing creation down, indeed slowing our minds down and calming our desires is where the process will begin. We need to be brave enough to ask ourselves what might happen if we started to firstly slow down and then dismantle the unbalanced systems presently controlling our political and economic destinies.

Concurrently, just to help the process along, Mother Nature will be withdrawing the benefits of freely available, highly explosive, readily accessible fossil fuel energy.

It is my understanding that, without the imminent crisis, man's journey would be but a few short generations to permanent oblivion. I fully appreciate that it will be very difficult for people to come to terms with how this crisis will affect their everyday lives, their aspirations and their desire for future financial security. Whether or not man has time to adjust to these environmental changes and to the imminent shortages of energy remains to be seen. Humanity is clearly a very adaptable creature but never before in the history of man and womankind has a change of direction been either so necessary, so critical, so imminent, or so compressed into just one generation.

Most extraordinary of all is that the absolute necessity for a complete change of direction is still, even at this critical moment, recognised by very few. Indeed, it is this last fact that is the most critical and **makes the imminent crisis entirely inevitable.** The history of the human race is most certainly not categorised by intelligent forethought and future planning. Quite the opposite in

No one said it wouldn't be hard.

The ice is melting.

Glaziers are retreating. The Arctic Sea has thinned by 40 per cent.

Greenland is melting.

If Greenland were to melt entirely all the world's coastal cities and a third of the world's population would be drowned.

fact. Mankind drives on relentlessly, greedily and desperately until a crisis of civilisation overwhelms it and change is forced upon it. It will be no different this time. Except for the fact we are approaching the 'Last Chance Saloon.'

Presently only a few will be unnerved by the arguments and the analysis. When the oil shock waves, however, start to really take hold, then and only then, will we all wake up to the critical state of affairs which we, the human race, have inadvertently, and yet inevitably, created in our natural, all-encompassing, environment.

beautiful planet earth: shame to spoil it

POPULATION CLOCK COMPARISONS

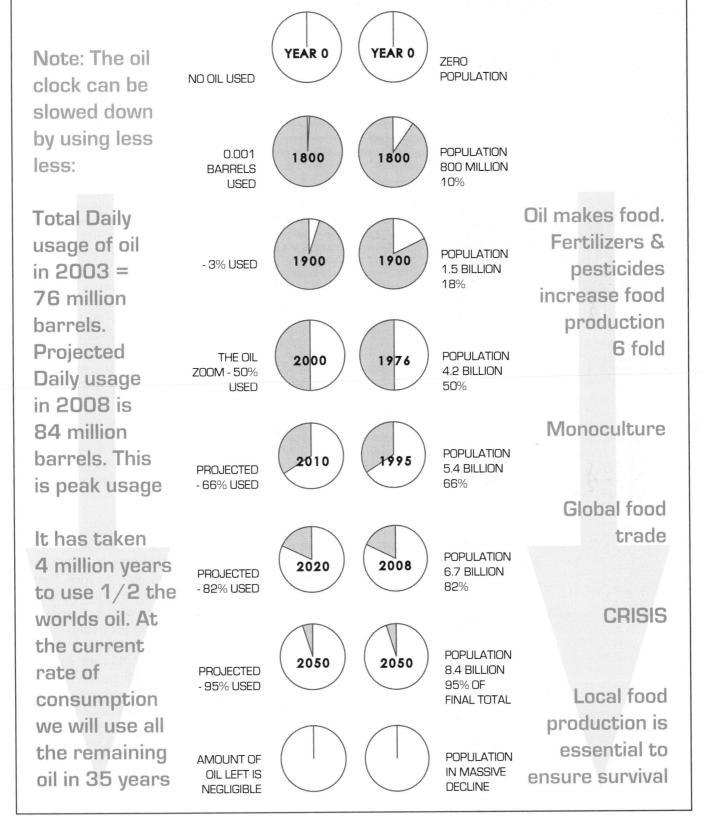

TOTAL EARTHLY ENDOWMENT OF OIL = 1.8 TRILLION BARRELS
THERE IS A DISTINCT RELATIONSHIP BETWEEN OIL DEVELOPMENT
AND POPULATION GROWTH: THE DECLINE OF ONE WILL LEAD TO
THE DECLINE OF THE OTHER

POPULATION OF THE EARTH AS A % OF THE POPULATION IN 2050.
THE POPULATION IN 2050 IS ESTIMATED AS 8.4 BILLION AND
REPRESENTS THE POPULATION PEAK: AFTER THIS DATE, DUE TO
ENERGY SHORTAGES THE POPULATION WILL DECLINE

Note: The oil clock can be slowed down by using less less:

Total Daily usage of oil in 2003 = 76 million barrels. Projected Daily usage in 2008 is 84 million barrels. This is peak usage

It has taken 4 million years to use 1/2 the worlds oil. At the current rate of consumption we will use all the remaining oil in 35 years

NO OIL USED — YEAR 0 — YEAR 0 — ZERO POPULATION

0.001 BARRELS USED — 1800 — 1800 — POPULATION 800 MILLION 10%

- 3% USED — 1900 — 1900 — POPULATION 1.5 BILLION 18%

THE OIL ZOOM - 50% USED — 2000 — 1976 — POPULATION 4.2 BILLION 50%

PROJECTED - 66% USED — 2010 — 1995 — POPULATION 5.4 BILLION 66%

PROJECTED - 82% USED — 2020 — 2008 — POPULATION 6.7 BILLION 82%

PROJECTED - 95% USED — 2050 — 2050 — POPULATION 8.4 BILLION 95% OF FINAL TOTAL

AMOUNT OF OIL LEFT IS NEGLIGIBLE — POPULATION IN MASSIVE DECLINE

Oil makes food. Fertilizers & pesticides increase food production 6 fold

Monoculture

Global food trade

CRISIS

Local food production is essential to ensure survival

Relying on God may not be the answer.

God may be relying on us!

Don't worry about it all too much.

Worry won't help.

Worry goes round in circles.

How can one think without worry.

Good question.

No easy answer.

Does God need a Sex Change?

Short answer? Yes. God has been predominately male for long enough. Time for a change. As it happens there's quite a lot of sex changing about at the moment. Male Polar bears in the Arctic are developing breasts. It is believed this development comes from the increasing number of hormone based chemical elements in the water supply in the Arctic. This will come as a surprise to some people but in fact the Arctic and the Antarctic are the fridge re-circling centres for the planet's water system.

People, black gold, an energy crisis, a crisis of global capitalism, environmental Armageddon, the division of man against man, each of whom believe with equal passion and fervour in their own legitimacy and their own integrity and their own particular gods. Much of the critical history of civilisation is the male or masculine principle battling with nature for supremacy. Man, and I mean specifically male in this context, has literally been raping the earth. Raping is beyond simple 'taking'. Raping something, or someone, is trying to take by force that which something or someone doesn't want to 'give.' Whilst men raped the earth, women tended menfolk and nurtured creation. Indeed women still remain, in spite of 'science' the essential vehicle for souls to incarnate upon the earth.

Early man up to modern man has been driven by a very important and fundamental principle of evolution: fear of the future. We store in order to retain something for tomorrow. We make 'pension plans' in order to store today's work to pay for later leisure.

News and media, mainstream politics, focus only on short-term problems. If you're not convinced of this observation just consider the Iraqi war. Now it is apparently over it is 'old' news. For a deeper analysis you have to start to look further afield than newspapers or television and yet, for the most part, newspapers and television are the two main places from which most people get their daily dose of capitalist propaganda. The big picture, the long-term view, is rarely, indeed barely, recognised. "Stupid white men" as Michael Moore calls our political leaders, are just that: stupid. At least twenty or thirty years of reflective training in philosophy and an equal period of service and compassionate humanitarian work should be the bare minimum for world leadership contenders. Perhaps it is not merely a coincidence that the Earth is running out of oil just at the point when the climate is beginning to climax and our political democratic dictatorships are getting increasingly out of touch with reality.

In essence, of course, the reason why our politicians are hopelessly out of touch is simply because they hold in their minds, in their general, small, individualised consciousness, only one tiny fragment of knowledge. Politics is about understanding and controlling our immediate environment – not what the world will look like in thirty years. In that sense, present day politics is probably not so different from Roman politics, or even Mesopotamian politics. It's about manipulation in order to retain control. Amongst other meanings the word 'politic' means dissembling, shrewd, scheming, crafty, cunning or artfully contrived. (This definition from 1580 – Shakespeare's time – and taken from the faithful Oxford English Dictionary).

Politicians may consider themselves motivated by a desire for the common good. Indeed this motive may be, quite sincerely, the force that draws them towards 'Politics'. But merely wanting to 'do good' does not necessarily guarantee wisdom, not even political wisdom. The very worst mess is often made with the very best of intentions.

We are presently entering a period of unprecedented crisis but established political powers are yet quite convinced that the current world problems – a Middle East conflict and global recession, to name but two – are just temporary phenomena. Just cycles in the system. The good times, the economic boom times will return...Crisis? What crisis? It is primarily an attitude of mind.

True, the times are uncertain but the eternal will of the planet is unlikely to be deviated from its primary evolutionary process by the over-inflated, lunatic egos of a few crazed politicians and some psychotic terrorists. They may even be a part of the original plan. Amidst these great uncertainties of our time it is understandable that people would like to return to a state of innocent simplicity. A clear view. Fundamentalist movements, whether they derive from Islam fanaticism or Christian primitivism, essentially originate from the same confused and uncertain source of being. This confusion is real and the need to believe in one particular, one specific, one clear religious idea, one overall generalised feeling of being at one with one's innermost faith – is a very, very potent human aspiration. It is the substrate, the foundation of religious thought and feeling.

Most people argue (and it would appear, from the historical records, with good cause) that 'religion' is responsible for most of the world's worst problems. If you include the primary American religion in this category, money, then you've pretty much covered the whole of human life. So all we need to do to solve the world's problems is to banish money, all religious endeavours and all spiritual fervour. Might as well banish life, I suppose, and have done with it. Religion has many origins but the *primary motive* is the *removal of uncertainty*. The more one can remove uncertainty and thus the more 'certain' you can become, the more comfortable the feeling.

Fundamentalists from all the major religions fall into this category. There is no difference, in spirit or kind, between Franklyn Graham (son of Billy Graham, the evangelical US preacher and friend of George Bush) racing off to Iraq with thousands of bibles, and Islamic fundamentalist fanatics who believe, with equal intensity and sincerity, in the supremacy and omnipotence of Allah. Fanatics on both sides are actually in the same team: convert or annihilate.

Meanwhile, virtually all religions preach, from their real spiritual heart, peace and good will.

Private saving in the US collapsed in 1997 for the first time in history.

The savings rate fell below zero per cent in 1997 and in 2001 it collapsed to minus six per cent. Economists are worried. The government is grateful because it has kept the economy going. No one has really asked the important question:

Why are people buying and borrowing as if there's no tomorrow?

The reason no one asks the question is because the answer is un-palatable. Ordinary people are getting increasingly worried about whether there's actually going to be a tomorrow.

Volume Six - 2003
Tim Trader

Tim had made several million pounds in the last six months, had lost half of it and then made it all back again. He'd paid £600,000 for his house in Richmond: three beds, three baths and a double garage. The house was his. Owned outright. The collateral the house provided and the cash that he had in the bank enabled him to have a large extended margin call with his brokers. He had an open credit limit of nearly £10 million. He could bail out at any time and he'd be filthy rich. Still, it was a shock to the system losing £30,000 in half-an-hour. Was he losing his nerve? He sat down with his coffee and cigarette and glanced at Bloomberg again. He blinked! He blinked again! Fuck! Zeus was going back up: 180, 182. He should have ridden this one. Christ! Perhaps he was losing his touch. He checked last minute.com to see if they'd hit rock bottom yet but they were solid. The Dow was up 160 and the FT was just closing at 6500, up nearly two per cent. He hesitated for a moment and then started kicking around the screens. He found the 'City Index' and took a sell position at 6500 at £10 a point. If the Stock Exchange went up tomorrow by more than 10, he would make four hundred pounds a point.

The next day the Footsie Hundred closed down 230

Meanwhile, the vast, **vast** majority of people, devout, sincere people, follow their own religious beliefs with good intentions. The global shrinking that has taken place at an unprecedented rate over the last fifty years, and the explosion of inter-cultural, inter-religious experience **should** have dispelled the idea that **one** religion has the **monopoly** on spiritual and religious truth but, in fact, the **opposite** is rather more the case. The sudden explosion of inter-racial-cultural connections created much knowledge and compassionate interaction but it also induced fear, and fear increases uncertainty, and uncertainty is uncomfortable and this, in turn, produces a return to fundamentalism.

Up until now, religion, its prophets and theology have been male-oriented. There may be a simple reason for this: The Male Ego. That's why it may be time for Mother Earth to make a re-appearance.

Recently, modern physics, in its exploration of the inner, tiny, molecular world, discovered that all things probably arise from a singularity. By which is meant one single point, **one** single source, one single specific non-moment in time when everything in the universe was a void. You can't call this void **empty** space because 'space', as such, didn't exist. Nor can you **exactly** pinpoint the moment in time when the singularity exploded because time, at **that** particular moment, didn't exist either. This great original explosion created the most breath-taking, un-believable, truly miraculous waves of galactic cosmos building. Our sun is just a little orange blob that probably wouldn't even reach the 'top one million stars in the universe'.

It is very likely that waves, travelling through time, echo and re-echo across the vast cosmic litany of life. It is more than likely that engineered and designed into these waves are the eventual solutions to all cosmic dilemmas. It may be that we are currently perched on the crest of a little earthly wave on which the climax to vital evolutionary processes is beginning to find its fulfilment.

Some men say women are **irrational**. By which I assume that **they** believe womankind are capable of holding one or more **apparently** contradictory and paradoxical concepts simultaneously. I would rather call this attribute multi-rational. I believe this female multi-rationality derives from the understanding that more than one person can be right, even when they hold quite conflicting views. I believe that **too** entrenched a **sense of right** leads to a sense of righteousness and, in the wrong hands, this sense of righteousness wants to overpower and then subsume all other life into its own image. Mother Earth, the spirit divine indwelling in all our souls, has no need to divide right from wrong. Mother Earth is very tolerant, very giving and very forgiving. Mother Earth is however subject, quite simply, to the law of excess. This law states that creation of any system will become unstable if it does not respect and preserve a sustainable and renewable existence.

I wonder how many people are aware that about the year 2000, the millennium year, the two thousandth birthday of the Christian saviour and Lord, the planet passed, for the first time, the peak production of people's souls!

Let me explain.

About the year 2000 the number of people who had died upon the planet was exactly equal to the number of people presently alive on the planet. About six billion. You might wonder what such a silly statistic has to do with anything? Well think of this. **If** you believe in reincarnation **then** you believe that **everyone** has had a **previous** life and everyone will have (probably) a **future** life.

However this could <u>not</u> <u>have</u> <u>been</u> physically possible <u>until</u> the year 2000.

Why? Because in the year 1999 more people were presently alive upon the planet than had ever died. In total. In other words, if six billion people were floating about on the planet in the year 2000 not all of them *could* have had a previous life, because only 5,999 billion people had actually died during the course of human history.

The point is that we may be passing a threshold of extraordinary significance. It may well be that a wave of Old Souls is presently incarnating. I can only imagine that Old Souls, the ones who've already had a previous shot at inhabiting the contradictions of life in human body, will be somewhat smarter than the great lustful wave of New Souls who currently seem to inhabit bodies and personalities that (even whilst brutally immature) yet reach the dizzy heights of president of this or that country. I can see no other way of explaining it to myself.

It brings me rather abruptly however to consider a simple question. Do we have soul? Do you have a soul? The answer is yes. Everyone has a soul. How do you know that we have a soul? This question is not going to be answered here for you upon this piece of paper. It's up to you, and for you alone, to know if you have a soul or not.

The likelihood is that most souls presently on the Earth are on their first lifetime. In this 'first' life they will 'make' their soul, and the residue of this 'soul' is then available for re-cycling of some sort. This is not the moment to be too specific.

The **soul** that you make **whilst** you live will be the one that you take to your **death** and all the repercussions and consequences that entails.

In other words, New Souls presently constitute the bulk of humanity. It is strangely wonderful to imagine, even for a moment, even if you only consider it as a spiritual fantasy, that Mother Earth, Mrs Planet and Miss Atmosphere are waiting patiently for the wisdom of Old Souls to return to commence the healing process by getting to grips with the adolescent evolutionary mess created by humanity's numerous previous civilisations.

Souls incarnate in waves together. Perhaps in this particular evolutionary wave very Old Souls are returning once more to the earth. How this process takes place is clearly beyond the present realm of physical science to understand. Indeed present physical science, in many cases, flatly rejects the idea of a soul

points and Tim was down another £2,300 but he was not too fazed. No one could win all the time and as long as everything in the long-term moved steadily upwards he would make money. Indeed, even if it went down steadily and he chose the right stocks, he would make money selling short. The only thing you really needed to make money on the markets was volatility and a good intuition about which direction it was going to go.

When Tuesday morning arrived it was a beautiful, clear blue, warm September day. Tim had arranged for a limo to drive them down to Manhattan. In any event, Stella had an aversion to the tube. Tim wanted to show 'Stella the stunning' off to his old broking pals and he wanted to do it in style. To impress them. Stella looked drop-dead gorgeous in a black, tight, micro-knit mini and matching black jacket. Underneath she wore a lacy blouse and a see-through bra that intimated flesh and nipples and sex without actually being pornographic. It was enough, Tim was certain, to make his old broking mates salivate like the old dog droolers he knew them to be.

Eventually they were on their way, cruising delightfully in a long white limo towards the the office.

Straight ahead were the magnificent twin towers of the World Trade Centre. Tim glanced at his watch. It was nearly 9 a.m. They should have been there already at 9 a.m. He knew these guys well. They'd have marked out thirty minutes, perhaps forty, for their champagne breakfast with Tim and Stella and then they would be racing back to their 'strategy meetings.' Tim and Stella were chatting calmly in the back of the limo when suddenly they were interrupted by the chauffeur screaming:

"The World Trade Centre's on fire!"

Tim saw the second plane career towards the tower and then swerve at the last moment. The explosion followed about one second later but it seemed as if a whole new world had passed by and reintroduced eternity. The fabricated façade that separated reality from life was torn away. It was awesome, grandiloquent and just another dreamt up Hollywood series of special effects. Surely the screen would fill with credits. Where was the producer? The director? Who were all those actors incinerated in seconds? Who had changed the world forever?

Hundreds of people were trying to crawl into a small Italian restaurant where the TV was on. Somehow this made it more real for the

at all. Probably for the very simple reason that it cannot touch it, see it, smell it, hear it, taste it or, most importantly of all, measure it or weigh it. That is not to say some scientists haven't tried. If you remember, in my essay on alternative energy, I described the first two laws of physics. Everything is energy and the amount of energy is always the same. It is never destroyed.

Back in the Victorian age a couple of scientists came to the conclusion that if there was indeed a human soul then it should have mass (i.e. weight). But how would they measure the weight of the soul? They came up with the ingenious idea of leaving people who were just about to die lying on some very sensitive weighing scales. At the point of death they hoped to see a reduction in weight as the soul left the body. Their weighing apparatus was very sensitive and accurate to within fractions of a gram. Once or twice they got very excited when someone died and the scales indicated that a few grams had indeed disappeared. The evidence however was not conclusive and eventually they ran out of dying people to practise their experiment on. The scientists both died, not knowing, frustratingly, the answer to their question. Like everyone else they had to wait until they had died to find out.

Personally I find the idea that the soul is elusive rather attractive. It is like a lover that needs to be wooed. Of course modern cosmology, a direct derivative of basic physics, has pointed the way to the original universal soul. Back to God, if you will, and there are many people who have had their spiritual faith renewed by cosmological insight.

Up until now I have studiously avoided relating any personal experiences in my writing but I would like to share with you one particular revelation that took place when I was twelve years old. It happened, strangely, in a chemistry lesson at school. The chemistry teacher was also a physics teacher and also happened to be a Church of England vicar. He was called the Reverend Fardon. During this lesson the Reverend taught us the first two laws of physics. All is energy and energy never disappears. It is merely transformed. In order to prove this theory we trooped off to the laboratory. Each of us was given a piece of copper oxide. [That's a small piece of discoloured oxidised copper]. We first weighed the copper very accurately (to thousands of a gram) and then we weighed a glass retort. We put the copper oxide into the retort and heated it up with a flame over a Bunsen burner. The copper oxide eventually started to smoke (it gave off a gas). The smoke went upwards into another retort and this retort was then also weighed. The end of the experiment showed very precisely that the weight of the copper had reduced by exactly the precise amount of the weight of the gas that had been released during the heating process.

The copper oxide had weighed 1.863 grammes.

When the gas/oxidisation/discolouring had been burnt away the copper weighed 1.8 grammes.

The gas weighed 0.063 grammes.

When you added the weight of the copper (which is now bright shiny and new) to the weight of the gas you arrived back at exactly the original weight of the copper oxide. In this experiment, if you look a little beyond the basic physics, it is perfectly reasonable to perceive two further laws: -

Law One: **Everyone could have a soul because the soul may be weightless and exist in another dimension where the Laws of physical mass do not apply.**

Law Two: **The environment will be profoundly affected if we constantly heat it up and start to turn fossil fuel solids and liquids to gas.**

Of course it takes a spiritual leap of faith and revelation to recognise these physical 'truths'. I remember being weightlessly suspended in time for a moment. I had a distinct knowledge that I had always existed, for eternity and through infinity, and I said as much to the Reverend Fardon, who looked at me with such incredulity and astonishment that his look is forever imprinted on my memory.

"Hamilton", he said finally, if you spent more time with **that strange brain of yours** concentrating more on your work than your daydreams you might possibly one day produce some good work."

At this point he asked to see my experimental results. They were perfect. My copper and my gas, when the weights were re-combined, were precisely equal.

"Very good!" he said finally, "Carry on."

And of course I did: - with my daydreams.

The wakefulness of this insight has remained with me for the rest of my life. It has also brought with it many dilemmas. For a moment I had tasted the perfection of the perfectly designed universe. I was, literally, in awe and to this day in awe I remain. I also traced back to this specific moment the setting of the agenda for my destiny. I had experienced perfection. I was secure in the knowledge that everything and everyone will eventually fall back into perfection. In the meantime there was life and lots of it. I was young, excitable, impressionable, and it came as something of a shock thereafter that my physical, emotional and mental life might not always stay in this original pure state of perfection! Later I realised that it is impossible for life to remain in a state of perfection. All it **can** do is fall **in and out** of it from time to time.

Souls incarnate in groups, in families, in tribes, and back to the same tribes, usually in a similar geographic and cultural context. This is hardly surprising. The subject of reincarnation or rebirth is of course a huge one. Christians, atheists and many pragmatic, practically minded, physically oriented people will deny, quite categorically, even the possibility of a previous conscious existence, but there is a law "The Law of the Residue of Consciousness" which can be observed functioning from a place that is beyond the rational, measuring mind and outside the body.

The residue, or remnants, of human consciousness, indeed

on-lookers. It was an electronic confirmation of the hideous physical reality. Strangely, the TV was comforting. It shared the horror around. Tim was standing in the street, straining to get a view of the TV pictures and hear what was being said, when the first tower collapsed. He was not sure if he first saw it collapsing on the TV or on the reality video machine in his head. In any event, it crumbled and crashed in real time. There was no delay and no rewind button available.

For a few moments people stood transfixed but, as it crashed, a huge cloud of dust and debris started to roll towards them. It looked like a thick cumulus cream billowing up into an immense menacing cauliflower. It seemed to move very slowly at first and then it came funnelling down the street. Glass and plastic and debris started to shower around them and suddenly horror and shock turned to hysteria and panic. It was a holocaust, in the streets of Manhattan. The unthinkable was being thought out. The unimaginable had been imagined and a nightmare had been forever burnt into the fabric of the world's universal consciousness. That image, that one image, of the passenger plane hurtling into the tower was being shown across America and then across

146

the world time and time and time again. But there was only a repeat button. No rewind. No going back. It had happened and it could not be unhappened. In all the worlds that have ever been, or ever will be, the hand of time has only two motions: forward and eternity. No Star Trek doctoring of the laws of physics and no time-traveller can ever or will ever undo what has been done.

Tim watched with the crowds of others as the cumulus cloud of molten death and destruction headed down the street towards him. He grabbed Stella from the car and started to run whilst, all around, the walls and ceiling of reality were falling in on top of them. Stella stumbled in her heels; one had broken! Tim was pulling at her so she discarded her twenty million lire red Italian shoes she had bought in Milan and scampered in her pretty bare feet down Holocaust Alley.

Suddenly, the cloud behind them was no longer behind but around them and they were choking in a white smoking stink of burnt plastic.

Suddenly, Stella discovered her long silken legs were not just made to slip elegantly into the latest silk sheer stockings.

They were made to run and run and run.

even animal or plant consciousness, is always recycled. Naturally the most immediate question reincarnation or rebirth sceptics ask is: If consciousness has had a previous existence why do we not remember it?

Well, an understanding of the journey of the human soul is not understandable by the rational mind and is not properly communicable as a knowledge to another through the medium of words – written, spoken or otherwise. For those who are fascinated by the question of an afterlife, however, and for those who are wondering why we don't remember prior lives, my own experience has led me to the conclusion that 'forgetting' our past existence is a healthy, natural state of affairs. A new life is just that: a new life. Why drag a whole bunch of memories with you? If the theory of reincarnation is in any way a reflection of spiritual reality it clearly has a reason to exist in the way that it does. Maybe memories of past lives are just too painful, too burdensome. A new start, a fresh, clean slate, this is the best way to get an education. Starting from empty.

It may also be that the residue of consciousness is not personality specific. In other words, Fred Bloggs does not become, specifically and exactly Joe Bloggs. Personalities may dissolve, indeed do dissolve, but we are very attached to them and, generally speaking, consider them to be 'ourselves.'

In fact, the great Hindu-Aryan-Indian traditions of re-incarnation and the equally great Buddhist traditions still argue/discuss/debate this exact issue. I'd love to chat some more about it. Another time maybe. The primary purpose of this particular 'tangent' is that it is one more spoke in the wheel of life. Nothing is wasted. Everything is recycled, even old, derelict, human consciousness.

Unfortunately, **unlike** the depletion of the world's oil, 'spiritual' facts are much harder to come by. My observations and experiences have led me to the conclusion that souls reincarnate in waves. These 'waves' are created by natural resonance that was essentially a sonic vibration that went off 'bang' at the beginning of time. Recently the cosmologists measured one of these original Time Waves. Recently various old tribal souls have been surfing this original Time Wave back into human consciousness. It's like a ripple of old time flowing into the present.

Here is a 'spiritual fact' for contemplation:

The soul is forged by the process of living. All living beings have a soul.

But not all souls have had a previous life.

There are brand new souls in brand new bodies. In fact, most people alive today in the western world are brand new souls. Then there are a very few, very, very old souls, and a number of fairly old souls, etc. etc. I wish I could give you a decent spiritual statistic on the various numbers but that is presently beyond me. It is simply easier to understand by looking at the present population of the Earth. There are presently far more young people than old people, but this population ratio is changing. **Over the <u>next</u> hundred years there will be more and more old people as a proportion of the world population**.

The same applies to souls. Over the next hundred years there will be more and more old souls. If you don't like the word souls, read instead "residue of ancient consciousness.' Nothing is lost to nature. This is the secret of understanding her. Nature is forever generous but only within the limits of what is sustainable. Mother Nature cannot create more resources. She can't increase her volume of air or presently make more oil. She can only share out what she has. If we live beyond her means then we live beyond our means. This lesson will have been noted by the wave of old souls who are presently slipping, albeit a little reluctantly, back into this crisis-strewn, sorely sick little planet of ours.

So does God need a sex change? I think so. Rapid, radical, theological surgery. Perhaps men would be better just to capitulate and let women rule the world for a while!

The second law of Thermal Soul Dynamics states quite simply that the soul is forged, created, made, moulded, sculpted and shaped by fire.

Ancient Yogis created fire in their bodies so they could **burn** off the dross and discoloration that hides the original burning bright brilliant Orb in the original light of being. The soul is made. Quite simply. By the Sun.

Ancient Yogis stared into the sun until their eyes were burnt out of their sockets because they were so anxious to return to the **weightlessness** from which they had so recently come.

These souls are now beginning to return. They may well feel that they are not earthlings any more but aliens upon the earth.

Now for a silly interlude. Speaking of aliens.

A picturesque, 'Pythonesque' moment.

It actually concerns a little alien. The one that landed **yesterday** on 1st April 2003.

This **particular** alien landed his little pod **right** in the middle of civilisation. His job was to report back to his superiors on the state of planet Earth.

Here is his report, in synopsis form:

Planet Earth

"*24,000 miles in circumference.*

Distance from the original energy source: 150 million kilometres.

Biodiversity: Main viral species called human. Presently this viral species thinks it is in control of planet systems. The virus

> Ultimately it's not Doomsday at all. It's simply the recognition that an essential and necessary crisis is shortly to be coming our way.

> Space

> for

> Silence

Volume Six - 2003
Tinker and Shoe Box

Tim had lived underneath the arches at Charing Cross station for longer than he could remember. Over the years he had collected coloured rags and scarves and sewn them on to a huge grey overcoat. At a distance he looked like an ostrich. Closer to, he resembled a feather duster. Tinker had a huge mop of grey-black hair, unwashed and unkempt, and a large black straggling beard. His hair flopped in front of his face and Tinker peered out from amidst this tangle with two brown eyes that were barely ever half open. Tinker operated his life on the principle of minimum input and minimum output.

His staple diet was rough bread, which he bought stale from the bakery, and sardines, which he ate with greasy fingers direct from the tin. Inside, his world smelled of himself; stale, strong beer that had dropped over his beard and scarves, and a fishy sweatiness from his diet. His universe was entirely self-contained. Transformed into Zero worship. He had not decided to do this intentionally. That internal combative dual conversation machine we mistakenly refer to as a mind had not engaged in Tinker's consciousness. Tinker did not engage in

is presently prolific but depletion is imminent. Chances of making next stage of evolution very small.

Action to be taken? None advised. Viral species appears particularly aggressive. Suggest leaving them in their self-made predicament and let natural laws of equilibrium re-assert themselves.

Note: Western souls are mostly new and recently industrialised.

They are very busy with **things. Indeed very busy generally."**

At this point the alien stopped writing his report for a minute and tried to draw his breath but it was hard. There wasn't much oxygen left.

He scribbles one or two more notes:

"There is a small section currently designated lunatic or fringe who are suggesting radical environmental surgery but they are mostly ignored or **occasionally** locked up.

There is one thing though. They have invented a game called cricket, and another game called football and in fact all sorts of games. They may be of interest to us as a **social cultural diversity.**

As for the population? Well mostly at the moment they seem to be murdering each other to get their hands on some poison so they can release it into the atmosphere and therefore annihilate themselves. **Delusional** elements and **psychosis** unfortunately seem to be **most prominent** in those who **think** they are in control of the planet. The laws of sustainability have been studiously ignored and crisis in most of the viral systems is imminent."

On this positive note, our little alien climbs back into his space pod and sods off back to Planet Wod.

Out there in the far distant galaxies other planets are going through fairly identical processes but yet in other dimensions none of us can even begin to imagine.

We are nearing the point when accelerated evolution is fast becoming an absolute necessity. This alternative energy revolution will not be a **choice**, it will be an **ongoing** organic necessity. It is, and will remain for some considerable time, a race against time. Many of the processes have already been decided for us. We will only have one choice this time. To co-operate. To learn to like each other a little more, to tolerate each other a great deal more or **die**. One chance saloon. One chance planet. Planned in this way for the very simple reason that no better plan is available. The choices facing evolution are simple: Miraculous, multiple, marvelous, biodiversity or **no** biodiversity at all. What's your choice? Exactly. It's all going to happen quite shortly.

This is **our** future we are talking about. Nature is not wasteful. The planet has a planetary consciousness.

One question I hope I will be asked very early on in the proceedings is how compatible a new Gaia-based earth survival philosophy is with conventional religious beliefs. Since a theological analysis is beyond the present scope of this book it is a difficult question. To answer briefly: -

My own experience and observations gathered mostly through being in various different monastic disciplines, from different theological/spiritual backgrounds is that spiritual essence is not reducible to dogma and belief in one particular system. Ultimately when the soul departs the body we will not be judged on what we left behind but on what we did and on the clarity, purity and deepest motivations of our hearts. I think it is a strangely beautiful development that spirituality, the spirit of self sacrifice and development of a new world based on the conscious recognition that we all exist within the same single source of being will arrive because of very basic, very physical laws. The fall of hydrocarbon man just running out of fossil fuel energy will bring an entirely new dimension to our future.

When I look at the state of Western consciousness today, the most obvious feature is a sense of being seperated from the cosmic source of original being. Industrialisation and specialisation has made us all into individuals but at the the cost of losing our attachment to a greater universe beyond ourselves. This isolation creates an ever deepening void as 'connections' beyond us – to Earth itself, to each other are increasingly severed. To fill this increasing void, we have made ourselves increasingly busy with things and activities. This process is shortly going to come to an end and these changes will not come about because our political, spiritual or religious leaders call for change. These changes will come because the principles for change (and the necessary energy) are being re-established in the very soul of the Earth from which we are not actually, in reality, separate. We only *think* that we are.

Don't be fooled by it all. It's a **great game** that **must** be played out. There is no choice but to take it to the brink and yet....One war equals the possible cost of an entire planetary future. All the work of evolution could be wasted. Mother Earth has given birth to the human race but has yet to steer it past the rocky waters of adolescence. It's not difficult to understand really. Fortunately some people can begin to see that the approaching crisis is probably not before due time. Had we been allowed to travel much further down the road of excess and greed it may have been terminal.

Different racial souls have different properties which also probably represents mankind's best chance of survival, for it will be our differences ultimately that will unite our knowledge of being. In this Gaian scenario no one has to give up any of their religious beliefs. One's religious beliefs are very important because they are one of the most important factors in the making of the soul. In making as much soul biodiversity as possible. It will perhaps come as a rather remarkable revelation to many but, in fact, *the world we will inhabit when our soul has left our body will be the world that the soul imagined when it was in the body.* For those who have spent little or no time imagining a world 'beyond' the one that simply fills physical, emotional and mental needs as quickly as possible, dying will

self-discussions; whatever thoughts he had remained glued to the inside of his skull. All his internal cognitive processes coalesced into a state of suspended animation. It was thus quite exceptional when, one day, he found himself peering out beneath and between his curtain of scarves and rags to watch a young girl whom he had never seen before. She stood, a lonely ragamuffin, clasping a cardboard shoe box closely to her chest.

The Brazilian rain forest is disappearing at the rate of Wales every year. The world's rain forests are the lungs of the Earth. All forests are designed to breathe in the pollution that humanity breathes out. If we continue to increase our rate of pollution and simultaneously decrease the ability of the Earth's forests to fix carbon dioxide then we are running in opposite directions simultaneously. It is not difficult to understand why such a process puts unprecedented pressures in the system.

come as something of a shock. When a physical body/mind dies for the first time, the newly formed soul is very surprised for the simple reason that it is also the very first time the soul can actually stand outside of itself and therefore recognise it's own existence.

Gaia, the Earthly, planetary intelligence which forms the foundations of human consciousness uses the residue of ancient consciousness to form the next wave of souls.

For Mother Earth and her High Priestess Gaia to fail to get us through this next evolutionary cycle would be heartbreaking to her.

Any mother losing her child would be heartbroken. Even now as I write Mother Earth is calling like a great whale to her cubs in the sea:

Come back come back come back to me.

All the systems are presently slowing down. Energy levels in all their forms, oil, electrical, personal, private, popular, global and local are finally slowing down. Shortage of energy will reduce financial and economic growth. These are natural laws at work. **We should not be frightened by them.** On the contrary, we should **welcome** them. From physicality to spirituality is not as far as you think because, in reality, they are perfectly and intimately related.

Humanity has spent much of this first wave of evolution **worrying** about dying. That is understandable but in the next phase such a worry will be misplaced.

We now need to worry about whether we will have a planet worth returning to.

The planet is not a hotel. We can't trash it and leave. It is, in reality, evolving humanity's **only** home.

Knowledge is a gift that needs to be learnt but, more importantly, knowledge is a gift that needs to be earned.

Does God need a sex change? Quite definitely! The male Gods have had their say. What is now urgently needed is the gentle reviving principles of Mother Nature to be honoured. The male gods have had their day, well not quite. They still run amok but their day is coming to a close. The first, principal law of evolutionary life always promises a return to equilibrium.

The Coming Global Energy Crisis

The Twilight Years of Hydrocarbon Man

When I started writing the no 19 bus in 1997 I started to think a great deal about the future. This should come as no surprise since I always intended the no 19 bus to be set in the future. I'm sure most people can sympathise with the enormity of the task. Most of life is full of unknowns; but the future? Surely the **very definition** of the future is that **it is unknowable**. Over the last few years from 1997 to date [as I write it is July 10th 2003] I have found a number of my predictions were spookily accurate. In 1997 I started sketching out my plot for all the forty characters that are going to get on a bus together at about 6 pm on the 2nd May 2012. Why did I choose a war over oil in Iraq, terrorism, Global economic stagnation and deflation? Do you know I can't really remember all the reasons. I was certainly, even then, pretty desperate about the state of the world. I saw the last few years just prior to the "Millennium" party as virtually obscene.

In 1997 I was aware of the research regarding the imminent world energy crisis. I knew for instance that the US was running very low on internal oil reserves and I was equally aware that their oil guzzling gobbling habits were getting increasingly difficult to satisfy. It was obvious to me that if you are very rich and powerful and desperately short of something you urgently need, you will buy it in from elsewhere, if you can, or *failing that* you will just go and **take it from someone who has lots of it.** The US and Iraq fitted perfectly into that specific category. The US as of 2002, [according to the BP statistical review of World energy] states that the US has about 30 billion barrels of oil left. It has used over eighty per cent of its own oil.

Today the US uses about 30 per cent of the all the oil produced worldwide: about seven billion barrels a year. At this rate of consumption, the U.S. only has four and a half years of it's own oil left to use.

Iraq on the other hand has about 112 billion barrels and has *used virtually none of it.* Iraq, has the worlds **least exploited** reserves and the US has the **most exploited** reserves. **The US uses up its own oil at the fastest rate it physically can.** The Iraqis have been stopped from exploiting their oil reserves by international embargoes imposed by the US. There were, and indeed still are, obvious inequalities in this situation. Presently the US is

*More Extracts from the novel no 19 Bus: -
Volume Three - 2007
Alex De Ville*

Alex sat in the back of his large Daimler Double Six and cruised contentedly through the abnormally quiet London roads without a glimmer of guilt or self-consciousness. The petrol crisis had, as far as he was concerned, managed to clear the roads of riff-raff. He looked with amusement at the huge queues at the bus-stops and they looked back with feelings of undis-guised disgust. The journey from his Hampstead mansion to the Houses of Parliament would normally have taken forty-five minutes but today his chauffeur managed to get there in just twenty. The only irritation was the fact that his chauffeur would insist on continually honking at the savage waves of cyclists who, in the absence of general traffic, had decided that the roads now belonged to them.

A week, he thought, one hundred anti-tank missiles at $10,000 to buy and $15,000 to sell. Half a million dollars profit, less expenses. He picked up another mobile, plugged it into his scrambling device and pressed some buttons. It was a useful gadget that he'd come across when supplying some surveillance equipment. The radio message was encoded in the box and then decoded at the other end. It meant no one, not even the CIA, could tap into his telephone calls. The only drawback was that he had to type the message and then wait for the written reply. It was time consuming and he was in somewhat of a hurry to leave. It was the Easter recess at Parliament and he wanted to get up to his estate in Scotland in time to prepare for the

trying to correct these inequalities by taking over Iraq. But I'm jumping ahead again. Back in 1997 I simply saw that the geo political ferment in the Middle East was bound to get worse and worse. Today, six years later I am equally certain that the crisis in the Middle East is only going to get worse still. Just consider for a moment:

Over 63 per cent of British people believe that the primary reason for going to war in Iraq was oil.

Now that's just 63 per cent of **British** people. What on earth do you think the Middle East Muslim countries are thinking? There may be some political pretence from the Saudi Arabian Royal family and the Kuwaiti governments that the US and the UK was dealing, legitimately with the Iraqi threat from weapons of mass destruction but most of the British people now realize that was a load of.... And yes...I'm going to really say it. The *absurd idea* that we were going to Iraq to "liberate" the Iraqi people was a world spun by politicians and media alike. We now know that there were no weapons of mass destruction of any significance. We went for the oil in order to preserve our rather privileged way of life.

But let's move on. Between spring 1997 and Christmas 2002, I wrote the first six volumes of the no 19 bus. I hope you have enjoyed some of the extracts printed alongside these more serious essays! If you've been following all the characters you will have noticed that so far they are simply portraits drawn up to the present day. 2003. The ones alongside *this* essay are the same characters drawn up until 2007. We are getting into the area of futurology.

Between 1997 and 2003 I became increasingly aware that the "oil" crisis was deeper, *more potent and more ultimately terrifying than I had originally imagined.* Over the years I started studying the subject of oil depletion and then I started to study the coming Global energy crisis; only after some years did it really begin to dawn on me that this crisis is exactly what we need and *it is coming just in time to save us from ourselves.*

So where to next? It will have been obvious to most people that the essential issues portrayed in this series of essays have been about oil depletion and the fact that there are no **readily available** substitutes for oil. But oil of course, is just one element, albeit the most important in the **Total World Energy Systems.**

Just take a look at this Pie Graph.

Primary Energy Sources in World, by Source 1999

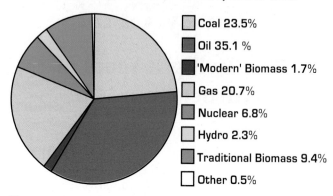

- Coal 23.5%
- Oil 35.1 %
- 'Modern' Biomass 1.7%
- Gas 20.7%
- Nuclear 6.8%
- Hydro 2.3%
- Traditional Biomass 9.4%
- Other 0.5%

First a general analysis. What does this graph tell us?

90 per cent of the worlds energy comes from Fossil fuels.

The remaining 10 per cent is nuclear [6.8%] and Hydro. Traditional Biomass mostly means wood. It is still a hydrocarbon. Now let's look at this second Pie Graph 2 which just covers **industrialised countries.**

Primary Energy Sources in Industrialised Countries, by Source 1999

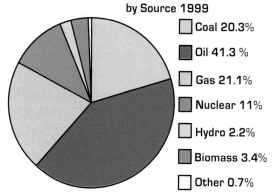

- Coal 20.3%
- Oil 41.3 %
- Gas 21.1%
- Nuclear 11%
- Hydro 2.2%
- Biomass 3.4%
- Other 0.7%

The **main** difference is the amount of oil used [41.3%] An increase in Nuclear power [to 11%] and a reduction in the burning of traditional bio mass from 9.4% to 3.4%.

What can we learn from these graphs?

Firstly: our dependence on fossil fuels is almost total.

Renewable energy like wind/wave/solar is so negligible it doesn't even get a mention. It is *hidden away* in the Pie Graph that says other [0.5% to 0.7%] What these Pie Graphs also tell us is that there **isn't any great statistical difference** in the energy usage **by type** between the average country in the world and industrialised countries.

Now look briefly at Pie Graph 3 which indicates primary energy usage in Developing countries.

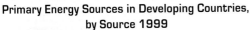

Primary Energy Sources in Developing Countries, by Source 1999

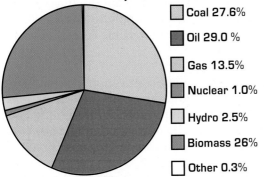

- Coal 27.6%
- Oil 29.0 %
- Gas 13.5%
- Nuclear 1.0%
- Hydro 2.5%
- Biomass 26%
- Other 0.3%

The biggest difference is vastly more biomass [and somewhat less gas and nuclear] but oil still represents **29.0%** of consumption,.

The main point to realise from these graphs is that *oil depletion* will impact all countries.

In developing countries the situation may be better or worse. I'm not sure if I have enough information or analysed the situation in sufficient depth to be able to ascertain the degree of difficulty each individual country will face when energy shortages become apparent. In some ways developing countries are more dependent on imported oil and gas for the very **basics** of life like heat and food production/food transport etc whereas the Worlds Industrialised nations are much more dependent on oil for **luxuries**. On the other hand developing countries are still probably **closer** to self sufficiency in food production and probably more adaptable in returning to local manufacture and local agriculture. They may also benefit from the inability of rich countries to steal all of their valuable food production under the pretence that this is going to make them wealthier.

One of the first consequences in the Global financial system of these imminent changes will be the inability of developing countries to service the vast debt burdens which they now owe to Western Banks. Presently they service these debts from foreign currency earned from exports. When at some point, in the probably not too distant future, the cost of importing/exporting fresh food becomes prohibitive many third world countries will be **unable to service these foreign debts.** They'll be unable to ship food to the Industrialised countries and hopefully they will have more food to feed their undernourished communities. Of course I realise food isn't a one way trip. Many poor countries import food from heavily subsidised industrialised countries [The US in particular] to satisfy their middle classes. The first oil shockwaves will affect

'Duck Shoot' that he had arranged for some Arab clients. He waited impatiently, clicking his fingers annoyingly on his red despatch box. Still, he reflected, chaos had its advantages. If it hadn't been for all the economic and social and geo-political problems then there wouldn't have been a hung parliament in 2006 – and Alex, a Conservative Member of Parliament, would never have had this chance for power. He glanced at his scrambling machine once more.

Alex returned another message to Mr Cash-Okay and arranged for the fifty per cent deposit, amounting to $275,000, to be transferred from one of his trading accounts in the Cayman Islands.

"Excellent!" said Alex. His humour was beginning to improve. He picked up a magazine 'Arms and Armaments' and flicked through it. There was nothing new except for a sonic personal landmine that didn't explode in a conventional sense but simply sent out electronic sound waves so powerful that they would shatter someone's eardrums and incapacitate them. The article was entitled 'Humane Weaponry'. There was a bit of a blurb about the latest laser directional rifles which could fire effective stun bullets over six hundred yards. Alex thought these might be very popular with the government. It would not be long, in his opinion, before they would have to deal much more effectively with the growing number of demonstrators and riots. The 'softly softly', we are trying to understand and deal with the crisis' was simply not working.

It needed a firm hand. Anarchists were anarchists. They had no respect for the rule of law and should

World Trade **but it will not collapse overnight.** On a medium term trend however [ten to twenty years] most world trade in food [at least perishables] will probably have come to an end.

As you will have gathered *my* "philosophy" leads me back to what is local and available.

I've just dealt briefly with the **world energy mix** because it gives a general overview of our energy requirements. Now I would like to turn my attention to the UK. My concentration on the UK originates from the fact that I have always lived here and the countries future welfare is very much on my mind of late. Here are three more pie graphs. They represent the total UK electricity production 1990, 1995 and 2000. In other words this represents all the output from our power stations.

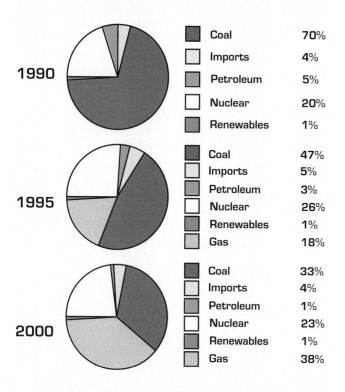

1990		
Coal	70%
Imports	4%
Petroleum	5%
Nuclear	20%
Renewables	1%

1995		
Coal	47%
Imports	5%
Petroleum	3%
Nuclear	26%
Renewables	1%
Gas	18%

2000		
Coal	33%
Imports	4%
Petroleum	1%
Nuclear	23%
Renewables	1%
Gas	38%

There is **one really startling change** in the energy mix between 1990 and 2000. During these ten years **coal** usage **dropped** from 70% to 33% whilst **gas** usage went from virtually zero in 1990 to 38% in 2000.

Oil, as you can see, is **not used** very much in power stations to generate electricity.

Thus one could say that **gas is replacing coal.**

This trend is apparently set to continue but it will shortly become clear that over the next few decades we will not just be facing a precipitous collapse in Oil Hydrocarbon Energy, we will also be facing [within the next 20 to 30 years] a similar collapse in gas.

A few statistics first. World gas *ultimate* reserves are generally accepted to be in the region of 7,000 trillion cubic feet. We are currently using gas worldwide at the rate of about 100 trillion cubic feet. Thus, in broad theory, we have about 70 years left. Of course similar principles apply to gas as oil. We will not simply use 100 trillion cubic feet for 70 years and then just run out!

Secondly gas production and supply is estimated by nearly all world energy authorities to be **at least double** over the next thirty years. If this is the case then gas reserves will be reduced dramatically from 70 years to **less than 20 years in 20 years time.** This is probably an underestimate. If you cast your mind back to UK gas consumption over the last ten years it has increased from nearly nothing to 38% of our primary power needs. If other countries follow this same pattern over the next ten years gas supplies will come under increasing strain. There will simply be major gas shortages as well as oil shortages. You have to remember that when **oil starts to deplete the demands on gas will be even higher.** Many economists who recognise that oil may become scarce over the next few years happily tell us that when oil runs low we will then *liquefy gas to propel our cars!* But in reality we are **not** just going to experience an oil crunch **we are going** to experience a gas crunch too.

In fact in the US a gas crunch is already taking place. According to a study by Richard Duncan US production of gas peaked some years ago in 1971. Canadian gas [a great deal of which is imported to the US] will peak in **2005** and Mexico [The US only other source] may have peaked already. These two countries supply the **additional** gas that the US needs. Meanwhile **200** more power plants are planned to come on stream in the US in the next ten years. 97% of these power plants will run on natural gas. In fact there have *already been* a number of gas shockwaves over the past year or so. Prices at one point jumped 40% in one day. On June 7th 2003 the energy secretary of the US administration Spencer Abraham called for a government industry summit on **natural gas** to "Look for options for increasing supply and REDUCING DEMAND" Industry experts responded by suggesting that the federal government opens up all its **national parks for exploration.** How desperate can you get for fossil fuels? Apparently the energy industry consultants even had the temerity to suggest that they could do this "without damaging the environment" The matter has become so serious that the Chairman of the Federal reserve Alan Greenspan was asked specifically about this question at his last monthly meeting with the US administration. [July 2003] When asked if there was anything he could think of to resolve the gas shortages he simply replied "NO".

Meanwhile General Electric, Americas' biggest corporation and provider of much funding to political causes is very busy making huge numbers of gas turbines. This scenario is not unlike the Chinese automobile industry. It is being created without any forethought being given as to where the fuel supplies might come. Gas shortages are already a reality in the US.

There are two main differences between oil and gas. Oil is easily made into fuel for transportation purposes and it is also easily transportable. Gas has to be cryogenically frozen [energy intensive] to turn it into a liquid fuel and the same applies when it needs to be transported by sea/container ship.

This is why when **the US started running short of its own gas** it turned to the two countries *geographically closest* to it for more. Supplies from Canada and Mexico can come as a **gas** through pipelines. If the US has to **ship gas** from elsewhere, beyond the American continent it will have to be cryogenically frozen and transported in specially designed refrigerated container ships. It will then have to be unfrozen at the other end and then introduced into the domestic gas system. In fact facilities to do exactly that are already being prepared in California.

As one might imagine oil and gas are quite related geologically. The middle east has over forty % of the worlds gas reserves. Who has the rest? Well apparently Russia has 35%. Indeed cynics might suggest that the recent state visit of the Russian head of state President Putin, to meet the Queen, might just be the beginning of various diplomatic overtures. The UK is going to **need Russian gas**, in the near future, the date is uncertain but probably in the next four or five years. Over the **next few decades** it will become increasingly dependent on Russian supplies. In fact the **whole of Europe** will be in the same situation. Added to which a major pipeline is being considered between Russia and their old enemy China.

Russian Gas will be seriously in demand.

Perhaps we should give some thought to the **balance of power** this might present to Russian Politicians. Such geo economic resource crisis have been the flaring point for many of the worlds worst conflicts.

Presently the Russians have vast gas supplies. According to the BP statistical review of World Energy about 2,500 trillion cubic feet. Europe, unfortunately, has very little gas and virtually no oil. It is for this reason that France gets over 70% of its primary electrical power from nuclear power stations. However Germany and Sweden have both decided to *phase out Nuclear Power altogether.*

In fact in Europe the only two countries to have any **significant** reserves of oil or gas are Norway and the UK. However reserves of gas in the UK are now reaching the point where we are *no longer self*

be dealt with accordingly.

The accident happened just as the last few ducks were being released from their cages. Several of them had flown towards the turret but, in their terror, they had tried to go higher and higher directly over the heads of the shooters. Abed, who had been growing very bored with his lack of success, raised his gun higher and higher over his head until he was almost falling over backwards. At the very last moment, just as he was about to topple over, he pulled the trigger. The muzzle of the gun was now virtually resting on his father's headdress and when he fired he just missed blowing the back of his head off. Even so, the hot blast was sufficient to remove his father's headdress, leaving an enormous red scorch mark on the back of his balding skull. Prince Abdullah screamed in agony and turned round to face his son. He had his shotgun in his hand and, for a moment, Alex thought he was going to shoot him. Instead he turned the gun round and, wielding it like a baseball bat, hit Abed upon the head. Then he screamed again because the hot barrel of the gun had now burnt his hands. For a while there was pandemonium. Abed, who had recovered quickly from his father's blow, tried pouring a glass of champagne over the scorched area in order to cool it down but it did not achieve the desired effect and Prince Abdullah hopped around yelling and swearing dreadful Arabic blasphemies. Eventually Mihimoto arrived. Within minutes he had procured several ice packs which he applied to the Prince's burnt bald head and scorched hands.

The next morning broke early with some commotion. Abed had been

sufficient and we will have to start importing gas quite soon. I'm afraid it is beyond my present knowledge to analysis and therefore to describe the **gas** depletion scenarios over the next thirty years.

All I know for sure is that it will become increasingly tense. I've also had enough headaches trying to understand the academic science of oil depletion. All I know for certain is that one thing tends to lead to another and oil shortages will also, eventually, precipitate Gas shortages. It is not difficult to understand why. When oil starts to deplete the pressures on Gas production will be greater. Only one thing seems certain; **we will need all the oil and gas we can get our hands on in the short term.** In the medium term [10 to 20 years] I think the situation could get much more critical for different reasons. In 20 years Russian gas supplies will be seriously starting to deplete. At that point the Russian people may, quite naturally, decide to keep Russian gas for Russians. Would you blame them? If, in twenty years, **we are all seriously short of hydrocarbon energy** what would you do with your hydrocarbons? Exactly. You'd keep them for yourself. In fact many other factors could alter the strategic supply of gas. It is likely that as hydrocarbon shortages appear more frequently, more ominously and more severely then those with the military power might try to appropriate them but I hope you feel, as I do, that by 2020, we will have stopped such selfish nonsense so perhaps *this* won't happen after all.

One last point on the UK's total electricity production. Presently 23% comes from Nuclear power. In twenty years Nuclear power will only provide 4% of our power. All the present nuclear reactors will have shut down by then. There are presently no more plans to build any more nuclear reactors. In any event *even* if we did decide to build nuclear reactors it takes at least ten years to get them up and running and the *first five years* of their electricity production is needed to pay for the energy costs in building the power station in the first place. So we can pretty much write off any more nuclear power in the UK. I hope that most ecologically minded people will regard this as excellent news. Presently the energy boffins at HQ UK government plan to replace the **loss of nuclear generation** with **gas and renewable.**

More about renewable shortly.

It is dawning on me that we are approaching not just an oil crisis but a general hydrocarbon energy crisis. I wonder how long this fact can be hidden from the general public. Not much longer I think.

Of course the precise timing of the crisis is the great unknowable but at some point major changes to our use of energy will have to happen whether we want it to or not. So I am going to make a prediction. The depth of the crisis will be exactly deep enough and potent enough and horrible enough to make us

do the right thing for Mother Earth. Science and statistics are jolly good fun to play with but there is a place for philosophy and intuition which is not presently given due credit by the powers that be.

When the general energy crisis starts to actually impact on our daily lives no doubt many people will recommend returning to the burning of more coal and the immediate creation of more nuclear power plants. In fact I think these two issues, **coal and nuclear,** will become the **two most critical issues** of the first few decades of this century. Nuclear power still has a few enthusiasts and no doubt it will claim a few more when it becomes increasingly apparent that we are not going to be able to generate sufficient electrical power to maintain us in the "comfort zone" to which we have all become so attached. It will be a matter of some considerable importance. This is understating the case. In fact so far, since I always *hedge* my bets, **I** think **it may become a focal point** of our discussions much more imminently than you might think. If this is the case then the crisis may not be as bad. If we **don't think** about all of this then we are in for a very bumpy ride.

The issue of the World's available energy is critical to understanding the deeper implications of the new world that is about to arrive. Oil depletion has been given the most significance in this series of essays because oil is the most important hydrocarbon. This importance can be summed up in one simple word.

Transportation

The school run, driving into town for the shopping. Driving to work and back from work. Visiting friends and relations. Going on holiday. Jumping in the van or lorry to deliver something to someone somewhere. Catching the 11.15 flight to Barcelona on Friday night and the 8.05 flight back from Barcelona two days later. Indeed many business people take return flights to Switzerland **every single day.** Some of them are just dropping off vast wodges of cash to hide in the " Oh so secretive" Swiss banking system. Some are honest financiers travelling to the World's financial hub.

Transport includes oil container ships and the cargo ships containing raw materials. Wood, Coal, Meat, Steel and millions and millions of tons of general consumable product. 90% of garden furniture is shipped from the far east. Food? It comes from everywhere, all over the world, every single day. By ship and by plane. **World air freight is at literally epidemic proportions.** We ship over 100 million tons of air freight a year. Air freight brings us fresh flowers on Saturday morning which were quite possibly cut on the fields of South America on the Thursday before.

TRANSPORTATION is not just the basis of **TOURISM**.

TRANSPORTATION EQUALS TOURISM

Without transportation tourism doesn't exist. It is for these reasons that oil is given the priority in these essays. I hope it is clear why this is so. I do not wish to labour the point. But the **Global energy mix** is also critically important. We get our electricity, our primary daily power from coal, gas and nuclear power. The availability of these fuels is clearly going to be important. A brief word of the sources for my statistics in this essay. Most of them are drawn from International Energy Outlook. The most respected, most prestigious and most frequently quoted of all the international energy organisations.

It is certainly worth analysing their most recent report published on 1st May 2003. This is a staggeringly comprehensive report which details World projected energy consumption up until 2025. It covers all types of energy. Oil, Gas, Coal, Nuclear and renewables. **Anyone** who is interested in the World energy situation needs to be aware of this report. So what does it say?

Here's the introduction.

"Worldwide oil demand is projected to reach 119 million barrels per day by 2025 [43.5 billion barrels per year] This is an <u>*increase*</u> *over current world capacity, [presently 77 milion barrels per day,] requiring an* <u>*increment*</u> *to world production capability of* <u>*more than 42 million barrels*</u> *per day. OPEC producers are expected to be the major suppliers of increased production..."*

And here's another extract.

"The projected trends in growth for oil production are sustainable without severe oil price escalation. There are <u>*some*</u> *oil market analysts, however who find this viewpoint overly optimistic, based on what they consider to be significant overestimations of both proved reserves and ultimately recoverable resources."*

It is worth noting that the International Energy Outlook [we will now abbreviate this to IEO for convenience] is the major report used by governments and economists to **support their preferred position**. Their preferred position is of course, business as usual, a permanent economic **growth phase without interruption and without any problems**. According to the rather rosy scenario painted by the IEO report, energy growth over the next 25 years, **is going to rise dramatically**. Here is an extract from the IEO report 2003.

"The outlook presented in the IEO report 2003 shows strong growth for worldwide energy demand over the next 24 years.

caught in bed with Ahmed by his father, Prince Abdullah. The back of his head was ferociously sore and he'd lurched into his son's bedroom with the single purpose of berating him further. Alex, rushing out of his bedroom, was regaled by the Prince chasing the young naked Ahmed down the long stone corridor.

"Now we come to the most important item," he said coolly. His expression had not altered. *"We need to purchase a little uranium."*

"Uranium?!" Alex wasn't sure if he had quite heard him correctly. *"I'm sorry,"* he said without pausing for thought, *"that's something I don't deal with."*

"That's a pity!" said Mazatoum and then he paused. The room went silent; an uncomfortable, wriggling silence as far as Alex was concerned. *"We were really thinking of this as a kind of package. We're not talking about very much; just a few hundred kilograms."*

Alex panicked inside whilst trying to look composed on the outside. 'A few hundred kilograms' he thought to himself. 'My God! How much is that!' He wanted to ask what it was for but you never, ever, asked questions like that when it came to arms dealing. The end purpose was never any concern of the seller. Nor was the eventual destination. Alex felt trapped.

"Perhaps you're worrying about what it is for?" said Mazatoum smoothly.

Alex wanted to know and didn't want to know. In any event, he was intelligent enough to realise that he wouldn't be getting a truthful answer.

Total World energy consumption is expected to grow by 58% between 2001 and 2025."

The IEO also optimistically predicts Global economic growth of 3% a year.

'Every year. Year in. Year out. For the next 22 years.

Anyone reading this report could be forgiven for thinking that there is no energy crisis in sight. Not even the merest hint of one. As far as the IEO is concerned it's business as usual. **There is absolutely no mention of the concept of Peak oil production and depletion.** You may have noticed the comment about some oil analysts who consider the reserves estimate as overly optimistic? Well that's referring to us. *The ones who think that the crisis is more serious and more imminent than most people care to imagine.*

The IEO, *in common* with most Flat Earth economists, regards **reserves in years to production ratios** as the only important factor. Oil depletion simply isn't considered. According to the IEO we will be using: -

42 million barrels more oil every day in 2025

and the price will be **absolutely stable!** Now if I was reading this essay for the first time (and not writing it) I would need to ask some pretty serious questions. Firstly; how can there be such utterly divergent views? My predictions; based on geological science *predicts general decline* most conventional scenarios *predict general growth?* Many of the world's leading oil petroleum geologists are suggesting that perhaps as **soon as 2007** oil will reach peak production and then decline **every year by about 3 %.** Meanwhile major international organizations like the I E O are suggesting that oil supplies w**ill grow at 1.8% a year.** The difference is staggering. But in fact there is probably a bigger issue at stake here. If the IEO is correct in its predictions then.

Carbon Dioxide emissions are going to increase dramatically.

[there's more on carbon dioxide emissions later]

If the IEO is correct then I will almost certainly have to join the ecological doomsday brigade. The ecological doomsday brigade think there's no hope for humanity. They believe that the planet will become uninhabitable and the human species will most likely become extinct.

The choices are stark.

If the I E O is correct and carbon emissions are due to increase dramatically then planetary warming and ecological catastrophe seem certainties.

But if the oil depletion/peak oil theory is correct and the IEO is wrong then the world economic system is going to suffer an equally devastating catastrophic decline!!

Could there be a middle way?

Theories of course are rather like magazines or newspapers. One tends to subscribe to the one that fits most easily with one's own views and preferences. Diehard Conservatives tend to buy the Spectator [not the New Statesman.] Ecologists and the new wave of green thinkers will subscribe to the theory of peak oil. *One can only hope and imagine that young ecologists are ready for a total change of economic emphasis.*

Governments, corporations (including the media) businessmen, bankers, brokers and anyone who has a vested interest in keeping the **present system** up and running will prefer the rosy picture painted by the IEO. Indeed the above mentioned groups will regard the IEO as definitive and they will regard the theory of "Peak oil", if they bother to regard it at all, as the rantings and ravings of a few crackpots, *[a category in which I am certainly hoping to be included.]*

If, on the other hand, the IEO is correct *then* we have an enormous environmental crisis on our hands because according to the IEO **there is no energy supply problem on the horizon for at least the next 25 years. According to the IEO we can continue to have a jolly good hydrocarbon burn up without any constraints at all.**

It is true that past forecasts from the IEO have been **quite accurate.** So it is not unreasonable for many people to **assume** that their **future forecasts** will be *equally* accurate. The essential point is that the IEO has *always forecast continuing World growth* both in economic terms and energy terms. **In fact this is really their starting point.** They are not analyzing the fossil fuel resource base. They simply start with a basic irrefutable assumption based on the past. The Capitalistic World Economy has grown every year for the past fifty years and will continue to do so ad infinitum. We must remember we are talking about continual World Growth. The Western World has seen recessions of course when their economies didn't grow. But the World economy has grown every year since the war. In fact a World recession is defined in most economic circles as "Growth of less than 2.5 % " World growth is the IEO's starting point. From this **assumption** the IEO then works out the energy requirements such growth will require.

It is hardly surprising, that these two issues, economic growth and energy requirements, are intimately connected. To the vested interests/power elite economic growth is sacred. Increasing world trade and maintaining or indeed **increasing** domestic consumption is not only regarded as **essential** but almost a divine right. The environmental problems connected to energy growth are just a nuisance. Capitalists who **consider growth to be paramount** still think that environmental degradation and resource constraints are problems that will be solved by more growth because more growth equals more money and money **solves all problems**.

The main point is that the vested interests will not be convinced by the scientific or academic proponents of "Peak Oil". Accordingly we will carry on as we are doing. One might wonder then what makes me so convinced that "Peak Oil" is the more likely theory to be correct? To answer this is not easy. Peak oil will give humanity the opportunity to reflect on the effect our intense industrial activities are having on the environment and on our "spiritual" and "psychic" health. Personally I don't want another 25 years of unsustainable growth and I don't want to see our rather precious and delicate ecosphere damaged any more. Possibly beyond the point where the damage is beyond our human capacity to repair. There is something inside me that craves fundamental changes to the way we live. I know I'm not alone in holding these sentiments but I also know I'm in a minority, albeit a growing one. My intuition and my analysis tells me that the science of oil depletion, [the Hubbert curve] is probably correct. If it is correct this is not good news for the power elite because economic growth will be severely and ongoingly curtailed.

Before I move on however let's just stay with the IEO predictions. Let's assume, **just for the moment,** that they are correct. Let's assume that oil production **can** increase by over 50 per cent over the next 25 years until oil production reaches the IEO projected total of 119 million barrels per day [43.5 billion barrels per annum.] If these projections are correct, the total amount of oil consumed between 2001 and 2025 would be about **900 billion barrels**. Now this brings us back to how much total recoverable oil there is left on the Planet. Dr Campbell and other highly influential and respected oil geologists believe that we have about 1000 billion barrels. So if we use up 900 in the next 25 years we would then only have about two and a half years left.

In other words by Mid June 2027 we will have absolutely no oil left whatsoever.

This seems to me like nonsense. Of course the I E O **believe that vast oil reserves** will be discovered

"Call it the 'balance of power' if you like," continued Mazatoum.

"Something we need to protect ourselves. You can be assured it is not required for anything aggressive. Simply a necessary deterrent in these difficult and dangerous times."

Chloe - 2007

The roads were much busier than she had expected. For the moment at least the fuel crisis seemed to have eased off. Still she was grateful to her husband for queuing at four different garages to get the car filled up. It had taken him all afternoon. He reckoned he had used £5 worth just sitting in the queues. Still, with petrol at £1.50 a litre that didn't take very long.

At first it all seemed to go quite well, she was definitely making progress! She turned down into a residential street. At first it just seemed abnormally quiet, then she realised that the lower part of the street was thronging with gangs of boys. At the end of the road several cars had been overturned. Chloe turned right into another small residential street, trying to block out the terrible wail of sirens.

The road looked calm but it wasn't to last. A huge mass of bodies suddenly came surging towards her from nowhere. They were brandishing sticks and throwing stones, bricks and car wheels through the shop windows as they went. As they ran passed her many of them glanced in, their faces distorted with wild pleasure. They banged on her bonnet and roof with their baseball bats. Chloe sat paralysed in the middle of the road

between now and 2025. Or at least I assume they do. Although they make astonishingly precise predictions up until 2025 they make absolutely no comment as to what might happen beyond then. But let's continue to assume their predictions are correct, what would happen between 2025 to 2050. Will fossil fuels and particularly oil continue their meteoric and indeed positively heroic annual increases? The fact is that the IEO predictions are simple fantasy. They take the present situation (oil production at 26 billion barrels per annum) assume growth of three per cent per annum (the minimum necessary to keep the world economy charging ahead) and then extrapolate from this trend how much oil is going to be needed. Then, when they have decided **how much oil** is going to be needed they look up some tables which indicate the **amount of reserves** and assume that those people will be producing those reserves on demand to keep the world satisfied according to its present desires.

There is no *science* in the IEO oil predictions. They are simply *economic* predictions.

As an academic body it fulfils its role perfectly. *It maintains and indeed encourages ultimate future confidence in the system.*

In fact even the most utterly and absolutely optimistic predictions for total world oil recovery only specify about 1.6 trillion barrels. In this happy/unhappy scenario, depending upon your point of view, there would be about 700 billion barrels left in 2025. If future growth then continues at the same level there would be just *16 years of oil left.* Somewhere there is a terrible flaw in the thinking processes of the people who produce the I E O reports. In fact when one looks back over history it is not difficult to find examples of people who believe the very opposite of what reality is showing them. This is just such a case.

It is also very interesting to note what the IEO predicts about growth in renewables during the period 2003-2025 such as wave wind and solar. Here is another extract from their summary: -

"renewable resources are not expected to compete economically with fossil fuels in the mid-term forecast. IEO 2003 projects that consumption of renewable energy worldwide will grow by 56 per cent from 32 quadrillion btu in 2001 to 50 quadrillion btu in 2025"

According to the IEO report 2003. This total of 50 quadrillion btu's includes Hydro-Electric schemes which in fact form the bulk of the

increase. Wind capacity over this 25 years is expected to grow by 300 per cent but by 2025 renewables excluding Hydro-Electric are only expected to provide *less than one per cent* of worldwide energy consumption.

[NOTE. Before we continue. The term "btu" stands for British thermal unit. It is an industry standard for the measurement of "energy" units. Quite often different fuel sources are converted into "btu's" for the purpose of comparison. A Quadrillion is a big number. With apologies to those who understand here is an explanation of big numbers. A billion is a thousand million. A trillion is a thousand times bigger than a billion and a Quadrillion is a thousand times bigger than a trillion. For convenience during the rest of this essay the term "Quadrillion btu's" will be simply referred to as Quads.]

Read that again. ***LESS THAN ONE PER CENT.*** Somewhere in the vast mystery of life, amidst the drama of daily existence **a crisis of some sort** is unfolding. The theory of "Peak oil" brings this crisis to a head very soon. The rose-tinted projections of the IEO only delays the utterly inevitable by a generation.

It is **important** to recognise that the IEO predictions for 2025 **are absolutely frightening in themselves**. Such massive increases in consumption simply cannot be desirable but yet the powers that be continue to support the whole economic infrastructure which is taking us down a path of no return. One of the reasons that I hope the theory of Peak oil is correct is because I think a crisis coming sooner rather than later would be preferable for the planet and preferable for the chances of Homosapiens getting a bit further up the evolutionary tree.

In fact if the theory of Peak oil is correct it would mean that the **decline** in world growth would tail off **gradually from around 2007/2008** rather than **precipitously some years later**.

It would also be preferable if we could actually plan for this decline rather than wait for a developing crisis.

According to the BP statistical review 2003 world gas production and consumption is expected to grow by an average of 2.8% a year from 90 trillion cubic feet to 176 trillion cubic feet. **In simple terms gas consumption is set to double.** Most of the

---STOP PRESS---

Here are some very interesting Graphs which just came into my posession. The first graph is called the Growing Gap: this graph was published by Texaco in 2002. It illustrates very clearly the fact that oil discovery peaked in the 1960's and that production/consumption (see the black line) is now running way ahead of discovery.

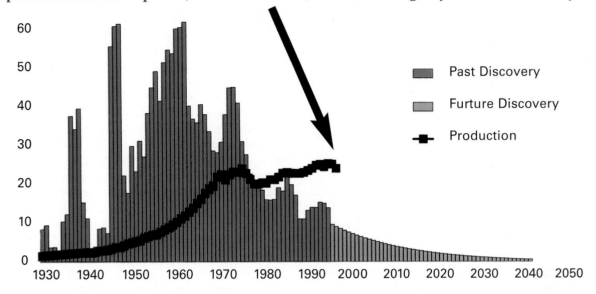

I also recently came across an extract from a report by Petroconsultants 1995. This reports costs US$30,000 and is only bought by oil companies and Governments. Shortly after this publication, the report was suppressed. The information is too alarming for general consumption. I quote from the 1995 report: -

"Production is expected to enter a plateau lasting from 1997 until 2001 (under a base caes scenario of demand and supply) at sixty-six million barrels per day before declining to fifty-two million barrels per day by 2010. By 2050, world oil production will have fallen to about eighteen million barrels per day - about one quarter of todays present production."

Astute readers will recognise that the production figure quoted above (sixty-six million barrels per day) in 2001 differs from the figures used throughout this book. The reason is that the Petroconsultants report is only dealing with conventional oil. It does not include polar oil or deep sea oil or non-gas liquids which make up todays total daily consumption of seventy-six million barrels per day

MORE THAN 80 PER CENT OF THE WORLDS OIL LIES IN THESE TWO BELTS.

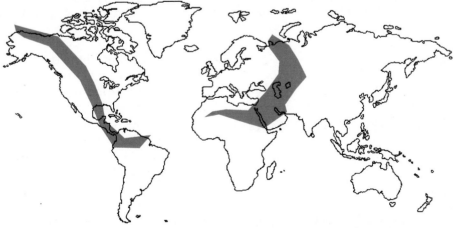

The oil field across the U.S.A. is nearly depleted. The oil field across the Middle East is not yet depleted. The reasons a resource war exists between the U.S. and the Middle East is illustrated here in perfect graphic detail.

increase will come from industrialized countries who use gas for electricity production, domestic heating and various intense industrial and chemical processes.

So gas is **projected to double** in usage over the next 25 years. Of course the IEO figures for **increased** gas consumption **run in parallel** with their forecasts for an equally dramatic increase in oil consumption [1.8 % per year growth every year for the next 25 years] But if the theory of Peak oil is correct then we will not be able to increase our oil usage at this rate and if we can't what will we do? The answer is *we will use more gas*. If we can. In the US the treasury and energy departments are trying to instigate plans to start trading world gas in the same way as oil. Why? They are running out of gas. The US will need an **additional** 19 trillion cubic feet per year by 2025!! The critical point at which world gas supplies will peak is variously estimated at 2015-2025. It will be sooner if there is less oil of course and more gas is used. Since the late 1970's when the US started to realize that their own supplies of gas and oil would not be sufficient to fuel their industrial growth they have, naturally enough looked elsewhere around the world to buy it. [Stealing from Iraq is a new twist on the same theme.]

During the last thirty years or so the US has forced, literally, other countries to *sell* their reserves of oil and gas. They "forced" them to sell by the creation of various World trade bodies such as the World Trade Organisation [WTO] and the International Monetary fund [IMF]. These two organizations have, under the auspices of US corporations, **written the rules of free trade.** The most important of these rules states that;

"Wherever resources are found they must be available to the highest bidder, whoever has the money to buy the resources has a legally defensible right to them."

If countries didn't agree to these terms they were locked out of any access to International capital. Even small developing countries were forced to abide by the same rules.

Hydrocarbons are going to be in increasing demand and the US as the worlds biggest user is going to do absolutely everything within its power to get hold of them.

The only people who could stop them are the American people themselves. It is my personal opinion that they will not only come through with the goods they will repay their dreadful Karma to the world by designing maintaining and then donating technologically innovative ways of living within the limitations of the earths energy systems.

Wars have already been fought over hydro carbons and more are probably inevitable. We will not stop war tomorrow. War will eventually evaporate as hydrocarbon resources deplete.

One of Hitler's main objectives in the Second world war was to gain access to Russia's southern oil fields. The reason the Japanese attacked Pearl Harbour was to take over the Far Eastern oil fields. The main difference over the next ten to thirty years is that these resources will be starting to rapidly dwindle away. When one considers the enormity of the issue, ten to thirty years, is no time at all. The crisis will be upon us sooner than we think. The desire for power, hydrocarbon power, is not going to **abate** it is going to **increase**.

My personal hope and the purpose of my thesis is that a series of oil shock waves will destabilize the system sufficiently to create the impetus for dramatic political and economic "revolution" **without being so severe** they actually destabilize the foundations of society. I think we are in for an interesting ride. Bucking bronco style. I hope I will be playing a great deal of cricket in the afternoons. A low hydrocarbon high physical intensity activity. Something for the future perhaps? One of the best features of this revolution is that it will, of necessity, be gentle. Hydrocarbons make life very busy, explosive and they are very useful for building up enormous military arsenals. The new sustainable world that beckons is non-violent benevolent and based on the rebuilding of trust, integrity, self sacrifice and the renewal and reconnection of local communities.

Coal

Coal as a part of the global energy mix has been **in decline** for some time. But although we are **using less of it as a proportion of our total energy use.** We are actually using **more** of it than ever before. As the earliar Pie Graph showed us; coal is being used **less and less** in the Western industrialised nations but *in Asia* the situation is somewhat different and is very frightening for reasons that will shortly be made clear to you. Coal usage in the Far East, and most *specifically in China* is growing at an absolutely phenomenal rate.

China alone is projected to increase coal usage from 1,282 million tons to 2,917 million tons. In other words it will be using two and a half times as much.

One point that needs to be made about the increasing usage of coal. Unlike oil it is almost certain that there is enough readily available coal at a reasonable economic cost to insure that the IEO predictions can become reality.

According to the IEO The world as a whole between 2001-2025 will use almost exactly **one and half times as much energy**. In 2001 the world consumed 404 Quads. By 2025 according to the IEO we will be using 640 Quads. This is a difference (640-404) of 236 Quads. During this period 2001-2025 Asia will have **increased** its primary electricity usage by 210 Quads to 434 Quads. Now you must remember that these statistics come directly from the world's leading Energy Authority. What it says quite simply is that in the next 20 years the world will need **one and a half times as much prime electrical power** as it does now and that *all* of this additional power will be required by the Far East and most specifically China. Now let's stick with Asia and look at their oil consumption.

Between 2001 and 2025 according to the IEO China will increase it's oil usage from 4.8 million barrels per day to 10.9 million barrels per day. In the whole of Asia oil usage is going to increase from 14.5 million barrels per day to 29.8 million barrels per day.

So Asia, as a region, is going to *double* its oil use but in order to do so it is actually going to have to *treble* its oil imports for the very simple reason like everywhere else it is **running out of its own oil**. The same statistics apply to gas which is due to *increase* in usage in Asia from 13.9 quads to 35 quads. This is an increase of nearly 250 per cent. Where will the additional oil and gas be coming from? Easy answer. **From the same places everybody else in the world is going to have to get it from**. Mostly the Middle East or Russia.

World consumption of oil in 2003 is 75 million barrels per day. Now let's get back to that **additional 15 million barrels** of oil Asia is going to want over the next 20 years. I want to ask a question. I want to ask a question of oil engineers, politicians and oil businessmen. I want to ask this question of economists. In fact I want to ask this question to anyone who can give me the most scientific, the most detailed and the most honest appraisal of the energy situation in the World.

Where is this additional 15 million barrels per day of oil going to come from?

whilst the wave of bodies swarmed by.

It reminded her of driving through occasional herds of cattle in the Cornish countryside. Behind the rioters came a dozen policemen on horses. Dressed in battle gear, they held huge plastic shields and batons. Their heads were covered with black motorcycle helmets. Even the horses' heads were covered. Chloe was now stopped exactly in the middle of the road. The police had gathered up into line. Then they charged towards her, towards the retreating hordes of screaming, gesticulating thugs. Then they were gone. They passed her and suddenly the street was absolutely empty. Some shopkeepers immediately dodged out of their shops to survey the broken glass and wave useless fists of defiance at the retreating rioters.

The silence was pleasant and, strangely, Chloe felt no fear. For a few moments she had hoped that the rioters would tear her from the car and dismember her, but her prayers had not been answered. She would gladly have sacrificed herself to the wanton destruction.

Chuck Sackville - 2007

In need of employment once more, Chuck took a job down in Brazil setting up a 'Paper Mill' from scratch. It was one of those enormous logistical operations which thrilled Chuck. Agreement had been reached with the Brazilian government to clear one million acres of rainforest in southern Brazil and set up the largest pulp and paper mill in the world. When Chuck first flew over the land it was simply one

You must also remember that *we're only talking about Asia's increasing needs.* I have not yet included the **projected increases** from the rest of the world which will not be inconsiderable. **It strikes me, at this point that I** <u>don't need</u> **to be very** <u>specific</u> **or** <u>accurate</u> about any of these statistics.

Common sense and intuition will suffice to reach the conclusion that these projections for total world energy increases over the next 25 years are not compatible with any scientific, pragmatic or sensible view of future realities. The hydrocarbon resources to fill this demand gap cannot come on stream on time due to physical production constraints.

I would hope, by now at least, that some people are beginning to get quite concerned by what they are reading. If your reaction to what I'm writing is anything like the feeling I've had whilst investigating this then it is at times quite terrifying. Unfortunately it's not the end of the story not by a long way in fact the real terror is only just about to be unfolded. Let's return to China's projected coal increase.

Let's recap. Coal used in Asia in 2000 was 1,282 million tons. Projected coal used in 2025 is 2,917 million tons.

Now from the BP statistical review of world energy 2003. This is the very first sentence from their report: -

"Coal was the fastest growing fuel in 2002 on the back of a huge 28 per cent reported rise in Chinese consumption. World coal consumption increased by almost seven per cent. Well ahead of the ten-year annual average trend of less than one per cent."

It is truly worth pondering these "facts" for a moment. This *28 per cent* is over **twenty eight times** the increase projected by the IEO just two years ago. In fact the IEO predictions for Chinas coal use between **2001** and **2005** [1,383 tons to 1442 tons] indicated a growth rate of about **one per cent** a year.

So just two years into the IEO predictions.

China's coal use has gone up 28 per cent in just one year [2002.]

I'd like you to bear this fact in mind because it will be very relevant when we come to our next terrifying subject.

Carbon Dioxide Emissions

World carbon emissions will rise from *6,417* *million* metric tons per annum in 2001 to *10,361* *million* metric Tons by 2025

This figure should seriously alarm every human being on the planet.

This Statistic is from The IEO Report 2003 on page 191.

We simply do not need an increase. Oh Lord! we desperately desperately need a decrease!

And **these increases** are based on the IEO **predictions** that China **will only increase coal usage by an average of one per cent** until 2005 and then about 3.2 per cent until 2025!! If China was to increase coal usage as they have done in 2002 then the Carbon Dioxide emission figures would **go into orbit.**

It is not alarmist to suggest that a reduction in Carbon Dioxide emissions may be become a matter of life and death for the planet. No that's silly. The Planet will be just fine whatever happens. It's the human race who will suffer the ignominy of annihilation.

It makes one ask? When will the crisis point be reached? Although there are still a few dissenters **virtually every scientist in the World has recognized that stabilizing carbon dioxide emission is a matter of some priority.** But nothing is being done about it. Forget the Kyoto protocol. It's a bunch of political spin. So, if we actually need a decrease how much should this decrease be?

Scientists from the World Watch Institute estimate that we should reduce carbon emissions by 80 per cent. **Yes you read that correctly** we should;

Reduce carbon emissions by 80 %.

I quote directly from their book *"State of the World 2002"* [page 30]. I should point out that this is a prestigious organization. Its 19th edition, published in 28 languages was dedicated to the Johannesburg World summit. It has a foreword by Kofi Annan the secretary General of the United Nations: -

"Stabilizising greenhouse gas concentrations at 450 parts per million, for example, requires that annual carbon emissions drop well below current levels within the next several decades, then to around 2 billion tons by 2100 and ultimately to less than 1 billion tons. <u>This entails a cut of roughly 70 to 80 per cent in Global carbon emissions."</u>

That would actually mean that instead of carbon emissions rising from 6,417 million tons to 10,361 million tons, we should, for the health of the planet and its inhabitants actually reduce the total carbon emissions from 6,417 million metric tons to 1,283 million metric tons. [1.2 billion tons] This represents a reduction of 80 per cent. You may think that I am now just being alarmist or simply silly. But there are

unending canopy of thick jungle and useless vegetation. In three months he had shipped in two hundred eighty-ton earth movers and bulldozers and cleared right down to the fresh soil the million acres required for the site. In six months they had laid the foundations to the mill: two hundred million tonnes of steel and four hundred billion tonnes of concrete. A year later the mill was up and running; the cheapest and most efficient in the world. It even had plans for its own dam making hydro electricity. The whole process had gone almost without a glitch. The only delay had occurred in moving the several thousand indigenous primitives out of the forest. The mill was now producing three hundred thousand tonnes of paper a year. Virtually every magazine and newspaper, from the New Yorker to the Cincinnati Herald, from the Enquirer to all the promotional material for McDonald's restaurants, poured out of Chuck's new factory. It was his greatest achievement to date. He had supervised and managed the building of the world's largest productive unit in the shortest possible time and he was very proud of himself.

In Chicago a little-known scientist, Charles Jefferson, proposed a theory that the planetary weather system was presently just simmering. He went on to propose a further theory that, at some point, quite possibly in the very near future, the weather might stop simmering and come to the boil, thereby dramatically altering the rate and intensity of the climatic changes. He anticipated that this could mean a doubling of rainfall in many areas already prone to flooding, and severe, almost permanent, droughts and fires in other areas. He proposed that, in

the facts in front of you from the world's leadings authorities.

At our present rate we will actually be increasing carbon dioxide emissions by 70 per cent precisely at the time we should be planning to reduce them by 80 per cent.

The difference in these two figures, the volumes it would represent and the changes to our lifestyle which would occur were these reductions to take place are;

"Utterly momentous to think about."

But we have to think about them. Nature may be finding a way to help us cut down fossil fuel burning by withdrawing the increasing availability of oil but if we try to replace oil consumption by burning coal we will be in serious trouble.

These facts and statistics are correct and verifiable and the sources are impeccable. It also doesn't really matter which particular figures you enjoy using or make you feel the most comfortable. You may also think that this statistic.

"The need to reduce carbon dioxide emissions by 80 per cent"

is some kind of nonsense. Maybe the World Watch Institute from which they are drawn is not reliable. Well very recently and **indeed to their credit** the British government recently stated that it **has the ambition** to reduce C02 emissions by 60 per cent by 2050. Of course Government **ambitions** set *so far out* in the future have very little chance of becoming political reality. It is very unlikely to happen through any policies concocted by the present bunch. The fact is that economic growth and energy supplies are precisely related to one another. To actually establish a scenario whereby carbon dioxide emissions are reduced by 60 per cent in the next 47 years when world economic growth is forecasted to increase by 3% a year is palpable nonsense. It would require a massive, utterly mindbending, reduction in industrial activity. Such a reduction is not presently on the political agenda.

Could it be on the agenda of Mother Earth?

For our planets ultimate health it would probably help if carbon dioxide emissions collapse. But such a collapse would require a concomitant precipitous collapse in the entire global trading infrastructure. Economics, banking, finance, manufacturing, tourism, trade. In fact **every single commercial activity that presently takes place**. And not just in the Western industrialised nations but *where ever humans move and consume end-use energy*. Of course the stated ambitions of the British government probably aren't worth the paper they are printed on. If it's anything like the Kyoto protocol it's a matter of making lots of fine promises and then ignoring them. Ultimately it will be **events beyond political control** that will start to initiate the essentially needed changes.

The "Peaking of the millennium oil wave" will shortly be seen to be an inescapable reality. The reactions to this event will be momentous. For all of us. How **severe a shock** the global trading economy gets his hard to measure precisely. There is good news and there is bad news. They often come packaged together these days. Here's the good news. If world trade collapses then so does the desperate need for Asia to industrialise by using their vast internal coal resources to make more electricity to make billions of items for **export** to the rest of the world. It wouldn't solve of course their internal domestic growth problems. The Chinese are desperate to industrialise. It is difficult to see a solution to this dilemma. The only imaginable solution would be for the West to de-industrialise, whilst simultaneously creating technical solutions to the problem of making economic activity sustainable and then exporting this technology to the countries still going through the processes of industrialisation. How this is to be achieved if, as seems likely, the Industrialised nations means of producing wealth is to be severely curtailed is a matter that is yet to be resolved. I do not see how we can stop China burning vast amounts of heavily polluting Coal but if my intuition serves me correctly I can assure you that buying imported teak garden furniture from Asia, fresh flowers from South America or mangoes from India will be the *least thing* on your mind in 2025. To get anywhere near a benevolent scenario will take a human, political and spiritual energy the like of which humanity has never seen.

Now you have been presented with my thesis "The theory of oil shock waves and the repercussions for the global economy and the planets environment" What are my final conclusions? In a nutshell? Trouble ahead.

During the last six years of writing *I have been increasingly astounded* by the almost total inattention the world political leaders are devoting to the utterly critical notion of hydrocarbon depletion and the imminent global energy crisis. I do not regard appropriating Iraqi oil fields as a particularly intelligent or pleasant reaction to the oncoming shortage of hydrocarbons. Every single day, indeed almost every single hour I ask myself *why* we are not really *addressing* this issue.

My short answer is that it is **too huge** in scope for

most human analytical systems **to deal with comprehensively or intelligently.**

My <u>simple</u> answer is that **those** people who run world affairs also **think** they rule the Planet.

My <u>detailed</u> answer however requires a little more **subtle analysis of the mind sets** of those who presently wield political and financial influence because the **sheer enormity** of what is facing us is hard to look at straight in the eye without blinking.

Conventional Mindsets

If I am correct in my analysis, and the subject of hydrocarbon depletion and environmental pollution becomes the major issue of our times we will no doubt ask ourselves why this enormous issue came to be broached at *such a late point in our evolution* since it was very clear, even several generations ago, that we would **eventually** reach some kind of barrier through which we could not pass. The IEO statistics may be right or they may be wrong; we will not know **exactly** until 2025 when we can look back and compare them with their predictions. What we must hope however is that **in making these predictions they may well have initiated processes which will ultimately make their predictions invalid.**

One of the other important factors is simply timescale. The hydrocarbon crisis is not going to suddenly explode one-day **it is going to explode over a very long period of time.** About 30 years. There will be a number of explosions. How intelligently we react to each of these explosions will determine how painful or how painless each following explosion will be.

If I am correct these explosions could have been foreseen and, to a large extent, the violence of these explosions could be greatly mitigated if we all to started to adopt, right now, an **entirely different approach to our lifestyles.** This is perhaps the major issue of our times. We are addicted to our lifestyles and would rather that they were not interrupted presently. So perhaps the **biggest** reason why this issue is not presently in focus is because;

It would lead to a potent self examination of the foundations of our lives.

There are also some very **practical** and **simple** reasons why these issues are not being confronted. Quite simply *conventional mind sets* do not have the **facility** to see beyond their own personal framework. Over the last few years I have spoken to many oil industry people and it is astonishing but the vast majority of them are quite **oblivious** to the problems we are about to face. Of course Oil industry executives can hardly be expected to start making a song and dance about the fact that the raw material of their industry is a **finite** resource; which

order to safeguard the planet for future generations, carbon emissions should be reduced permanently and immediately by three-fifths; the amount needed just to stabilise the carbon emissions in the atmosphere at their present levels.

David Sadleigh - 2007

David had been hit very hard by the fuel crisis. As a kitchen salesman following up his cold calls, he had often been sent up to one hundred miles away from home four or five times a week. He had not sold a kitchen for eight weeks.

The underground was bursting at the seams. He couldn't get a seat so he sat on his suitcase of samples and tried to read up about the latest Neff and Bosch ovens.

It's really going to piss down, thought David sadly. And he was right. The large cold drops quickly became a blank wall of black rain. David retreated to the doorway of an estate agent and watched it teem down. As he sat on his case of doors and looked disconsolately out at the rain he observed, with keen interest, the kebab shop across the road. The smell of greasy lamb and chip fat drifted enchantingly across the wet black tarmac. The blanket of rain was now very thick. He'd probably get soaked just crossing the dual carriageway, even though there was not much traffic on it. It was quite amazing what the latest fuel crisis had done to the economy. He had tried to sell his old Volvo Estate and buy a tiny, fuel economic car but everyone was doing the same thing and old thirsty Volvos were now two to a penny. He could not even swap

is disappearing at increasingly faster rates; and is getting **increasingly hard** to find. Of course some of them are becoming aware of the forthcoming problems but they cannot **think** about the consequences. They are too busy trying to find oil for our present purposes.

Oil Reserves Revisited

There is some *very interesting analysis* to be done on the Oil industry's "oil reserve" data. It is a little appreciated fact but in order to keep **some stability in oil reserve reporting** it is much better that some oil reserves **are kept in one's back pocket for a rainy day.** I will shortly explain in more detail why this is important and why it will help us understand why the oil industry is ignorant of its own imminent demise. Just a word on the derivation of the word reserve. To be "reserved" is to hold back. It also means to keep for future use and enjoyment. Presently our oil reserves are being torn out of the earth at ever increasing velocity. This is hardly keeping them for a rainy day. Growth requires that we tear them out ever faster.

It would seem that we are just about to travel back to where we began. **To the very scientific physical basis of the oil industry.** How do oil companies actually discover oil and how do they physically drill for it? Indeed even **before discovering** an oil well what exactly is it? I suppose most people simply imagine an oil well as a hole in the ground at the bottom of which oil waiting to be sucked up. Well such a picture is not entirely off the point. But oil wells are actually a rather fascinating bit of the Earth's natural geology and if you'll forgive me I'm going to spend a few brief moments describing the nature of oil well formation. Since I am going to be brief and others may wish to pursue the matter in more detail I would like to take this opportunity of thanking M. Hubbert and all the other Pioneer oil geologists who correctly predicted in 1956 that oil production in the US would peak in the early 1970's. I'd also like to highly recommend a book called "Hubbert's Peak" by Kenneth S Deffeyes. Published by Princeton University Press.

The history of oil is interesting in itself but how far do you go back? 2000 years ago boiling oil was poured over the battlements of castles on to the invaders. In one famous battle boiling oil was spread on the sea and set fire to in order to chase away the invading armadas.

But what about oil geologists? Who are they, what do they do and most importantly of all **should we trust them?** Here are a few of my conclusions as to why, for the purposes of my thesis, I have trusted in the **oil geologists science** rather than **political spin** from government energy departments or from *Flat Earth economists* who cannot see the brick wall they are currently heading into at such breakneck speed.

It goes without saying but in order to produce oil you *first have to discover* its whereabouts. As one might imagine the worlds biggest, most powerful and historically most important world industry has spent some time in trying to improve its ability to find oil quickly and profitably. In those early heady days of Texas oil 1880-1930 most exploration was fairly random. In fact it was during these heady pioneering days that the term wildcat was spawned. A wildcat is literally a "hole drilled for oil". I have been presently unable to ascertain the precise first derivative use of the word but it means rather like it sounds. Wildcat. The Oxford English dictionary defines it as an "unsound financial enterprise" It was probably a mixture of the wild gamble being taken by the early oil prospectors, to whom failure meant bankruptcy, but success could mean fortunes, and also the *wildness* of a really good gusher spiffing and spewing up like a big black cat needing to be tamed. In fact some of the very first huge oil finds were so powerful that they stayed "wild" for weeks or months until they were tamed. Since those early days oil discovery techniques have become somewhat more refined. Indeed oil discovery involves some of the most profound and highly advanced science available to mankind.

Now let's take another step back to the geology of the oil well itself. This is such a vast subject I shall try to reduce it to its essence; with apologies to oil engineers for the generalizations involved in this process.

1. Oil is found in basins. It needs to get trapped by specific geological conditions.

2. Oil is usually found in oil bearing rocks.

3 Oil generally exists between 7000 ft and 15,000 ft beneath the Earth's crust. There is no oil beneath this depth because it is too hot.

4. Oil formation requires quite precise geological conditions of global warming.

5. Oil needs to be internally and geologically capped by a crust of some sort. A salt crust like the one in the Middle East does the job perfectly.

When all these particular geological conditions have been fulfilled to a greater or lesser extent the oil has to be boiled for millions of years. In fact **unless** the oil has been boiled for millions of years it doesn't become oil.

So there's the oil lurking in dark reservoirs in underground sealed caverns. How do the oil geologists find it? One oil engineer I spoke to said that, in the early days, it was a mixture of art, science and hard work but **mostly good luck**; but today ...*it's all a matter of science.*

The first analysis is seismic. This is literally sending shockwaves down into the earth and then reading the shockwaves response on increasingly sophisticated and incredibly expensive computer software. The Oil companies were some of the first corporations to use massive Cray super computers. One might think of seismic shockwaves as an internal cardiogram of the sub geological structures of the Earth. These shockwaves can indicate the **possible** presence of oil. It is never certain but technology has narrowed down the possibilities for the very simple reason that it has been economic to do so. After all why drill more holes than you have to? Drilling an exploratory hole, a wild cat, is a very expensive business. Seismic surveys are really like X-rays. They enable oil geologists to make up a map of the underground geology of the Earth. If the X-rays are promising the seismologists will prepare a report for the oil exploration company. They will basically say one of three things.

We do not think that there is much likelihood of there being any oil here and we would definitely not recommend drilling or...... we think there is some chance of oil and it might warrant further exploration or...*this looks very promising, let's drill some wild cats!!*

The next process, on land anyway, is to bore small holes down to the depth of the presumed oil field. Down these tiny holes go explosives. When they explode more shockwaves are produced. These shockwaves are more powerful and accurate than those produced by surface seismic sensoring machines. These shockwaves travel back up through the earth. The **rate** the shockwaves travel will be affected by the **internal geological structures** of the sub-surface of the Earth. Oil seismologists can now read these Shockwave reports and make very much more accurate assessments of the general viability of the oil well. More reports are made. A decision may be made to do some real exploratory drilling.

Virtually the whole of the Earths land mass has now been surveyed with the first type of seismic survey. In fact satellites now have the ability to probe beneath the earth through all kinds of clever science like thermal imaging which can reveal fault lines and borders between tectonic plates where many of the major oil basins exist. This science is very advanced. The oil geologists who have most used this science are coming rapidly to the conclusion that *there are no more major oil basins* to be found on the planet. In other words there are no more Middle Easts. Some people actually believe that you can more or less drill for oil anywhere. This is a complete fallacy. Wildcats are very very expensive. Two or three dry holes is usually enough for an oil company to shut down their prospecting. This has recently happened for major oil companies in the Caspian who have been disappointed with their exploratory drilling.

it for an eight-year old Renault Cleo.

Debbie - 2007

Like most babies, this one was wrinkled and slightly odd looking but Debbie had never seen a newborn baby before. Her baby book had only shown perfect six-month old babies.

Debbie had been expecting a nice, rounded, plump baby and the shock to her system when she was finally and exhaustively presented with a little wizened monster was extreme. Otherwise, apparently, the baby was fine. Debbie called him Noel, partly because it was Christmas Eve when she gave birth, and partly because of the singer from 'Oasis' – the great hero in her life. Little Noel – the incestuous production – lay screaming in the small, rough crib by her bed. The crusty old spinster from the Social Security Office came brandishing an insipid bunch of flowers and a card. She stayed only five minutes, wished her the best and disappeared. Within a few days Debbie and Noel were deemed ready to leave hospital and they both returned to St Josephine's.

Debbie had never smoked but now she started. She bought cigarettes for £4 a packet and sometimes she smoked a whole packet in a day. Then she'd stop. Then she'd start again. Mostly, she cried herself to sleep at night and tried to push away the terrible thoughts that reared themselves ever more frequently.

After a month she was so desperate she put her last three pound coins in the gas meter and put her head and the baby's head in the gas oven. The baby had been screaming

If a wild cat strikes oil there is much jubilation. If a wild cat fails to find oil there is much disappointment and a lot of unfortunate expense which will have to be eventually paid for by the successful Wildcats.

At this point, when oil is first struck, **very rough estimates** will be made up of the oil wells total oil volume. It is usually apparent quite quickly if one has hit an oil field and the original seismology which had "intimated" that an oil cavern **might** exist could be used to estimate the total. These would be called *estimated reserves.* Later after a great deal of investigation and after the oil well is pumping these estimated reserves may be put into **proved reserves.**

Now this is a very important statistic as you might imagine. There are various things that can change the reserves in an oil field. A good sign however is pressure. If the oil really gushes out rather than dribbles then the oil cavern is probably quite full. Some of the most powerful oil wells of all time have been reputed to produce at up to 200,000 barrels per day. Clearly this is the best sort of cavern to find because the pressure inside the Cavern forces out the oil without the expenditure of external energy systems.

Soon after the oil well comes on line the oil geologists get a far better appreciation of the **flow rates** measured in barrels per day (bpd) from this they can more accurately assess the "probable" total reserves in the oil well. Of course actually how much oil is precisely recoverable from the oil well will not be known until no more oil can be recovered economically. The operative word here is economic. When a good sizable oil well starts gushing oil and the flow rate is very strong the cost of recovery per barrel may be quite low. To give you an idea; in Saudi Arabia it is estimated that the raw cost of extracting one barrel of oil is only $1.50 a barrel. On the other hand extracting a barrel of oil from the North Sea has been estimated at anything between $8/12 dollars. When an oil wells flow rate starts to drop off various methods are used to increase it again. Steam or sometimes gas may be forced back down into the well to increase the pressures. Sometimes pumps are used to pump the oil out or horizontal drilling methods are employed, as opposed to the more conventional vertical drilling. According to most reports I've seen even the very best most up-to-date and technically efficient secondary recovery methods will still leave about 50 per cent of unrecoverable oil in the ground, at which point the well is capped as its' useful life has come to an end. Now for the important bit. Reserves **begin** life as **possible**, or a very rough estimate, become **probable**, and are then finally described as **proved.**

An individual oil well recovery pattern follows quite clearly the bell-shaped curve used by Hubbert to predict the peak of American production in 1971. It is this particular bell-shaped curve that also indicates to those who have been analysing the oil situation that the peak of world oil production is likely to occur quite soon.

When the oil starts flowing the oil petroleum geologists hand over their data to the oil company's management and of course their accountants. It is actually the accountant's job to finally state what is called "proved reserves". *The geologists only make recommendations.* If you look at the BP statistical review of world energy oil reserves they are called "proved". Now it's important to try and understand what the oil accountant's job is. Primarily the accountants are there to **produce figures** about the oil company's reserves and therefore its profit (or return on capital invested). For various reasons oil company account executives tend to be rather cautious in stating "proved reserves" There are two main reasons. In many countries there are quite legitimate safeguards to ensure that oil companies don't overestimate their new discoveries. Why? Well partly if an oil company falsely overstated reserves then they might delude potential investors to buy shares or invest. So in some respects it is simply honest. In fact one retiring recent old executive recently said it "wouldn't be cricket to claim all the reserves for oneself. Much better to leave some for the chap coming along after you." Then there are tax and consequent profit implications. Thus the accountants, more frequently than not, will be *even more cautious* about finally stating proved reserves. This particular scenario in one form or another exists in most major international oil company structures.

In other words reserves are generally understated.

In practice what this means is that *as the years go by* total stated reserves are **revised** and then **backdated**. This tends to even out the reserve figure and what it does is produce the following bar graph. the left hand scale on this graph represents the total number of years of proved reserves of oil. In other words, in 2002, this graph indictes the world has forty years worth of oil at present consumption rates - about one thousand billion barrels.

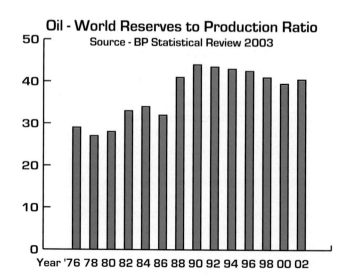

Oil - World Reserves to Production Ratio
Source - BP Statistical Review 2003

Year '76 78 80 82 84 86 88 90 92 94 96 98 00 02

This shows that from 1976 to 1992. The **reserves to production** ratio increased slightly **from 30 years** in 1976 to nearly **42 years in 1992** and then slipped back slightly to 40 years in 2002 if you then extrapolate this trend it appears that the reserve production ratios are actually quite stable. To quote Hamish McRae once more from the Independent newspaper in June 2003: -

"The ratio of production to reserves has been remarkably stable in recent years. Oil remains at about 40 years' supply (gas at 60) we are finding both oil and gas at roughly the rates we are using it up. At some stage in the next 20 years we may well become really worried about the shrinking reserves and I think we should be worried about the environmental costs of excessive energy use right now but the world does have some time"

Hamish continues; *"This prospect raises at least three big questions. First and foremost is there a general energy crisis looming? I think the answer to that is no, at least not yet."*

For those who have been able to follow the technical labyrinth that oil analysis creates there are some very serious questions to ask about Hamish's interpretation of the BP statistics. First and foremost there is one statement which is **patently false**, very simple to verify and **astonishingly and dangerously complacent**. I refer to his statement "we're finding oil and gas and roughly the same rate we are using it up. In fact this is quite categorically a falsehood.

uncontrollably for hours and hours. Debbie had no idea how long it would take to kill them both. She hoped she would just fall asleep and that would be that. After a few minutes she felt pleasantly drowsy. The smell was awful. The baby was still screaming and then suddenly he stopped screaming and smiled at her. It was the first smile Noel had ever had. For a moment she was transfixed and then she staggered up to turn off the gas.

Desiree - 2007

Desiree was now feeling very hungry. She's have to walk up to the kebab house and get herself a chicken and chips. Hurriedly she poked her old feather duster into the holes in the wardrobe and gave Gerald a quick tickling. Then she slipped on an old raincoat over her underwear, pulled the door to very carefully and splish-splashed away down the grey concrete pavement. She was tossed about by the wind and sometimes it caught embarrassingly under her raincoat and lifted it up, revealing her exotic scarlet underwear. She looked up at the sky. May? God had to be joking, surely! It pissed cats and dogs and then, when the sun came out, you sweated like a Polish fattie in a sauna. There were some sharp crickle-crackles of thunder. Not a clap but a long drawn out drum roll, as if the sky could not vent its anger properly. Desiree didn't like it. It felt ominous, eerie. She ordered her chicken kebab and chips and waited. Bugger! She thought to herself. It didn't half take a long time to charcoal a chicken.

Fifteen minutes later she ran out of the shop with the kebab wrapped up

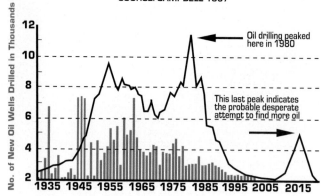

GRAPH NO. 4 - WORLD OIL DRILLING
SOURCE: CAMPBELL 1997

Oil drilling peaked
here in 1980

This last peak indicates
the probable desperate
attempt to find more oil

THIS GRAPH SHOWS THAT THE NO. OF OIL WELLS DRILLED PEAKED
AROUND 1980. SINCE 1980 THE NO. OF NEW OIL WELLS BEING
DRILLED HAS FALLEN PRECIPITOUSLY. MOST EXPLORATION IS NOW
COMPLETE. BY 2008 WE WILL ONLY BE FINDING ABOUT 1 BARRELS OF
OIL FOR EVERY 10 WE CONSUME. THE RED BARS REPRESENTS THE
ACTUAL AMOUNT OF OIL DISCOVERED.

According to the world's leading oil consultants Petroconsultants we are finding **about** six billion barrels a year on a falling trend. This figure excludes some deepwater discoveries of oil which distort the figures. For technical reasons deepwater oil will not fundamentally alter production or the onset of "Peak oil". Deepwater is the operative word. What it really means is that we are going to have to go into the backend of nowhere to get a little bit more. Deep water, over 6000 feet below the oceans surface is serious oil drilling. You'd better believe it.

In other words we are finding less than one barrel for every four we are using. Many oil consultants think the ratio is more like one in five.

Now how could Hamish make such a horribly inaccurate statement? Was he lying? No. He wasn't. He wasn't even trying to be duplicitous. **He has simply misinterpreted the BP's data.** He has assumed that because the reserves to production ratio is unchanged then **discovery to production** is unchanged but **reserve reporting** and **actual physical discovery are quite simply** <u>not the same thing</u> at all.

Physical discovery is also not a straightforward process for the reasons just described above. You may sometimes read in the newspapers about a huge new oil field find in the daily papers. More often than not this is a **known** oil field which is just beginning to be properly charted and explored.

British Petroleum along with many other oil companies **backdates** its reserves as I described earlier. Again; this is **not** a conspiracy. Nor is it in any way fraudulent. In fact it is simple common sense and sound financial housekeeping. By keeping reserves "in reserve" the company **can even things out from year to year.** This gives the *appearance* and the *feel* of stability. Each year, every year, it appears we still have forty years of oil left. However this particular little accounting trick is just about to come to

an end because the major oil companies do not have many reserves left in their back pockets. Here is an extract from Dr Campbells most recent book. *"The esscence of oil and gas depletion."*

"One great contribution to this end [the accurate reporting of reserves] would be a new requirement for oil companies to report the date of their discovery of their oilfields with any revisions to the estimates of their size being attributed to that date. It would soon reveal that companies are replacing reserves less by discovery than by imaginative accounting."

Hamish is wrong.

He has not been **misinformed** and he has **not intentionally tried to deceive us** or indeed deceive himself. He is merely ignorant of the way in which reserves are reported. We are going to come back to Hamish again shortly but before I do I would like to take this opportunity to say, in writing, directly to Mr Hamish McRae **that his error is entirely understandable.** In fact I have some considerable measure of admiration for Hamish as the final part of this essay will describe.

In conclusion therefore:- **proved reserves are not necessarily quite what you think.** In fact they have been mostly understated. This is surely good news! It means there is in reality probably more oil than we think! Now let's make one final comment on the BP statistical review of energy 2003. Here is a chart. I reprint it in full for the simple reason that you may be interested to know what the oil wealth is of the various different countries around the world.

OIL - PROVED RESERVED
Source: BP Statistical Review

	At end 1982 Thousand million barrels	At end 1992 Thousand million barrels	At end 2001 Thousand million barrels	At end 2002 Thousand million barrels
USA	35.1	32.1	30.0	30.4
Canada	8.3	7.5	6.5	6.9
Mexico	48.3	51.3	26.9	12.6
Total North America	91.6	90.9	63.5	49.9
Argentina	2.6	1.6	3.0	2.9
Brazil	1.8	3.0	8.5	8.3
Colombia	0.5	1.9	1.8	1.8
Ecuador	1.4	1.6	2.1	4.6
Peru	0.8	0.4	0.3	0.3
Trinidad & Tobago	0.6	0.6	0.7	0.7
Venezuela	21.5	62.7	77.7	77.8
Other S. & Cent. America	1.0	0.8	1.9	2.0
Total S. & Cent. America	30.2	72.5	96.0	98.6
Azerbaijan	n/a	1.3	7.0	7.0
Denmark	0.5	0.7	1.1	1.3
Italy	0.7	0.7	0.6	0.6
Kazakhstan	n/a	5.2	8.0	9.0
Norway	6.8	8.8	9.4	10.3
Romania	n/a	1.6	1.0	1.0
Russian Federation	n/a	48.5	48.6	60.0
Turkmenistan	n/a	n/a	0.5	0.5
United Kingdom	13.9	4.1	4.9	4.7
Uzbekistan	n/a	n/a	0.6	0.6
Other Europe & Eurasia	67.0	4.1	2.3	2.4
Total Europe & Eurasia	88.8	75.0	84.1	97.5
Iran	55.3	92.9	89.7	89.7
Iraq	41.0	100.0	112.5	112.5
Kuwait	67.2	96.5	96.5	96.5
Oman	2.7	4.5	5.5	5.5
Qatar	3.4	3.7	15.2	15.2
Saudi Arabia	165.3	260.3	261.8	261.8
Syria	1.5	1.7	2.5	2.5
United Arab Emirates	32.4	98.1	97.8	97.8
Yemen	-	4.0	4.0	0.5
Other Middle East	0.2	0.1	0.1	0.1
Total Middle East	369.0	661.8	685.6	685.6
Algeria	9.4	9.2	9.2	9.2
Angola	1.6	1.5	5.4	5.4
Cameroon	0.5	0.4	0.4	0.4
Rep. of Congo (Brazzaville)	1.6	0.8	1.5	1.5
Egypt	3.3	6.2	3.7	3.7
Gabon	0.5	0.7	2.5	2.5
Libya	21.5	22.8	29.5	29.5
Nigeria	16.8	17.9	24.0	24.0
Sudan	0.4	0.3	0.6	0.6
Tunisia	1.9	1.7	0.3	0.3
Other Africa	0.4	0.3	0.3	0.3
Total Africa	57.8	61.9	77.4	77.4
Australia	1.6	1.8	3.5	3.5
Brunei	1.2	1.4	1.4	1.4
China	19.5	24.0	24.0	18.3
India	3.4	6.0	4.8	5.4
Indonesia	9.6	5.8	5.0	5.0
Malaysia	3.3	3.7	3.0	3.0
Papua New Guinea	-	0.3	0.2	0.2
Thailand	0.1	0.2	0.5	0.6
Vietnam	0.5	0.6	0.6	0
Other Asia Pacific	0.5	0.8	0.7	0.8
Total Asia Pacific	39.2	44.6	43.8	38.7
TOTAL WORLD	676.7	1006.7	1050.3	1047.7
Of which OECD @	116.7	108.9	84.5	72.0
OPEC	443.3	769.9	818.8	819.0 1
Non-OPEC £	170.4	179.8	166.1	150.9
Former Soviet Union	63.0	57.0	65.4	77.8

We can see that the United Kingdom has proved reserves of only 4.7 billion barrels, Norway has 9 billion and Russia has 60 billion. **No other country in Europe has any significant oil.**

The USA, it might be noted, has 30 billion barrels [it originally had about 160 billion] **and the world total of proven oil reserves is 1047.7 billion barrels.** In other words almost exactly one trillion barrels. If you remember this one trillion is the figure I used as total world ultimate endowment but of course BP's list is **proved reserves.** It doesn't include **other** probable understated reserves, waiting in the wings to be *backdated into proved reserves* nor does it include the "yet to find". Well let's follow this through.

BP's proved reserves are 1047 billion. The oil geologists estimates of the "yet to find" is about 10 per cent. Maybe 200 billion barrels? So this would make a total of 1247 billion. To which you then have to add the *probable reserves* which are yet to be backdated into proved reserves. This is a hard one. No really reliable data exists. Most industry estimates vary between 50 and 100 billion barrels. In fact some say they may be beginning to overstate reserves to try and keep the market from panicking. For the sake of **clarity** let's be **generous** and use the **upper** estimate. This now makes total proved reserves; total probable reserves; and the "yet to find" 1047 plus 200 plus 100 = 1347 billion.

From first glance then it appears that the world ultimate total of oil could be actually 347 billion barrels **more** than we have assumed. **But this brings me back full circle** to the "proved reserves of the Opec countries" as shown on a chart in the first essay. Here it is again to save you looking back for it.

ORGANISATION OF PETROLIUM EXPORTERS

	ABU DHABI	IRAN	IRAQ	KUWAIT	SAUDI ARABIA	VENEZUELA
1980	28.0	58.0	31.0	65.4	163.3	17.9
1981	29.0	57.5	30.0	65.9	165.0	18.0
1982	30.6	57.0	29.7	64.5	164.6	20.3
1983	30.5	55.3	41.0	64.2	162.4	21.5
1984	30.4	51.0	43.0	63.9	166.0	24.9
1985	30.5	48.5	44.5	90.0	169.0	25.9
1986	31.0	47.9	44.1	89.8	168.8	25.6
1987	31.0	48.8	47.1	91.9	166.6	25.0
1988	92.2	93.0	100.0	91.9	167.0	56.3
1989	92.2	92.9	100.0	91.9	167.0	58.0
1990	92.2	92.9	100.0	94.5	257.5	59.0
1995	92.2	88.2	100.0	94.0	258.7	64.5
2003	92.0	88.0	112.0	94.0	267.0	64.5

THIS IS 'DECLARED'RESERVES IN BILLIONS OF BARRELS

Now if you look at the **BP statistics for proved reserves it showed Saudi Arabia at 261.8.** Iran at 89. United Arab Emerates at 97. Kuwait at 96. If you remember in my first essay on oil we discussed the spurious upward revision of the Opec countries oil reserves. For political reasons and quota reasons they have almost certainly been overstated by about 300 billion barrels. Thus if you deduct this total from 1347 billion you arrive back at a world total of ultimate Oil of 1047 trillion barrels. Or thereabouts. **When you take the reserve adjustment into account the World ultimate reserves are almost exactly equal to the BP present proved reserves.**

A **10 per cent** change, even as much as a **20 per cent error** in these statistics would not make any real difference to the coming energy crisis or the oil shockwaves. This is a very important point. Arguing about the possible existence of a few hundred billion barrels of oil is getting increasingly irrelevant to the real issue at stake. If there is a bit more oil I imagine, ultimately we will *all be very grateful.* If there is a little less oil. Well! The crisis is on its way that much sooner.

When Hamish McRae uses the BP oil data reserves/production ratios he makes a very common mistake. He thinks that we have 40 years' worth of oil left at *current consumption rates.* He appears to have absolutely no concept of what "peak production" means. I'm not going to go over it again. If you're feeling a bit lost I suggest you finish this essay and then re read the first oil essay.

Hamish along with other economists always talks about "forty" years worth of oil at "Current consumption rates" but of course his entire theory of "growth " also requires growth in oil supplies! If Hamish uses the IEO figures, which I imagine he does because they suit capitalistic economic philosophy, then oil production and consumption has to actually grow at over 1.8% a year.

While companies like BP are not **intentionally** trying to deceive one might ask **why** they haven't questioned the unusual leaps in Opec reserves over the years. The reason that they don't question them is **probably political.** I am sure BP does not want to begin an argument with Opec or send shock waves through the oil industry. Can you imagine the political mayhem if the oil industry executives came straight out and stated that the projected growth over the next 25 years is not going to be possible because we have all been fudging our figures and making it appear as if there is plenty of oil and therefore **no Hydrocarbon** crisis looming! The oil industries problem is that **the longer** they leave recognition of the problem the greater the collapse in confidence will be.

Who the hell is going to tell the general public that the Hydrocarbon party is shortly to be coming to an end? Any volunteers?

Ironically this may be causing an unnecessary problem. If I'm correct a great many people will be grateful that something is really going to change. Fundamentally change and change quite soon. The "tipping point" to borrow a modern idiom will actually probably occur when general public perceptions are raised to the point that confidence in the present system of government and world financial management starts to erode.

Just recently some retiring oil industry executives have started to try and draw attention towards a more informed discussion regarding the concept of "Peak oil" and its possible repercussions. Those still working within the industry itself are clearly reticent to speak about it because they are almost certainly worried about the price of their shares, the perceptions of the oil industry within the government investing markets and their pensions. I would expect to see many more oil executives popping out of the woodwork shortly to give us their professional opinions. It is interesting to note in passing that just recently ex Labour cabinet ministers like Mo Mowlam, Clare Short and Robin Cook have a **great deal more** to say about government and its failings now that **they are <u>out</u> of office**. The same applies to those retiring from the oil industry; once they are freed from corporate constraints they may be freer to speak their own minds. The oil industry is a law unto itself. It has been critically important in developing the resources for the world to grow. It does not presently want to relinquish this hard won mantle and accept that it is fast approaching it's twilight years.

So much for the oil industry then. We can't really expect an honest appraisal of their own internal situation because they are too close to it. But what about **Economists?** Why aren't they more concerned about the developing situation? When I started this essay I began by asking myself some very important and vital questions. Why, if a global energy crisis is literally just around the corner are the oil companies not warning us about it? Why are politicians not aware of it? Why is the mainstream media not in **hot pursuit** of perhaps the *most significant story ever!* **The fact is that for the Media to really investigate this issue it would have to start investigating its own validity and if it did so it might discover its own duplicity.**

Finally, why are our economists travelling down the road of perfect euphoria and optimism? I hope the reasoning and analysis in my essays goes some way towards understanding these aberrations. **It is not an oil company's executive job to be a sooth-sayer or a futurologist**. It is their job to *produce oil* on demand to make a profit and to satisfy share-holders. Economists, naturally enough take their energy information from respected oil companies like BP and International energy agencies like the IEO.

The job of an economic forecaster is to observe and analyse trends, extrapolate them, and then try to project these trends into the future. If the energy agencies aren't hollering down the grapevine about

---

under her arm. Two minutes later she was lying in the road, unconscious.

In her hurry, she had run into one of the few bloody cars left on the road. She remembered the initial bang and then she remembered, vaguely, being put in the back of an ambulance.

The next thing she remembered was waking up in hospital the following afternoon and the next thing she remembered was Gerald still locked in the wardrobe.

Dolly - 2007

Dolly partied away most of 2003 in a haze of simmering nothingness which steadily evaporated into even less. Even she could feel that the wheels were seriously going to come off. Nobody could quite put a finger on it but something was beginning to boil over and, to cover up the fear, Dolly dived deeper and deeper into recklessness.

Did she have some sixth sense that the party was about to come to an end? Or was it just her? Was the fact that she'd got terribly and desperately into debt just a one off? Her personal misfortune? Her stupidity? Somehow she knew that was not the case.

Everyone was in debt. At one point, when things got really desperate in early 2004, she had been forced to try and get a loan from a 'shark'. She was amazed how many of them there were. The back pages of The Mirror and The Sun were crammed full of them advertising their usury alongside all the mobile phone ads. The interest rates they wanted weren't just exorbitant; they were

an energy crisis how can economists be expected to know about it? In a sense it just goes round in circles with everyone passing the buck for the final responsibility of analysing and externalising all the inter-related facts.

Now I know I've picked rather on Hamish McRae in my book [something for which I have already apologised]. Part of the reason for this is that I actually have a great admiration for his generally balanced analysis of the economic situation. I attach no blame to his ignorance about the forthcoming energy crisis. There is however another very important reason. Hamish McRae actually wrote a book in 1994 called 2020, which is certainly worth reading. Since I have been thinking about the future I found his book very illuminating.

Just recently I have come across many studies of "Peak oil" in which mainstream economists are called "Flat Earth economists". No one in the articles described exactly why they were called Flat Earth but I have since come to a few of my own assumptions as follows.

Just over 500 years ago everyone [at least in Western Europe] thought the Earth was flat. Eventually Magellan circumnavigated the globe and slowly the idea arose that the world was actually round. A sphere in fact. 500 years ago **believing that the world was round** was heretical. Christianity in particular believed the Earth was flat. Hell was below, down into the burning boiling lava and heaven was above. Clouds, cherubims, and a benevolent Jehovah with his angels. When the idea arrived that the earth **might be round** the world view was quite literally turned upside down. Even so, even though circumnavigation had categorically proved that the world was round still some people insisted it was flat. Such an attitude kept dogma, belief and tradition to be **superior** to logic and reality. So Flat Earth economists are those who believe in some magical unsustainable reality. In other words it is more convenient and less risky to keep believing in what one has always believed in. Flat Earth economists think that there is just one world view. Here is Hamish once more. This time the quotation is taken from his book called *The World in 2020* published by HarperCollins in 1994. This extract from his preface.

"What I have written differs from most exercises in futurology. These either take the form of scenario building, where different possibilities are outlined and the reader is left to choose between them, or they paint a picture of exaggerated optimism or pessimism. The first approach is a useful one for businesses as a way of outlining the range of possibilities for which they might plan - and excellent work is done in this field by Shell, which pioneered the approach, and by the Organisation for Economic co-operation and Development (O E

C D) in Paris, which held a conference in the summer of 1991 on long-range prospects for the world economy, and to whom I owe a considerable debt. But scenario building is unsatisfying - some may well be more or less right, but others will be spectacularly wrong. The second approach is equally unsatisfactory because the authors tend to have a powerfully opinionated view of the future which readers are obliged to except: the future will be wonderful, or it will be dreadful, and all the evidence is piled up to support the view. I recognise the genre-I have contributed to a myself in the past.

I have tried to find a middle way, first by looking at the world as it is now, then by examining the various forces for change and trying to judge how these forces will alter the world over the next generation, and finally by drawing attention to some choices the industrial world in particular has to make. I know this book has weaknesses of its own-many of the details will turn out to be wrong, but it would worry me more if, through some flaw in the analysis, I fail to spot some really big global change."

Let us now turn to the **very first sentence** in the **very first chapter** of Hamish his book. It is almost certainly the most telling.

"The success or failure of any country over the next 30 years hinges on growth."

And later in Chapter 1.

"Solving many other problems, even including environmental ones can be much easier if there is the wealth generated to pay for solutions"

These few statements represent the conventional economists view that **growth is everything.** Productivity is the economic mantra. An annual continuous increase in gross domestic product and consumables. More things. More trade. More activity.

If we now leap ahead to chapter 6 there is a section headed.

"Is there enough energy?"

"There is no global energy crisis, set-aside, for the moment concerns about the effect on the climate of the build up of atmospheric carbon dioxide from burning fossil fuels. There will be ample energy to support economic growth to beyond the end of the next century. Coal, in particular and natural gas are in plentiful supply. At present consumption rates there is enough coal to last the world for more than 200 years and enough natural gas for some 60 years. Oil supplies are tighter, of which more later. Past predictions of the oil market have been spectacularly wrong but there is little doubt that

the oil market will tighten as resources are used up and that the price will rise as a result. In 1987 proven oil reserves were 32.5 years consumption. Were there to be no cutbacks in consumption and no new discoveries there would in theory be no oil left in 2020. That will not happen. Long before the last drop of oil has been pumped from the ground the price will have risen and either more oil discoveries or conservation programmes will have been put in place. Plenty of such substitutes for oil exist. The coal gasification programme pioneered by South Africa. The use of alcohol mixed with petrol and experiments in France to convert rapeseed oil into diesel fuel. The use of shale oil and Tar Sands and conversion of natural gas to liquids. The most sensible expectation is for the price of oil to rise, probably in sudden jumps, if past performance is any guide until the substitutes come on stream. Much of the developing world will be under great pressure to conserve oil. The pressure will be particularly acute when the periodic oil shocks occur. The timing of these cannot be predicted but they're more likely to occur as the underlying supply of oil becomes tighter. So expect an oil shock in 2015 rather than 2000."

Let's first recognise that this book was written 10 years ago in 1994. Well we've just had a nasty little oil shock. 2000-2003. A glance at the BP Statistical review of energy 2003 tells us the about the crisis. Not by making political comments about it but by simply giving a table of the spot prices. I print the list in full to give you a sense of the relationships between oil price hikes and political upheaval.

YEAR	Brent Crude Price in US$ (per barrel)
1976	12.80
1980	35.93
1998	13.11
1999	18.25
2000	28.98
2001	24.77
2002	25.19
2003	38.00 - high point

Some people will still remember the oil shocks of the 1970's. They would do well to remember they were but the tiny little tremors before the earthquake. I will leave you to study the table in detail and leave you with just one observation. Oil spot prices for Brent crude in 1998 were 13.11 American dollars. In 1999 the price leapt by 40 % to 18.25 American dollars. In 2000, the price jumped yet again to 28.98 American Dollars.

AN ANNUAL PERCENTAGE INCREASE OF 58%.

IT WOULD SEEM CRUEL TO POINT OUT TO HAMISH THAT, IN FACT, WE HAD QUITE PRECISELY WHAT HE DIDN'T EXPECT; AN OIL SHOCK IN 2000.

obscene. She felt that the walls were closing in on her and that the doors to escape from the walls were shrinking rapidly. It didn't really help to know that everyone else was in debt.

2004 crept by her, just skirting a sense of complete panic. In 2005 it suddenly grew much worse. Her bonus was slashed, her salary renegotiated. She tried to remind herself that she was still very lucky to have a job in the City. She'd seen most of her contemporaries washed up onto the unemployment register. Dolly couldn't imagine what it would be like to go, suddenly, from £100,000 a year to virtually zero income. God! Get hold of yourself she screamed. If only, she wondered, if only she could stop shopping but, as hard as she tried, she simply couldn't do it. Tamara had told her there were places you could go to cure shopping addictions. Indeed, she'd recommended the Hubert Elloneurf clinics. He was a genius apparently. Tamara, who was in and out of a lcohol and drug addiction centres faster than anyone could count, was very sorry Hubert Elloneurf didn't go in for detox.

"You should go and see him!" she said.

Her father had given her one very simple bit of advice which she had stuck to. *"If times get really hard"* he said, *"go back to the basics: power, water and food."*

It was a simple little formula which had worked very well for her clients, most of whom were now more concerned with simply keeping the value of their portfolios intact. Dolly had considerable success with getting them to invest in municipal

As you can see the spot oil price jumped again dramatically in 2003 to around 38 dollars. This is an increae of over 300 % from 1998. It has since dropped back to about 27 dollars as I write in JULY 2003. It is interesting to compare these increases with the increase around 1976 to 1980 when the oil price went from 12.80 to 35.93 This is an almost identical price rise as the one 1998 -2003. Of course the oil shock in the 70's was enormous. If we were to suffer a similar increase in real dollar terms, in other words adjusting for inflation the price of oil could jump to over 200 dollars a barrel. It wouldn't stay in this price range for long of course because demand would collapse very quickly and the price would collapse as a result. But what it would do is create volatility and instability.

OIL IN AMERICA AT THE TURN OF THE MILLENIUM WAS GETTING VERY EXPENSIVE.

THE PRESIDENT OF THE U.S. IS AN OIL BARON.

AMERICA WAS RUNNING OUT OF ITS OWN OIL. IRAQ, A REGIME EVERYONE COULD LOATHE AND WHICH WAS THEREFORE RIPE FOR SORTING OUT HAPPENS TO HAVE THE WORLDS LEAST EXPLOITED RESERVES OF OIL. SINCE THE END OF THE WAR THE OIL PRICE HAS SETTLED DOWN BUT THE CAT IS OUT OF THE BAG. WE ARE NO LONGER FOOLED BY OUR POLITICAL LEADERS WE JUST DON'T KNOW WHAT TO DO ABOUT IT.

We may not quite have noticed it in our personal lives but the economic future barometers are wobbling furiously and the wobbling can only get more acute in the short term.

Here is Hamish writing in June 2003: -

"First and most obvious. Is there a general energy crisis looming? I think the answer to that is no, or at least not yet."

Economists think that World growth benefits the whole World whereas in fact it only benefits those to whom the wealth flows. To the rich countries of course. Like us.

Or in other words making **money and creating wealth**. It's not difficult to understand why mainstream economists should hold to this view. For them money solves all problems. Make more money and solve more problems. In order to make more money we need to make more things [manufacture] and do more things [services]. In order for this whole system to work growth is essential. Up until now of course the Westernised industrial capitalised centralised corporate political power structures have felt immense wealth flow towards them. Whilst wealth was flowing came power in almost equal measure.

It is not entirely unsurprising they would like this wealth to continue to flow towards them.

Hamish does not understand the concept of "Peak oil". He is stuck, with other economists and politicians on the idea that 40 years of oil reserves means that we can use an equal amount of oil every year for the next 40 years.

Hamish believes an oil price shock will lead to **more exploration and therefore more oil**. For economists it is merely a matter of **economics** and not actual **physical resources**. I think if we were to convince Hamish that peak oil is a turning point for mankind and if he was to be convinced that after peak oil the depletion rate will be anything between three and five per cent per annum he might well start to revise some of his opinions about where the future is going. Growth will not be sustainable. Resource constraints will have a **massive unprecedented effect** on the structure of the global economy.

It is for the above reasons that conventional Flat Earth economists like Hamish are completely out-of-touch with the developing realities of the coming situation. Hamish is not **actively looking for crisis**. He is actively looking for reasons which will enable us to maintain the present economic status quo. The future he draws, the world you and I are going to living in, 2020 is, in his own words, *"a reasonably comfortable one"*.

Having given Hamish such a hard time I would like to finish with **his** conclusions which very much echo mine.

"What happens between now and 2020 will be of enormous importance for the future of humankind. This is the core issue for what is at present the developed world and it will soon become the core issue for the new cast of countries which would join it. If we as individuals make sensible and humane decisions in the way we live our daily lives, then the societies in which we live will become more sensible and humane. More than this, the developed world will become a better model for those other countries which will achieve developed status. If on the other hand we are lazy, corrupt and greedy, then the rich world will not just lose influence: it will, in any meaningful sense of the word, become less rich. This is an issue for all people, not just for politicians. The more we can understand about the way the world is changing in the run-up to 2020, the greater the chance we have of securing its future in the years beyond."

It is clear from Hamish's concluding statements that at least that we have some common ground. Indeed this is an important point. *We all want a better world,* a more humane world, a fairer world but perhaps we have different ideas of how we will get there. Hamish thinks its economic growth. I leave you to conjecture what you think I think it's all about. I gave up on that particular puzzle a long time ago. Hamish has a job. I suspect you have a job. I have a job. I suspect we'd all like to keep our jobs or at least our livelihoods intact. My view, having come this far, is quite simple. The most important development in mankinds immediate future is not being given enough intelligent **humane** thought. If we return to savages we have seriously failed. **More sensible and more humane**. [I am quoting Hamish]. Who could argue with such conclusions?

Economists are mostly optimists. They need to be. They are mostly quite wealthy and they are almost universally wedded, I'd like to say welded to the idea that world economic growth is good for everyone including all the poor countries. The environment can be *"set aside for the moment"* **man's ingenuity and technical brilliance will eventually solve the environmental problems**. In Hamish's world the environment is not connected to our spiritual centre it is simply a physical mass which provides physical resources. In Hamish's

bonds. Of course they were still bouncing crazily up and down but, overall, they had weathered the 'Bear' storm better than most other investments. Around her many other brokers and portfolio investors were being made redundant but Dolly survived and the harder survival became, the harder she and her wealthy friends partied. Dolly danced the wild dance of the soon to be condemned with as much abandonment as she could muster. It was her dying duty to party to the end. Always the last to leave. In the last resort she always consoled herself that she could turn to Daddy. He was so very rich.

Unfortunately, in April 2006, Dolly's daddy had a stroke. It had not killed him but it had left him paralysed down his right side and he was only able to mumble and mutter very slowly. Dolly had been on the verge of asking him for a loan. Now she couldn't do it. It was some months later that Dolly realised her daddy had been quite silly on the stock exchange. He had seen it bounce up and down a few times and had come to the conclusion that he knew when it was about to bounce. Unfortunately it always seemed to bounce back down again, only a little lower than before. He couldn't see that the system was in a state of shock. Apparently he had taken quite a few bets on the recovery of the technology stocks and much of his capital had disappeared. Dolly's mother put it down to the fact that, in retirement, he had got rather bored and felt that if he played a little here and there with the stock market he could both amuse himself and make a little extra money. Like so many other people, he did not feel the stock exchanges could go down any further. But they had, and like everyone else their wealth had been

world nature is a nuisance. **In this world nature has no active intelligence.** It is inert, albeit organic matter, which is **simply there to provide for all our increasing needs and to satisfy our all-consuming desires.** This view is narrow and limited. It is a view that is about to be challenged by nature herself. We are poised on the very pinnacle of hydrocarbon man's evolutionary cycle. The upward slope was all about growth and advancement. The downward slope is all about retrenchment.

Just to recap; Hamish in his preface, wrote, *"it would worry me, if through some flaw in the analysis I had failed to spot some really big global change."* Well Hamish probably has missed the big one but this is no discredit. His mind set was not tuned into the repercussions that the pinnacle of the hydrocarbon age will create. If I am to be of any use personally in this matter I would hope that I would be remembered *not for my predictions of the future* but for simply presenting **so many different possibilities** <u>for</u> the future.

Recently [2002] a former UK energy secretary made the following statement. This extract is based on the UK minister of energy's reply to a member of parliament who had been concerned by the issues raised by the BBC film of the 8th November 2002 called the next oil crisis. This energy minister expressed the view that "oil consumption will rise from 28 billion barrels today to 41 billion barrels by 2020." she also claimed "reserves will be adequate to meet this kind of demand for 25-30 years!" and she also made the following statement. "As with all commodities that are finite in supply substitutes takeover long before supply runs out."

As you might imagine the UK energy secretary is getting the very first hot copy of this book.

It is not difficult to understand this particular mindset. You have to remember that "peak oil" is presently just a theory and **will** remain a theory until the reality [oil shock] waves actually occur. Politicians do not anticipate a huge oil shock wave. They most certainly **do not want one** and they almost certainly do not want to create a fearful situation which might damage the confidence factor that keeps capitalism rolling along. They **most absolutely do not want** to alarm the general population unnecessarily about an event which may or may not happen particularly before an election.

Peak oil is a scientific assessment that comes from the world's leading oil petroleum geologists, who are in the best position to know about it, but politicians and economists do not want to give house-room to these theories.

It is true that UK politicians **should be aware** of these theories, because, if you remember on July 7th, 1999, Dr Campbell actually attended the House of Commons committee to inform the House about

"Peak Oil." But so far of course not a murmur, not a whisper, not a teeny weeny hint comes from the government about this imminent world crisis. Of course Tony Blair did join up with George Bush Jnr to invade Iraq and appropriate Iraqi oil. Ironically just today as I write (July 14th, 2003) I read that the first oil tankers out of Iraq since the war are going to a refinery in the UK!

And the media? Why isn't the coming crisis getting mass-media coverage? You would think that a global energy crisis and possible financial Armageddon might make a reasonably headline grabbing spot on the front page. But No! There is just more silence.

Are politics, the media and transnational corporations one and the same?

If you control all three you control the whole thing.

But of course nobody can own anybody else's mind.

Though the newspapers seem quite interested in the "real reasons for going to war with Iraq "oil" doesn't get anything more than a passing mention by Robert Fisk or some other columnist. (Clare Short was an exception). My view on this is that the science of oil depletion has not filtered through to the mainstream. After all if most politicians and economists and oil companies don't give the theory house room why should the Media? I think however that their present digging and a few other, as yet unknown factors, might begin to focus a little more attention on the matter.

"Peak oil" and its potential repercussions is a theory presently held by oil petroleum geologists and a few half poet/amateur philosophers like myself. **It is presently just a sideshow.** Of course that it is why it is *so dangerous* because if the theory is correct the World is totally unprepared for what's coming and the shock to the system will be incalculable. The theories of Peak oil can be easily dismissed, if you want to dismiss them. Presently the only people to really subscribe to these theories of Peak oil and the coming World oil shockwaves are oil geologists and oddballs. Not a great combination to get the world business leaders, politicians, economists or newspaper editors in a frenzy of excitement. It is for these reasons that the **crisis is of course inevitable.** It is simply a matter of waiting. Whilst waiting we might as well prepare the ground.

Well. I'm almost there. Before I disappear I would like to briefly mention the subject of statistics and sources. The word statistic from the Oxford English dictionary is derived from the word status. In other words "state". Statistics help us to describe the **state** that the world and all its myriad components and people find themselves. I have used many different statistics in the writing of this invitation. I have taken none of these statistics at face value. They are useful to help us understand the predicament [state] which we have created for ourselves. They are not an end in themselves. Statistics describe relationships through numerical and mathematical formulas. This is only one way of understanding the world. There are many ways to understand the world. In my recent investigations I have discovered that statistics are often misinterpreted, the sources are sometimes unreliable and in almost all cases, including my own, statistics are manipulated to provide evidence for an argument the answer to which has already been decided.

However since statistics are numerical and mathematical by nature it is always possible to subject them to the most rigorous independent scientific scrutiny. Broadly speaking statistics divide into two categories. The first category of statistics try to add up the sums of the past the second category try to take these calculations into the future. The first group are of course easier to verify because they deal with a quantifiable history. If they are well prepared and well researched these statistics can be regarded as quite reliable. A good example of this first type of group would be the total amount of electricity produced in the UK in 2002. According to the department of trade and industry about 2.8 billion kilowatts. A good example of the second kind of statistic is the amount of oil left in the earth and easily accessible for man's use in the next two generations or so. These statistics involve a very different kind of numerical science but the same principles apply. If they have been well researched, intelligently analysed and independently corroborated they can probably be trusted as reasonably reliable. The operative word is reasonable.

If the statistics which I have researched in respect of the world's energy systems are reliable then we have a great deal to worry about. Small things may be corrected quickly. Planetary energy systems take generations and beyond that aeons of time to correct themselves. If we presently underestimate the enormity of the task in front of us and let ourselves simply carry on [as we are doing] **with very little thought for the future** [except perhaps the terrifying state of our pension plans] then when the future rudely interrupts us with a crisis of globe swallowing proportions we will only have ourselves to blame. It is going to require the very best brains getting back to work with Mother nature rather than against her.

In order to give you a practical illustration of the uncertain nature of statistics. Today as I write, on 14th July 2003 a huge initiative has been put in place by the government to increase UK electrical production from wind power. It sounds very exciting. It even made the front page of the Daily Independent and major headlines in most of the business sections. I've already discussed wind power earlier but I need to discuss this latest

eroded by the collapse in property values.

Dolly sat staring at the e-mail for a long while.

Where on earth was she going to get the money now? She didn't dare try her own bank. The nasty letters had been getting more and more frequent. She thought about her other friends. Tamara was stinking rich and surely she'd do it. But she wouldn't! Or rather, she said she couldn't. She told Dolly that she had put all her allowance, and more, into a small art gallery with Damian Shyster and was broke until next month's allowance came in. On reflection, this could probably have been true. Damian had been hanging around Tamara for weeks.

Currently Damian was famous for his bronze replica of a plastic Barbie doll. He was a complete and total moron, thought Dolly, but then she found herself being caught off guard by the severity and vindictiveness of her judgements. It was so unlike her.

She tried Timmy De Vere Bligh on his mobile but he was down at Cowdray practising his polo and all she got was his mobile message: *"See you all down at my party next Saturday."*

Dolly was exhausted. She could pawn some of her mother's jewellery, but that thought only made her burst into tears again. She could sell her beloved BMW 2X3 but everyone told her that, because of the dreadful fuel crisis, there was absolutely no market in second hand cars.

She had only two hours to get the money into the bank before the close of business.

development briefly because of the **gross inaccuracies** of the Newspaper reporting. This is an extract from the Independent.

"A huge expansion of the government renewable energy programme involving the construction of enough offshore wind farms to power 15 per cent of British homes will be announced today. Patricia Hewitt, The secretary of State for Trade and Industry will invite firms to build up to 6,000 megawatts of wind farm capacity. Britain's first large scale wind farm North Hoyle is due to start generating power next year. The £70 million development will produce 6,000 megawatts from 30 giant Turbines the height of the London Eye. To be built by National wind Power with a grant aid of £10 million.... the government has set itself a target of generating 10 per cent of UK electricity from renewable resources by 2010. And an aspiration of raising this to 20 per cent after concluding that new nuclear power stations were not viable. The expansion of renewables is designed to enable Britain to meet its wider target of cutting emission targets for carbon dioxide by 60 per cent by 2050. Tom Faulks, director general of the Institute of Civil Engineers welcomed the expansion but cautioned. "We must not lose sight of the fact that the wind only blows a third of the time and cannot ever be expected to supply the major portion of the nation's energy requirements."

Now here is another brief extract also from the Independent Newspaper. The following day Tuesday 15th July 2003.

"In seven years time Britain will be generating enough electricity from offshore wind to power every home in the South East of England. Eight million households running on green, pollution free energy...that would be enough to power one in six of the countries households."

But hang on. If its enough power for eight million households and that represents one in six households then Britain must have 48 million households [just multiply 8 by 6] but of course we don't have that many households. In fact we only have 24,479,439 households or about half the total mentioned in the paper. [figures from UK census 2001] This statistic is out by a factor of two!

Sometimes I begin to wonder? Is the government intentionally trying to mislead us into complacency over our imminent energy situation?

The article in the Independent continues.

"Britain is still a long way from a full blown energy crisis but time is eating away the margin of comfort." Nuclear is off the agenda for the moment and much of our indigenous coal resources will be gone in a decade. The UK will become a net importer of gas by 2006 and of oil by 2010. By 2020 the country could be dependent on imported energy for 80% of its needs, much of it piped in from politically unstable regions of the world."

[End of article]

In actual fact current consumption of oil in the UK is 1.7 million barrels per day. Domestic production is running at about 2 million barrels per day. The current depletion rate is about 6.1 % a year which means that we will actually become a net importer of oil by 2005/2006. Not 2010 as stated by the Independent Newspaper. Perhaps the most significant and telling comment however is "Britain is still a long way from a full blown energy crisis" What I wonder do they think is meant by "A long way." Five years? Ten years? Fifteen Years? It is probably good news that the very concept of a forthcoming energy crisis is finally getting some airing in the press. If you've been following my arguments then you will realise as I do that is not a matter of **if we will have an energy crisis**...but simply when.

If I am correct there will be many people out there presently having very similar thoughts and sharing similar concerns. Down in the bowels of the internet the topic is beginning to get enormous coverage. We now need to bring this important discussion into the mainstream.

We are all concerned for our future.

After all; it is the only thing we all have <u>absolutely</u> in common.

We are going to have to share this future together. How would you like to share it? I hope in sharing my personal thoughts on the matter I may help to initiate this discussion. In keeping with the philosophy of localisation which is a constantly recurring philosophical theme during these essays I am first going to initiate this conversation in my local neighbourhood.

I apologise in advance to all my neighbours for the all the noise [music] and the late night street parties.

I hope others will be doing likewise in their neighbourhoods and we can soon all meet together to help design a future which we can be proud of.

Every star in the firmament has a soul as its destiny.

Every soul has a star at its journeys end.

I should like to invite everyone to share a journey

On the no 19 bus.

As you have been following this last essay some of you may have noticed that the forty characters/passengers on the no 19 bus have turned up again.

The novel portrays each of the various seasons of 2007. We start in the Spring of 2007. Easter to be exact; and then each character of the forty characters is traced week by week for forty weeks. In 2003 we are experiencing one of the first oil shock waves. In 2007 the shock wave is quite severe and there are growing indications that it might get quite traumatic. Since this is 2003 however there is still time to change the direction of the story. Indeed there is still time to begin to write our own story and still plenty of time to invent a plot which is altogether more gentle and more harmonious and infinitely more light hearted.

The past is the one thing we cannot change.

The future is the one thing we can change.

So that's my invitation.

Let's change the future together.

Stop Press

Extract from Financial Times Tuesday October 14th 2003.

"Japan has offered a financial package worth $7 billion in its latest attempt to persuade Russia to build a pipeline across Siberia to the Pacific instead of using a rival route into N East China"

Background to this article.

Last year China offered Russia 2.5 Billion dollars to build an oil pipeline from Siberia. Later in 2002 Japan offered 3.5 billion dollars to the Russians so that they would build the pipeline to them. China then upped their offer to 5 billion dollars. Now Japan is offering 7 billion. China became a net importer of oil ten years ago and is poised to become the world's second biggest importer after America.

Meanwhile, in Bolivia, resistance fighters have successfully thwarted government attempts to sell their Gas to the US. The resistance fighters say they want to keep Bolivian gas for Bolivians. In fact most South American countries, Brazil, Venezuela and Columbia have similar resistance fighters. Shortages are on the very near horizon. There are presently more than three attacks every day on oil and gas pipelines around the world. The Western press remains mute.

Conclusions

October 2nd, 2003

My conclusions on all this change from day to day. In fact I'd go further. My conclusions on this change from moment to moment. Today, for instance, my heart was so heavy and my despondency so great that I really just wanted to forget everything I'd ever written and everything I'd ever read. The depths of despair which I plumbed originated from two specific sources. I spent most of yesterday reading a book called "Behind the war on terror." by Nafeez Mossadeq Ahmed. If you would like to spend a day hovering somewhere between terminal depression, inexpressible sadness and inescapable helplessness this book should take you there. I came away bruised and battered. Our world is being run by monsters. They are not just dangerous and deluded they are probably certifiable. The horrible hotchpotch of global development is now fermenting into a wicked poisonous brew. Bush and Blair, and most of their associated political cronies are, quite beyond any reasonable question of doubt, indictable genocidal war criminals. Murder and manipulation in Iraq would just cover one small charge on their charge-sheet.

I find myself asking.

Where we will find leaders worthy of our respect?

Where will we find leaders with the vision to deal with the Planet's increasingly desperate ecological problems?

Where will we find leaders who are prepared to plan our retreat from the horror of Globalism and actually face the reality that war and brutality do not solve anything?

Where will we find leaders capable of recognising that our economic system needs a complete and radical overhaul?

Where will we find leaders with genuine humility?

The second reason I became immensely depressed today is the fact that I had to travel to North London. I never drive to London. Ever. Appalling though the service is I scuttle up on the train and tube. Today I had to go to the very last stop on the Northern Line. The journey there and back took about six hours. Just time to read "Behind the war on terror" and look around me. I try to be a keen observer of people in these situations without making it obvious that I'm staring. Whenever I look around in such an environment I'm struck by two things. Mechanical electrical/ fossil fuel power is being constantly used but people are almost totally oblivious to its primary role in virtually every physical movement of their everyday lives. I also observe in people a very powerful projection to try and maintain their own personal private space. The demands on our personal interior environment are huge. The demands on our exterior environment are equally huge. One feeds off the other. We cannot isolate ourselves from what is going on outside us but we have to try.

I feel an overwhelming loneliness of spirit. As if we are all but broken songbirds trying pitifully to live in our tiny personal cage. In that entire six-hour journey I did not detect one spontaneous conversation struck up among strangers. Not one. People glued themselves in books [mostly cheap novels] or magazines or newspapers or simply sat staring into space and simultaneously into their own incessant thoughts.

As I observe and analyse this process I am drawn further into despondency. Are we really so lost to one other we can't even make conversation?

Now for a moment I'm going to be self-indulgent. My wife will tell you, quite correctly, that these moments of self-indulgence are all too common and that they weaken me. I am entirely aware of what she's telling me and each time I sense myself falling into despair I think of her, at home, with our dogs and animals and I pray, earnestly, from the very depths of my soul and the bottom of my heart that I can promise her a brighter future.

It is perhaps not surprising that travelling on the Underground today is quite stressful. I imagine I was not alone in wondering what it would be like if the National Grid decided to collapse once more. I started to wonder how far it was between stations. Would there be any emergency lights? What if the power took hours, or even days to come back on? What if these power interruptions became quite common. What if the National Grid failed and then the back-up generated power failed simultaneously. What if, in that scenario, the steel tubing in which I was buried deep underground became utterly and totally black. What if, at the same time, I was standing, sweating profusely cheek to jowl with hundreds of other terrified human beings, all of us strangers to one another? I began to smell adrenalin. I saw the smell of fear growing in direct arithmetical proportion to the length of time we were entombed. At this point I began to realise that we may at least speak a little to one another. Why would we speak to one another? Because we might need to build up our own inner resources. Why? For the simple reason that sharing the experience makes us feel stronger. Conversation is the primary tool in creation for eliminating what is essentially the one terrifying truth about our inner reality. We are all ultimately alone.

I have to say I was rather glad when the Tube on which I was travelling suddenly whizzed out of its electrified tunnel into the sunshine.

Throughout the writing of the "Invitation" and the ten volumes of the novel I have had one other question constantly thrown to the front of my mind.

Why is the future which I see so clearly before me taking this particular shape? Is my vision of the future so unique? If it is *unique* then my vision is rare but if it is rare it is not common and beyond all doubt I'd rather have a common vision than a rare one for I believe that a common vision will be one that I may share.

Am I alone in recognising that our world is presently run by certifiable maniacs? No. I'm not alone. I'm just in a minority, at least at present. It's very hard to get one's mind tuned into the concept that the world has, literally, gone quite mad.

America and Britain are trying desperately to hang on to the broken shattered infrastructure of Iraq. Our two countries have bombed the living daylights out of the population for nearly twelve years. Through our United Nations sanctions, we have murdered millions of ordinary Iraqi people. Through our casual distribution of depleted uranium weapons we have caused generations of cancers, not only in Iraqi children but probably in our own troops. America and Britain have started a nuclear war. A radioactive war. The poisons they have spread will blight the Iraqi people for decades. Truly, if I was an Iraqi I might wonder what on earth had singled me out for such a violent retribution.

When I turned twenty one my personal taste in literature inclined towards oriental mysticism. A few years later my taste for literature, indeed the written word, disappeared as I opted for meditation instead. Later in life I find myself returning to the great spiritual classics. I would like to mention them all by name but in what order would I begin? Lists always imply priorities. However if I were to be prompted to provide an answer I suppose I would have to begin my list with an Indian classic. The Bhagavad Gita. Like all classics it has an eternal message which is constantly changing its meaning as it moves from reader to reader. There is much in the Bhagavad Gita that entrances me but I am most affected by the few words of the introduction to my own personal Gita which was printed in Bombay in India in 1973.

"Truly speaking, none has the power to describe in words the glory of the Gita, for it is a book containing the highest esoteric doctrines. It is the essence of the Vedas, its language is so sweet and simple that man can easily understand it after a bit of practice but the thoughts are so deep that none can arrive at their end even after constant study through a lifetime."

The present essence I extract from the Bhagavad Gita is this.

The crazed monsters who rule our world are but reflections of what is also inside me. If I make them "other" to me then I oppose them and if I oppose then I feed the fires that make them.

The story of the Baghdad Gita is quite simple. It concerns a discussion about the nature of life and soul between Krsna, the lord of creation, (God?) and Arjuna, a worthy warrior who is yet uncertain of the role he ought to play in life. This interplay is the deepest metaphor for the relationship each of us has to the world at large. The world out there.

But let's cut to the chase and conclude the Bhagavad Gita story. In essence it is this. Buck up boy and get on with it. If you want to trust God you can't question him. (her?). He/ she is beyond question and beyond doubt. Don't worry yourself over your inability to understand the mind of God it is a mind beyond the ability of mind to understand. Just get on and do your duty. Krsna rounds off his philosophy by mentioning that the soul is indestructible but flesh is impermanent and physical.

Personally I interpret the key to his instructions towards duty in this way. Stand-up. Straighten out. Prepare to be counted. The light in the mirror at the end of the soul's journey will be quite blindingly bright.

Studying the Gita can be a tremendous source of strength when one is slipping away into self indulgence and despondency.

Something else I learned, at least academically speaking, from my studies of the great spiritual classics was the observation that it is always darkest just before the dawn. I often find it hard to maintain the sense of optimism this philosophy requires. I hope with a fervent heart that before too long we will see in fact, that the darkest hour has already passed. When we all start to realise we are all on this journey together we may encounter a spiritual awakening. Our physical lives are undoubtedly going to become much harder over the next generation or two. We will not have the fossil fuel energy to support such a materialistic lifestyle but maybe something infinitely richer will replace it. Maybe we will touch the land again and grow reconnected to the Earth and its changing seasons. Today, when I look round at my fellow human beings in their steel tube whistling along on their fossil-fuel relentless journeys I really felt that there was no-hope. I just couldn't help it. The planet's gone crazy. People are almost entirely oblivious of their greater connection to the cosmos out there beyond them and we are all hurtling towards an energy crisis with almost perfect abandonment. Nuclear war, in the form of depleted uranium has been declared on Iraq but apart from a few brave journalists this does not make the news. We have in reality started a nuclear war by stealth and deceit. Millions are dead. Millions more will certainly die prematurely in great physical, mental and emotional distress. Our politicians commit mass murder in my name. Meanwhile whilst Iraq is raped, pillaged and brutalised for the sake of a few more litres of petrol. 30,000 hummers, (the mechanical equivalent of a personal armoured vehicle which does ten miles to the gallon) are being produced annually in the United States. I ask myself. How am I going to get out of this insane asylum? My answer to myself. There is no way out. We are all in this together. We have been assigned the task of sharing it together. The human journey cannot be taken alone.

I have been told, on innumerable occasions that I cannot change the world. But what is the world? And why can't I change it? In fact of course I change it every day because when I change what's inside me the world outside changes. It is the same world yet it is a new and different world.

So what are my conclusions?

I must work on changing what is inside me. There are many planks left in my eye; I am quite certain of that.

It strikes me finally that I can't change the world alone. It will need to be a joint effort.

So am I eternally positive about the future? No! I oscillate like a yo-yo. One-day up and one-day down. The oscillations make me feel quite physically nauseous. My anxiety frequently reaches a point where I can barely even breathe. Unlock this asylum and let me get out! I am quite literally suffocating. The air is becoming unbreathable. The water in the little river at the end of my garden is nearly all chemicals. I am locked in this solitary little cage. I see no key to this cage. I can see no way of getting out; I feel I am trapped for eternity. It takes all my patience but I wait. Hours are followed by days; days by months; months by years; years by eternity. My heart is nearly bursting.

Just when I have given up all hope and resigned myself to annihilation despair and human extinction I find a key forming in my imagination inside me. It is a golden key. A key of light and illumination.

For the moment however it only exists in my imagination.

In order to become real. In order to forge a key that could unlock the secret of harmonious **community** spirit the key will need to be forged by the coming together of the **universal** human spirit.

I am utterly overwhelmed by the enormity of the task ahead. I hope I will be up to it.

I hope we will all be up for it.

I have one last question. I have saved this question until the very end. It is a question I must ask of myself. It is a question I'm going to refer to for an answer to the Great Book of Change. The I Ching. The I Ching is a book of mirrors. In order to consult the Book of change one needs to formulate a question in one's mind and hold on to that question.

After some meditation I formulated the following question.

What is to become of us all?

Unfortunately the Book of Change cannot answer this type of question. It is too abstract. The Book of Change will only answer a question directed to the centre of one's own being. Thus I must change the question. The question must be something really rather personal. This is presently something of a challenge. My whole life seems to have been a series of questions followed by a series of only partially satisfactory answers. I ask myself this? Am I asking the right question at the right time? I now have to take a step back. In order to determine if I am asking the right question I throw a coin. If the question that I have formulated in my mind is the correct question to ask the I Ching then I will be informed of this decision by the coin coming up tails. If, on the other hand, the coin comes up heads it is telling me to think again and formulate a better question.

It is now 4:00am on 2nd September. I was born on the 4th September, 1954 at 5am. I have another 49 hours before I celebrate by forty ninth birthday. This is slightly symbolic for me. Ancient spiritual treatises regard one's forty ninth birthday as the completion of seven cycles of seven. When I was twenty I asked my spiritual teacher, Dawa Lama, what I should do. I did not like his answer. He told me I had an over active mind unsuited to a meditative life. He suggested three things; that I explore the world; rigorously examine the nature of my own thoughts and be as quiet as possible for twenty eight years. I think I have managed the first two of his instructions reasonably well but I have failed miserably with the last.

I'm having great difficulty in formulating my question. I have asked seven questions so far and each time I came up with a question the coin oracle told me that the question was not good enough. These were my seven questions.

1)   Could you explain why I am feeling so alone?

2)   What is my duty?

3)   Where will I find faith?

4)   Where will I find the necessary courage to continue my journey?

5)   Will the human race survive/succeed?

6)   Should I simply empty myself and not have any question at all. Should I make "emptiness" a question?

7)   Why?

All these questions were rejected.

Finally the formulation of my 8th question came up tails.

My 8th question was.

"Will you show me what is inside me and show me how I should prepare myself?"

I will not presently going to any more detail about how the Book of Change works or the precise details of how it is consulted. It is Chinese in origin. The authorship is entirely unknown. It is almost certainly a book that was constantly added to by various authors over generations. It is not a book, in my opinion, that should be used carelessly or too frequently.

After one has consulted the Book of Change one is left with something called a hexagram which is a picture contained within six lines. These are the six lines my question reveals.

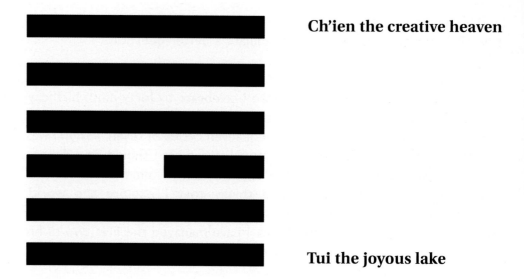

Ch'ien the creative heaven

Tui the joyous lake

The Chinese name of this hexagram is lu which means treading or conduct.

The particular Book of Change which I am consulting was first published in 1951. It was translated from the Chinese by Richard Wilhelm and has a forward by Carl Young.

I obtained the six lines by throwing three coins six times.

The interpretation of these lines is as follows.

The name of the hexagram lu means on the one hand the right way of conducting oneself. Heaven, the father, is above, and the lake, the youngest daughter is below. This shows the difference between high and low, upon which composure, correct social conduct, depends. On the other hand, the word for the name of the hexagram "treading" means literally treading upon something. The small and cheerful (Tui) treads upon the large and the strong (ch'ien) the direction of the movement of the two primary trigrams is upwards. The fact that the strong treads on the weak is not mentioned in the Book of change because it is taken for granted. For the weak to take a stand against the strong is not dangerous here because it happens in good humour (Tui) and without presumption so that the strong man is not irritated but takes it all in good part.

The interpretation as above is followed by the judgment.

Treading. Treading upon the tale of the tiger.
It does not bite the man. Success.

The situation is really difficult. That which is strongest and that which is weakest are close together. The weak follows behind the strong and worries it. The strong however acquiesces and does not hurt the weak because the contact is in good humour and Harmless. In terms of a human situation one is handling wild intractable people. In such a case one's purpose will be achieved if one behaves with decorum. Pleasant manners succeed even with difficult people.

This judgment is then followed by the image.

Heaven above
The lake below.

Thus the superior man discriminates between high and low,
And thereby fortifies the thinking of the people.

Heaven and the Lake show a difference of elevation that inheres in the nature of the two, hence no envy arises. Among mankind there are also necessarily differences of elevation; it is impossible to bring about universal equality. But it is important that differences in social rank should not be arbitrary or unjust, for if this occurs, envy and class struggle are the inevitable consequences. If, on the other hand, external differences in rank correspond with differences in inner worth and if inner worth forms the interior of external rank people acquiesce and order reigns in society.

This is the end of the Book of Change judgment and image.

So my thanks to the I Ching for the above. I could not have put it better myself. I think it quite precisely answers my question of the moment. I do feel small and weak but I will tread on the tail of the tiger. I will be eternally good humoured, well-mannered and polite. But I will worry the powerful. I will look inside myself first always. If I can maintain my courage and hold to my faith we may move the mountain.

Most of this book has been about the problems we are about to face together as a human race. The problems are immense but the solutions are simple. Indeed the solutions are so ludicrously simple we simply don't see them. All we have to do is slowdown. We need to slow down population growth whilst dramatically slowing our consumption of the earth's precious mineral and fossil fuel resources but most of all we simply need to calm our minds. When we calm the fire of desire in our minds the insatiable restlessness of our desires are cooled. Such a process brings us much closer to the living heart of spirituality. Amazingly we will realise we don't need all this activity and we certainly don't need all these things. Ironically and yet wonderfully we will have been brought back to this realisation by the simple withdrawal of gross physical energy.

Creation has already planned to make everything slow down by slowly but inexorably withdrawing the hydrocarbon energy which was responsible for everything speeding up in the first place. In other words we are going to be forced to slowdown whether we want to or not. It is now up to us.

Do we have the collective intelligence to slowdown just ahead of the hydrocarbon depletion timetable which nature has put in place or are we simply too selfish and too self absorbed in our material pursuits to notice that we are on the path to self destruction?

Thank you for your patience. I hope we may find the courage to walk together. The human world will either unite to celebrate its mutual origins or divide and die.

Stephen Hamilton-Bergin.

The Earthsure Foundation

Looking for solutions

Most of this book has been about the fact that a whole series of problems are looming on the horizon and that no one is really addressing the solutions. My fundamental purpose in writing all of this is to firstly bring the problems into focus. To determine the nature of the problem. The purpose of the Earthsure Foundation is to create an academy of the very best modern brains. The first principle of the Earthsure foundation is that the basic energy systems of our society will need to be rapidly redesigned. In my experience rapid redesign usually creates chaos. If we wait for the crisis it may be so intense and so overwhelming that we will not have the intellectual, scientific, psychological or physical resources to cope.

The Foundation is intended to operate, at least initially, in West Sussex. The Foundation will investigate how West Sussex can begin to adapt to the coming economic realities. By starting to think about it now and by considering all the implications before they overwhelm us there is a chance that we can anticipate and prepare for the worst of the crisis.

The Foundation will hopefully see the light of day shortly. It depends rather a lot on whether this book stimulates sufficient interest for local people in West Sussex to get together to discuss their future together with a radical new emphasis.

The Foundation is established on the principle that we will have to learn how to use a great deal less energy.

The Foundation will bring together local writers, philosophers, farmers, craftsmen, environmentalists, politicians, businessmen, planners, and anyone who can contribute to our understanding of where the future might need to go.

The Foundation is intended to operate as a forum so that local knowledge can be shared. There is no specific policy or dogma to preach and I hope it will always remain so.

The Foundation will take an active role in planting trees because planting trees is planning for many generations ahead.

The Foundation will set up scientific investigative committees to determine as reasonably as possible the science of Hydrocarbon depletion so we can better know what to expect when this depletion becomes a physical reality. It will also explore all alternative forms of energy with a specific emphasis on those that would be most suitable for West Sussex.

The Foundation will share freely and without seeking financial gain all information that might help others deal with the same problems.

The Foundation is not anti technology but pro technology but it is expected that all technologies supported by the foundation will operate on the principles of sustainability and renewability.

The Foundation will investigate how our economic infrastructure can be localised. It will emphasise growing and producing food locally and, as far as possible, organically.

The Foundation will investigate how employment can be generated locally using local materials and resources.

If anyone out there is interested in helping establish this foundation I would very much like to hear from them. I can be contacted on.

01444 47 11 11

More information on the Earthsure Foundation can be found on our website.

www.no19bus.org.uk

www.no19bus.co.uk

What you have just read was called:

"THE TRUTH ABOUT THE WAR AND OIL"

If you have enjoyed these essays and you would like to read no 19 bus - the novel, you can order on our website: -

www.no19bus.org.uk

If you would like to order by credit card over the telephone please call
01444 47 11 22

Or try your local newsagent or bookstore.

no 19 bus - the novel
ISBN 0-9545318-0-9

The human journey cannot be taken alone.

Stephen Hamilton-Bergin